Probability and Inductive Logic

Probability and Inductive Logic

Henry E. Kyburg, Jr.
The University of Rochester

The Macmillan Company
Collier–Macmillan Limited, London

Preface

The general aim of this book is to introduce the reader to the rather broad spectrum of philosophical ideas on probability and induction that are current in philosophical, mathematical, and statistical literature. I use the phrase broad spectrum deliberately, for probability has been taken as everything from an expression having merely the informal import, "don't take what I am about to say as Gospel, because I'm not really sure," to an expression applicable to a certain class of mathematical functions having certain formal characteristics; and induction has been taken to be everything from a solved problem to a pseudoproblem to a real but insoluble problem.

It is generally an advantage in attacking intellectual problems to consider a number of points of view; even if they conflict with each other, the intellectual community may approach the truth by exploring the consequences of the various views. The collection of problems pertaining to probability and induction, however, has been attacked from so many and such divergent points of view that it is no longer an easy task for a person following one approach to be familiar with the alternative approaches. In this case the advantage of a multiplicity of points of view is lost. Rate of progress, as a function of the number n of actively pursued points of view, is not a monotonically increasing function of n. For a given value of n, however, the situation may be improved by making it easier for each adherent of one particular point of view to become familiar with the other $n - 1$ points of view, and particularly by making it easier for the open-minded student to become familiar with all n points of view. This is the primary object of the following pages.

In conformity with this goal, I have striven to keep the formal machinery involved down to the absolute minimum, as well as to depend as little as possible on philosophical background knowledge. Although the book is relatively self-contained, and although the emphasis is always on the ideas rather than on the formulas, nevertheless there are passages that will be easier to read and more informative for those who have had some mathematics than for those who have not, and passages whose intelligibility would be enhanced by a background fragment of symbolic logic. Despite this, I strongly advise against skipping any chapters, particularly on the ground of their mathematical or logical difficulty. No chapter, except possibly the first (and easiest), could be skipped without coming out with a biased view of current opinions on the subjects of probability and induction.

On the part of students of philosophy who are interested in the big and broad problems of probability and induction, there may be a tendency to regard the mathematical-looking chapters as extraneous. They are not. The probability calculus is central not only to the consideration of statistical inference but also to many of those views of induction which seem on the surface to be purely qualitative. Furthermore, though one may regard statistical inference as a small or unrepresentative part of inductive logic, one cannot plausibly deny that it *is* a part of inductive logic. A certain degree of familiarity with the probability calculus is a necessary condition (though clearly not a sufficient condition) for talking constructively about statistical inference.

There may be a corresponding tendency on the part of those familiar with the machinery of mathematical statistics and probability to regard such chapters as the first and seventh as so much bilge-water. While there is something to this assessment, I think, when it is applied to some of the particular views discussed in these chapters, it is in error when applied wholesale to the *kinds* of problems to which holders of those views have addressed themselves. It is not that they are altogether on the wrong track, but that the branch lines they follow don't take them very far. It is important to see the reasons underlying these approaches and to face the questions that they are designed to answer.

My approach is not purely expository and historical, however. Some of the views in the literature seem to be flatly wrong; some seem to be misleading or irrelevant. Where this has seemed to me to be the case, I have given my reasons. Where two views seem to be essentially the same, I have attempted to exhibit their similarity, in the hope that at least the proponents of those two views could make their peace and present a unified front. Thus a secondary objective of the book is a reduction in the total number of points of view.

It is only proper to warn the reader that although I come to this task as one who has read fairly widely in both the philosophical and mathematical literature, I also come with my own point of view and my own set of solutions to some of the problems to be considered here. Nevertheless, my aim has been to provide an introduction, both objective and critical, to a wide variety of approaches to probability and induction. There is much to be learned from all of these approaches. The reader may judge for himself which approach seems most fruitful, for it is clear that the state of the art is not yet such as to admit of any final answers.

Questions concerning probability and induction are often treated together; a philosopher will often adopt a way of approaching both kinds of questions at once. But some people are concerned only with probability and not at all with induction, and others are concerned only (or primarily) with induction. Furthermore, there is a large group of writers who have arrived at conflicting conclusions concerning induction, but who share a common conception of probability. All in all, it therefore seemed better to treat probability and induction separately, even at the cost of having to refer to the same set of views in two places. Dividing the book thus into two parts, a part concerned exclusively with induction and a part concerned exclusively with probability, has the added advantage that those whose interests lie predominantly in the question of interpreting probability can concentrate on the first part of the book, and those whose interests lie mainly in questions about induction can concentrate on the second part of the book—though it should be noted here that most parts of the second portion of the book presuppose an under-standing of certain of the technical developments discussed in the first portion, particularly the probability calculus.

Such specialized concentration should be facilitated by the fairly extensive bibliographical notes appended to each chapter. These contain comments as well as titles and the names of authors, and take the place of footnotes. Page references for quotations and the like are given in the body of the text; the work quoted is cited in the chapter bibliography. These bibliographies are intended to be complete enough to lead the student to the specialized literature of the topics covered. But some use of the bibliography is required even for a thorough understanding of the topics specifically covered in the chapters; the text represents only a survey of the mountaintops, and to really get the lay of the land one must go to the original sources.

In addition to the specialized bibliographies that accompany each chapter, there is, as an appendix, a relatively complete bibliography of recent work in probability and induction. Those works which have struck me as being directly relevant to matters discussed in this volume, and which have been published within the last fifteen or twenty years, but no later than 1969, have been included. Those who wish to look for more recent materials (unless they also wish to uncover my oversights) should begin with the 1969 volumes of journals which are published on a calendar-year basis and the 1968–69 volumes of journals which are published on an academic-year basis. Another constraint is that I have tended to concentrate on materials found in philo-sophical journals; although there are some references to the mathematical and statistical literature, I have not attempted to achieve comprehensiveness in this area.

Much of the material in the chapters on induction is drawn from my article "Recent Work in Inductive Logic," *American Philosophical Quarterly* **1**, 1964. I wish to express my gratitude to the editor, Professor Nicholas Rescher, for permission to use that material. This book would have been a far more difficult and prolonged task, were it not for the great generosity of the University of Rochester in granting me a sabbatical semester. And I would not have been able to make use of that time in this way, but for the previous support of the National Science Foundation in my pursuit of the logical foundations of statistical inference; the assistance of the National Science Foundation is hereby gratefully acknowledged.

A number of persons have given me advice, encouragement, and assistance. Professor Bas van Fraassen has given me most gratifying encouragement, as well as excellent advice on the general structure and scope of the book; many of his suggestions concerning an early draft have become incorporated in the final version. Professor John M. Vickers has also earned my gratitude by providing painstaking, detailed, and numerous suggestions concerning a number of the matters discussed in the book, as well as concerning their exposition. He and his student, Mr. Frank McGuinness, have both made valuable contributions to the bibliography. Professors Isaac Levi, Richard Jeffrey, and Wesley Salmon have been unstinting in their efforts to make me understand their points of view; if I have failed to do their work justice, it is through no fault of theirs. I have also profited from discussions with Leonard J. Savage, Ian Hacking, Carl Hempel, and of course my mentor, Ernest Nagel. I wish to thank them all for their help and patience. Finally, I wish to express my gratitude to Miss Donna Anderton for the efficiency with which she attacked the sometimes tedious tasks of checking bibliographical items and preparing an index and the answers to exercises.

The responsibility for any errors of organization, of concept, of exposition, of bibliographical accuracy, or of answers to the problems, is, of course, that of the author.

H. E. K., Jr.

Contents

ix

Probability and Inductive Logic

PART ONE: PROBABILITY

1

Informal
Interpretations of Probability

'Probability' has many partial synonyms in ordinary usage: the probable is that which we distinguish from the certain; probability is likelihood, degree of confirmation, degree of factual support; the probable is the credible, that which is supported by the evidence, that which the chances favor. Probability is our guide in life.

It is easy to see that there are important philosophical problems involved in the interpretation of probability: for example, most contemporary philosophers agree that inductive (scientific) conclusions cannot be taken as certain, but must be regarded as (at best) probable. Some philosophers argue that inductive conclusions cannot even be rendered probable by the evidence in their favor. We can only understand such assertions (and *a fortiori* argue about them) when we understand the concept of probability, or, if there is more than one concept of probability, when we understand these several concepts and know which of them is at issue in a particular case. The same remarks apply to epistemological assertions (Are there any factual statements that we may take as *certain*, or are they all to be regarded as at best probable?); to theological arguments (Is our knowledge, if any, of the divine *probable*? Is it *probable* in the same sense as our knowledge of the other side of the moon?); to ethical argument (Does it make sense to say that an action is *probably* right, or that an end is *probably* good? Should we act on the basis of the highest probability, the highest utility, or the highest expectation, which is the product of utility and probability?); and of course in metaphysical and ontological argument as well the word 'probable' and its cognates are both useful and obscure in meaning.

'Probability' is a word that finds many uses in the sciences and in everyday life as well as in philosophy. Typical statements involving probability are: "Empirical generalizations can never be rendered more than probable by the evidence of their favor." "The probability of getting a six with a throw of a die is $\frac{1}{6}$." "The probability of getting a head on a toss of that coin is unknown." "If there is any probability that God exists, you should believe that he does." "The probability that an American male white-collar worker will survive his fortieth birthday, given that he has survived his thirty-ninth birthday, is 0.994." "I will probably be late meeting the train." "The quantum theory is probably true, in its broad outlines." "If all the crows anyone has seen are black, then probably all crows are black." "Crows are probably black." "The probability distribution of the quantity Q is given by the probability density function $f_Q(x)$." "The tales told by Marco Polo when he returned from the Orient were improbable but true." "If the probability of heads on one toss is one-half, then the probability of two heads on two independent tosses is one-fourth." "Induction is probable inference." "The probability of heads on the next toss of this particular well-tested coin is one-half." "I do not know what the probability of heads for this coin is."

It would, of course, be too much to expect that in all of these occurrences the word 'probability' had exactly the same meaning. We have, clearly, a variety of meanings or shades of meaning. We also have, in the philosophical and mathematical and scientific literature of recent years, a variety of proposals concerning the meaning of probability. One useful distinction can be made between two types of proposal concerning the meaning of probability: there is the type that take probability as a concept obeying a probability *calculus*—that is, a system of rules for manipulating probabilities and calculating some probabilities on the basis of others—and there is the type which takes probability (in some contexts at least) not as a formal or quantitative concept in a calculus, but as a qualitative concept that describes beliefs, evaluates hypotheses, or reflects commitment or lack of commitment to a hypothesis or an assertion. In this chapter I shall review some of the claims that have been made for an ordinary-language nonquantitative analysis of the word. Even such an analysis, however, may be more or less formal, may reflect more or less *structure* in the contexts in which the word is used.

The newest and most radical of the ordinary-language interpretations of 'probability' is Toulmin's. According to Toulmin, 'probably' is the fundamental word of the group with which we are concerned, and it functions in ordinary usage as a *modal operator*: that is to say, we may assert a certain statement flatly, thereby *categorically* committing ourselves to its truth, or we may assert it *guardedly*, by prefixing the word 'probably' to it. The statement we assert is still the same: "It will rain tomorrow," and "Probably it will rain tomorrow," have precisely the same factual content, on Toulmin's view. Both statements are true if it does in fact rain tomorrow; both are false if it doesn't rain. The whole difference between the former statement and the latter lies not in the content, but in the manner of assertion: the former is asserted categorically, unconditionally, while the latter is asserted only guardedly, cautiously. If I say that it will probably rain tomorrow, and it fails to rain, I am just as wrong as if I had asserted that it *would* rain tomorrow, but I am not as blameworthy. I have warned you that my assertion might turn out to be wrong.

The word 'probably' and its cognates do sometimes carry this meaning. For example, "I will probably come to your party" does seem to be a guarded way of saying, "I will come to your party (but don't *blame* me if I've just told you a falsehood)." Indeed there is an element of this kind of meaning in many probability statements. When I say, "There is not one chance in a thousand that this well-tested fair coin will land heads on each of the next ten times it is tossed," I am saying, among other more important things, that it is *possible* that the coin will land heads on each of its next ten tosses, and that if that should happen I should not be held *blameworthy*. The element of meaning, which one might call modal meaning, that Toulmin finds in certain ordinary-language probabilistic locutions, is surely there, but this element of meaning also seems to be present in many locutions which call for a technical, quantitative probability concept, such as the assertion about ten successive heads. Although this may be the kind of meaning which dominates some contexts, it is certainly not the most important element of meaning in most of the contexts of interest to philosophy and science, nor even in most contexts from ordinary discourse. We need not deny the validity of Toulmin's insight, but we must observe that it has little bearing on the kind of meaning that interests us most in science and philosophy.

The basic difficulty with the guarded-way-of-speaking interpretation of 'probability' is that one does not generally (and especially not in philosophical or scientific discourse) regard a probability statement as erroneous *merely* because the component statement turns out to be false, despite Toulmin's claims to the contrary. When I say that probably the next ten tosses of a coin will include at least one tail, and the next ten tosses all turn out heads, I do not regard myself as having made an error, provided the coin is a normal one and my calculations were correct. Similarly, when I say that there will probably be frost tonight, and there is no frost, I do not regard myself as having made an error—provided the grounds on which I based my assertion were indeed such as to render my expectation of frost justifiable or reasonable. One can, of course, be wrong in one's probability assertions. If I claim that in a fair poker game it is more probable that a hand will be a flush than a straight, my mathematics is wrong and my claim false. If, knowing that a certain coin is biased, I claim that the probability of two successive tails is $\frac{1}{4}$, I have misused the evidence in my possession. If I claim that there will probably be frost tonight, but I have misinterpreted or misevaluated the evidence, my claim is false. Furthermore, under the circumstances just outlined, these claims are false regardless of what happens—they are false even if there is frost tonight, even if the next two tosses do not yield tails, even if the hand is a flush. Indeed it seems quite evident that one can utter a falsehood in asserting 'probably S' only by making a blunder in the evaluation of evidence or by making a blunder in gathering evidence, regardless of whether or not S itself is true. Furthermore, the disavowal of responsibility ("Don't blame me if S turns out to be false") is irrelevant if the evidence has been misevaluated. Thus in most circumstances, if someone says 'probably S', he has spoken falsely and is blameworthy if and only if he lacks the evidence which makes it reasonable for him to believe that S. Whether or not S is true is beside the point. If this is so, then in most contexts, probability is not primarily a modal concept in Toulmin's sense of 'modal'.

To the extent that 'probably' has the sense that Toulmin has found for it, it is not of great interest to us; there is not much philosophical or scientific meat in it. A cautious man may assert that *probably* two and two are four; a less cautious man may assert flatly that certainly the universe is expanding. On the interpretation we are considering, the adverb 'probably' becomes a mere indicator of character (indeed an indicator of the character of the speaker as much as an indicator of the character of the statement), and makes no contribution either to the *content* of the statement or to the *context* in which it is uttered.

There are a number of other writers who take the view that the *probability* of ordinary (and philosophical) language is not the sort of concept that can be forced into a calculus, but most of them do not go so far as Toulmin does. William Kneale was perhaps the first writer to hold seriously and at length that the word 'probable' is in many contexts a word expressing *approval* or *justifiability*. To say that the statement S is probable, for Kneale, is to say that it is *worthy* of being acted upon, that it is in accordance with *acceptable inductive criteria*, and the like. Probability is therefore clearly relative to evidence (as it is not, for example, for Toulmin). According to Kneale, to say that S is probable is to say that you have evidence which *probabilifies* S. 'Probabilification'—Kneale's word—denotes the fundamental relation in the theory of rational belief. It admits of degrees: we can distinguish instances in which the evidence probabilifies S so intensely that S may be regarded as practically certain; and we can distinguish instances in which the evidence probabilifies S barely more than it probabilifies not-S. But there are also instances in which it is difficult to say whether or not the evidence probabilifies S, or to what degree. Probabilification is therefore not a quantitative concept in any useful sense of the word, and cannot be incorporated into a formal calculus; indeed, according to Kneale, the relation of probabilification cannot even be formalized. It is something which must simply be recognized, as we must recognize the validity of certain patterns of deductive argument. To some extent, at least, it must be an objective relation: whether or not the evidence probabilifies a statement depends on the evidence and the statement, and not on who, if anyone, has that evidence or has thought of that statement. But all of this is still not to say that the relation can be characterized by any sort of formal framework.

John Patrick Day writes from a point of view which is quite close to that of Kneale, with one important exception. He argues that the probabilification relation *can* be profitably formalized, and he attempts to provide such a formalization. He claims that we can find characteristics of probabilification arguments which will allow us to distinguish among orders of magnitude of the relation—the very probable, the probable, and the more probable than not. His formalization is complex, too complex to be summarized here, and suffers from two serious deficiencies. The first defect is that there is no way to apply his formalism to actual instances or arguments involving probabilities. Consider the probability statements listed earlier; there is no way for a person, having a given body of evidence, to reconstruct those statements along the lines of Day's formalism and to apply that formalism in such a way as to separate those statements into an acceptable group and an unacceptable group. Surely one of the prime objects of formalization is to provide objective standards according to which the concept being formalized can be applied. Given a probabilification argument, there should surely be some way in which one who accepts Day's formalization can discover the degree to which that argument probabilifies its conclusion; but there is not. The second defect is even more serious. Both Kneale and Day agree that there is a *doctrine of chances* which deals with a concept that enters into a probability calculus. They deny that this calculus has any direct bearing on the probabilification relation except in very special circumstances; but they do not deny that those special circumstances exist. The probabilification relation is thus intended to be a more general form of an ordinary probability relation. Whatever implicative relations hold for the general probabilification relation should therefore hold for the special case of the probability relation to be found in the *doctrine of chances*. Day supposes that the probabilification relation is transitive, i.e., that if A probabilifies B and B probabilifies C, then A probabilifies C; but this is simply false of numerical probabilities. Let A be the statement that a die is thrown and does not yield a one-spot; C be the statement that either a two or a four shows uppermost; and B be the statement that a two or a four or a six shows uppermost. We suppose that we can take the die to be fair. Then A probabilifies B, B probabilifies C, but A, far from probabilifying C, probabilifies not-C. Day's formalism therefore fails through inconsistency.

Nevertheless there is something to be learned from these various discussions of the meanings which probability can be given. Like any other important expression, 'probability' has many shades of significance, and admits a variety of uses. As Toulmin has successfully pointed out, one element in the meaning of 'probably S' is sometimes "Don't blame me if S turns out to be false." The import of the latter claim, according to Kneale, would be, "I am not blameworthy, however S turns out, because I have responsibly evaluated the evidence." The responsible evaluation of evidence, in turn, however, may be taken to involve probability; this is certainly true in cases to which the ordinary calculus of chances applies, and it is often claimed that it is true in all cases. Certainly we must not, as Day does, construe probability in such a way that it conflicts with the calculus of chances. Toulmin also claims that 'probably S' has the same factual import as S itself. While there may be instances in which 'probably S' is used in this way, such instances seem to be rare.

In all of these attempts to capture the ordinary-language meaning of probability, we run up against the same problem: to the extent that the concept captured does reflect ordinary usage, it does not help us to make our philosophical and scientific uses any more precise or meaningful. Either we are left with an instance falling under the "doctrine of chances" which we understood reasonably well in the first place; or else we have an instance which does not fall under this concept, and which therefore cannot be made quantitative by any amount of philosophical analysis; nor, indeed, in the latter case do we have objective standards against which to assess the validity or correctness of probability statements. Toulmin says very little indeed, Kneale and Day not very much more, about the evaluation of probability statements.

Even if the claims of these writers are correct, and there is no calculus or effective formalization appropriate to the concept of probability except in the very special cases to which the classical doctrine of chances applies, it will be to our advantage to do our very best to find, for as many kinds of context as we can, probability concepts that fit into some scheme for calculation, even if they only reflect part of the meaning of the colloquial 'probably'. To do otherwise is to accept the kind of defeatist negative judgment that has so often been proved wrong in the past (the impossibility of a heavier-than-air flying machine; the unsolvability of $x^2 = -1$). To fail to seek a philosophically and scientifically fruitful reconstruction of as many uses of the important concept of probability as we can is to give up before we have started.

EXERCISES

1. Discuss the element of "guardedness" (if any) in the meaning of the word 'probably' in each of the following statements.
   (a) There will probably be snow here for Christmas.

(b) The railroad is very reliable; probably the train will be on time.
(c) I will probably be able to get this paper finished in time to meet the deadline.
(d) The radio predicts fair skies for the day of our picnic, so it will probably be sunny.
(e) The radio predicts fair skies for the day of our picnic, so it will probably rain.
(f) There will probably be at least one head in five tosses of a coin.
(g) Probably the Yankees will win the pennant.

2. Which of the statements (a)–(g) might one regard as false if the occurrence alleged to be probable did not occur? Why?
3. Discuss the element of probabilification (if any) in statements (a)–(g). What is it that is probabilified? What evidence might one plausibly take to probabilify the categorical clause in each case?
4. Discuss three situations in which "There is probably an ace in Mr. A's hand," might be uttered; one in which the force of 'probably' is guarded assertion, one in which it reflects the probabilification relation, and one in which what is at issue is primarily the calculus of chances.
5. What did Hume have in mind when he wrote: "Upon the whole, then, it appears, that no testimony for any kind of miracle has ever amounted to a probability, much less to a proof..." (*An Enquiry Concerning Human Understanding*, Section X)?
6. And Bishop Butler, when he wrote, "To us probability is the very guide of life" (*Analogy*)?
7. According to the kinetic view of thermodynamics, it is correct to say, "An ice cube will *probably* not appear spontaneously in a glass of cool water." If such an ice cube did appear, would that refute this view of thermodynamics? Explain your answer in detail. Explain how someone might be inclined to accept the other answer.

BIBLIOGRAPHICAL NOTES FOR CHAPTER 1

Chapter II of Stephen Toulmin's book, *The Uses of Argument*, Cambridge University Press, 1958, contains the strongest claims concerning the use of 'probably' as indicating guardedness of assertion. Another defense of this idea about probability is to be found in his article "Probability," *Proceedings of the Aristotelian Society, Supplementary Volume* **24**, 1950, pp. 27–62. Criticisms of this view are to be found in John King-Farlow's article "Toulmin's Analysis of Probability," *Theoria* **29**, 1963, pp. 12–26, and in C. L. Hamblin, "The Modal 'Probably'," *Mind* **68**, 1959, pp. 234–40.

John P. Day's book, *Inductive Probability*, Humanities Press, New York, 1961, contains his formalization of the evaluative concept of probability. For an acute criticism of Day's point of view see Wesley Salmon's review of this book in *The Philosophical Review* **72**, 1963, pp. 27–41.

Probably the most defensible version of this general view of probability is to be found in William Kneale's book *Probability and Induction*, Oxford University

Press, 1949. Probability is taken there as a logical relationship but not a metrical one; it is understood to have an evaluative aspect.

Other articles which are relevant to this point of view are Siri Blom's textual analysis of the meaning of "probable" in classical texts of Aristotle, Locke, et al., "Concerning a Controversy on the Meaning of 'Probability'," *Theoria* **21**, 1955, pp. 65–98; and Findley, "Probability Without Nonsense," *Philosophical Quarterly* **2**, 1952, pp. 218–39.

2

The Probability Calculus

Most writers who think that probability can and should be a philosophically and scientifically important concept suppose that it has some metrical or quantitative properties. As we shall see in Part Two, the same is true of such alternative concepts as *degree of factual support* and *corroboration* which turn out to be intimately related to metrical probability concepts. There are a number of more or less distinct metrical probability concepts, but there is just one standard probability calculus which even the variant concepts approach as a special case. It is this calculus that is the topic of the present chapter.

Let us write '$P(H)$' for the probability of H. 'P' represents a probability function; 'H' the argument of that function. Given any H for which the probability function P is defined, there is exactly one thing, $P(H)$, which is the value of that function for that argument. Under most interpretations of the standard probability calculus, the values of the probability function are numbers: $P(H)$ is a number. But what is H? Before we can discuss the formal properties of the probability function P, we must be clear as to a certain amount of the formal structure of the elements for which the function is defined.

We speak of the probability of heads on the toss of a coin, of the probability that John Doe will survive his fortieth year, of the probability that a professional American male of thirty-nine will survive his fortieth year, of the probability of disintegration of a radioactive atom of X, of the probability of rain tomorrow. The phrase 'rain tomorrow' seems to denote a particular event; 'heads on the toss of a coin' and 'disintegration of a radioactive atom of X' seem to denote *kinds* of events; 'that John Doe will survive his fortieth year' seems to be a proposition or a fact; 'that a professional American male of thirty-nine will survive his fortieth year' seems to be a general proposition or a *kind* of proposition. There are four fairly standard interpretations of the elements for which the probability function is defined. We will consider these interpretations in more detail in subsequent chapters, but in order to set out the formal calculus of probability, we must consider them briefly here.

First, we may take these things to be propositions: that John Doe will survive his fortieth year is a typical instance. We will then speak also of the probability of such propositions as that it will rain tomorrow, that an arbitrary (or random) professional American male of thirty-nine will survive his fortieth year, that an arbitrary (or random) atom of X will disintegrate, etc. In general, the negation of a proposition is a proposition, the conjunction of two propositions is a proposition, and the disjunction of two propositions is a proposition. Thus if the probability function is defined for the proposition that John Doe will survive his fortieth year, we shall suppose it also to be defined for the proposition that John Doe will *not* survive his fortieth year; and if it is also defined for the proposition that it will rain tomorrow, we shall suppose that it is defined for the proposition that it will rain tomorrow *and* John Doe will survive his fortieth year, and for the proposition that it will rain tomorrow *or* John Doe will survive his fortieth year.

Second, we may take the things we speak of the probability of to be sentences. Many philosophers regard propositions as rather nebulous entities; and many of those who find propositions to be acceptable things in themselves still prefer to work in formal situations with the kind of hard linguistic entity that can be written down on a piece of paper or uttered. Thus they will say that in our formal probability calculus, we should take sentences, such as "John Doe will survive his fortieth year," as the objects for which the probability function is defined. As the negation of a proposition is a proposition, so the negation of a sentence is a sentence, and the disjunction or conjunction of two sentences is a sentence. Thus as far as negation, disjunction, and conjunction are concerned, the structure of the set of sentences for which the probability function is defined mirrors precisely the structure of the set of propositions for which, on the first view, probability is taken to be defined.

Third, we may take the arguments of the probability function to be events, or kinds of events. Thus we may talk of the probability of the event consisting of rain tomorrow, or of the probability of the event of John Doe surviving his fortieth year, or of the probability of the event consisting of the disintegration of an atom of X. Negation does not apply directly to events (it only applies to linguistic entities such as sentences or propositions), but given any event, such as the occurrence of heads on a toss of a coin, one may consider a complementary event: the occurrence of something other than heads on the same toss. Similarly, one may consider the events which consist in the occurrence of either (or both) of two other events, and one may consider the event which consists in the occurrence of both of two other events. The structure of the set of events is not so transparent as the structure of the set of sentences or propositions; we might, for example, balk at regarding the compound event of getting married and having a baby as the same as the compound event of having a baby and getting married. In order to develop the probability calculus in terms of events, however, we must regard the event consisting of the occurrence of event E_1 *and* E_2 as just the same event as that consisting of E_2 *and* E_1.

Fourth, we may suppose that the objects for which the probability function is defined are sets. This is the most common approach nowadays in texts on probability and statistics. On this interpretation of the arguments of the probability function (or *measure function*, as it is often called for this interpretation of its arguments), we must suppose that every probability statement contains an implicit reference to some set of events relative to which the probability is being asserted. Thus when we speak of the probability of heads on a toss of a coin, we are talking of the probability or measure of the set of tosses resulting in heads, relative to the set of tosses; when we speak of the probability that a professional American male of thirty-nine will survive his fortieth year, we are talking of the probability or measure of the set of survivors of their fortieth year among the set of professional American males of thirty-nine; and so on. It is clear that within the reference set, or the set relative to which the probability is asserted, the complement of a set for which the probability function is defined is a set for which the probability function is defined: we may speak, within the set of tosses of a coin, of the set of tosses which do *not* result in heads. Similarly, we suppose that, within the reference set, the union of two sets for which the measure function is defined is another set for which the measure function is defined. (The union of two sets is the set of all those entities which belong to one or the other or both of the original two sets.) Similarly, within the reference set, we suppose that the intersection of two sets for which the probability function is defined is another set for which the function is defined. (The intersection of two sets is the set of all those entities which belong to—are common to—both of the original two sets.)

In the presentation of the probability calculus, the set-theoretical notation will be used. It should be observed, however, that there is no loss of generality in doing this, since the operations of forming unions, intersections, and complements, which are appropriate only to sets, have analogues under the other interpretations of the arguments of the probability function. Thus if H and E are sets, '$H \cup E$' will denote their union, the set of entities that belong to H, or to E, or to both. But if we take H and E to be propositions, '$H \cup E$' will be their disjunction—that proposition which is true provided H, or E, or both, are true. And if H and E are sentences, '$H \cup E$' will be their disjunction—that is, the sentence constructed in English by inserting 'or' between the two sentences H and E, or in a formal language, by inserting a wedge, '$\vee$', between H and E. Finally, if H and E are events, then '$H \cup E$' will denote the event which corresponds to the occurrence of H or E or both in any order.

In order to make the going easier for those unfamiliar with the few rudiments of set theory that are required in what follows, let us set out here the basic notation and its meaning, under the set-theoretical interpretation. '$\overline{H}$' denotes the *complement* of H. It consists of all (and only) those elements in some universal set V, that are not members of H. It must be borne in mind that we understand what '$\overline{H}$' means only when we know what the universal set V is, '$H \cap E$' denotes the intersection of H and E. It consists of all (and only) those objects which belong to both H and E. '$H \cup E$' denotes the union of H and E. It consists of all (and only) those things which belong to H, or to E, or to both.

A set $\mathscr{F}$ is a *field of sets* if it satisfies the following conditions:

1. Every member of $\mathscr{F}$ is a set.
2. $\mathscr{F}$ contains a universal set V such that every member of $\mathscr{F}$ is included in V; i.e., if H is a member of $\mathscr{F}$ and x is a member of H, then x is a member of V.
3. If H is a member of $\mathscr{F}$, then $\overline{H}$ is a member of $\mathscr{F}$, where V is the universal set required for complementation.
4. If H and E are members of $\mathscr{F}$, then $H \cup E$ is a member of $\mathscr{F}$.

Since $H \cap E = \overline{\overline{H} \cup \overline{E}}$ is a theorem of set theory, it follows from (3) and (4) that the intersection of any two sets that are members of $\mathscr{F}$ is also a member of $\mathscr{F}$. Furthermore, it is easy to see that by applying (3) and (4) a number of times, it is possible to show that the intersection or union of any finite number of sets, members of $\mathscr{F}$, is also a member of $\mathscr{F}$.

Probability measures are often defined for a field of sets. Sometimes, however, they are defined for a sigma-field of sets. In order to define a sigma-field, we need a general notation of union which is applicable to an infinite set of sets. '$\bigcup\limits_{i=1}^{\infty} H_i$' denotes the union of the infinite set of sets H_1, H_2, H_3, ... It consists of all (and only) those elements x such that there is a number n such that x belongs to H_n. In other words, an object x belongs to the infinite union if and only if there is a set H_n to which x belongs. A set $\mathcal{F}$ is a *sigma-field of sets* if it satisfies the following conditions:

1. $\mathcal{F}$ is a field of sets.
2. If, for every number i, H_i belongs to $\mathcal{F}$, then $\bigcup_{i=1}^{\infty} H_i$ also belongs to $\mathcal{F}$.

There are certain properties of union, intersection, and complementation that we need to make use of in developing the probability calculus. Corresponding properties hold for negation, conjunction, and disjunction of propositions or sentences, and for the operations on events that are required for the probability calculus.

(1) Commutativity

$$H \cup E = E \cup H$$
$$H \cap E = E \cap H$$

(2) Associativity

$$(H \cup E) \cup F = H \cup (E \cup F)$$
$$(H \cap E) \cap F = H \cap (E \cap F)$$

(3) Distribution laws

$$H \cup (E \cap F) = (H \cup E) \cap (H \cup F)$$
$$H \cap (E \cup F) = (H \cap E) \cup (H \cap F)$$

(4) DeMorgan's Laws

$$\overline{H \cup E} = \bar{H} \cap \bar{E}$$
$$\overline{H \cap E} = \bar{H} \cup \bar{E}$$

Observe that if H and E and F are taken to be sentences or propositions, rather than sets, and if '$\cap$' is taken to be conjunction, '$\cup$' disjunction, and '$^{-}$' negation, and if '$=$' is interpreted to have the sense of the biconditional 'if and only if', then these laws all become tautologies of sentential logic.

We begin our presentation of the probability calculus by taking the probability function, P, to be defined for a field (or, alternatively, a sigma-field) of sets. If we take probability to be defined rather for propositions, or statements, or events, then we take it to be defined for a field (or sigma-field) of them, where 'field' has a meaning analogous to that defined for sets above.

○ I—AXIOM OF TOTAL PROBABILITY

$P(V) = 1$, *where V is the universal set of the field of sets for which the probability function is defined.*

This axiom is sometimes expressed: If H is certain, $P(H) = 1$. By the certainty of H various things may be meant, according to the nature of the arguments of the probability function and according to the interpretation of the function itself. If the arguments are types of events, to say that H is certain is to say that an event of type H *must* occur; if the arguments are statements or propositions, it is to say that the statement or proposition H is either logically true or known with certainty on some other basis. In the former sense, the type of draw from an urn which either yields a black ball or does not yield a black ball is a type which must occur (among draws from urns); in the latter sense, such statements as "the first ball drawn is black or the first ball drawn is not black" are logically true, and "the first ball drawn is round" and "*this* ball which I am now observing to be black is black" are types of statements whose certainty may under the appropriate circumstances be directly certified.

○ II—ADDITION AXIOM

If H and E are mutually exclusive, then $P(H \cup E) = P(H) + P(E)$.

If H and E are sets of events, $H \cup E$ is their union, and to say that they are mutually exclusive is just to say that their intersection is empty. If they are types of events, $H \cup E$ is the type of event that occurs when either an event of type H or an event of type E occurs. If H and E are propositions or sentences, $H \cup E$ is their disjunction or alternation. To say that two types of events are mutually exclusive is to say that if one of the types of events has occurred, then the other type of event cannot have occurred. To say that two sentences or propositions are mutually exclusive is to say that it is known (on logical or analytical or other grounds) that they cannot both be true. If the value of the probability function is always a real number, the plus sign on the right-hand side of the equation has its conventional meaning.

The addition axiom, as it is stated above, may be applied to any finite number of alternatives; but in the mathematical development of the probability calculus it is often considered desirable to be able to apply it to an infinite number of alternatives or to a union of an infinite number of sets. It must then be extended, and it takes the following form:

○ II*—EXTENDED ADDITION AXIOM

If $H_1, H_2, H_3, \ldots$ is an infinite sequence, and for every j, $\bigcup_{i \leq j} H_i$ and H_{j+1} are mutually exclusive, then

$$P\left(\bigcup_{i=1}^{\infty} H_i\right) = \sum_{i=1}^{\infty} P(H_i) = P(H_1) + P(H_2) + P(H_3) + \cdots$$

A set function of any sort which satisfies II is called *additive*. If it also satisfies II*, it is called *sigma-additive*. Thus in formal presentations of the probability calculus, the probability function is often introduced simply as an additive (or sigma-additive) non-negative set function defined for a field (or sigma field) of sets, whose maximum value is 1.

○ III—MULTIPLICATION AXIOM

$P(H \cap E) = P(H) \times P(E|H)$.

This "axiom" is nowadays generally presented as a definition of the conditional probability of one statement E, *given* another, H: $P(E|H)$. In some older treatments, conditional probability is taken as a second primitive concept, and related to unconditional probability through the multiplication axiom. (Note that '$P(E|H)$' is not defined when $P(H) = 0$.)

The conditional probability of E, given $H, P(E|H)$, is a set function satisfying the probability axioms, defined on a certain subfield of $\mathscr{F}$, namely the set of sets $\mathscr{F}_H$ of all sets of the form $X \cap H$, where X belongs to $\mathscr{F}$. In this subfield, H plays the role of the universal set V.

As an illustration of the axioms, let us look at a typical classical example of the application of the calculus to the throws of a die. (We shall carry through the illustration for sets as arguments of the probability function; the modifications necessary to deal with types of events, sentences, or propositions, are simple enough to make.) Consider the set of events consisting of the throws of the die that result in one of the six numbers 1–6. This is the overall set V we are interested in; it is the universal set of our discussion; in discussions of probability it is often referred to as the *reference set*, for it is to this set that the probabilities of other sets are referred. Since in this framework, every throw of a die *must* result in one of these numbers, we take the measure of this set to be 1, in accord with the first axiom. Similarly, the measure of the set of throws that result in a 1 or in some other number is 1, and the measure of the set of throws that result in a number smaller than ten is 1.

Consider the set of throws, T_5, that result in the number 5, and the set of throws, $T_{1,2}$, that result in either the number 1 or the number 2. These two sets are mutually exclusive, in the sense that we know that, as dice are constructed and the game played, a single throw cannot belong to each of these two sets. Ordinarily one takes $P(T_5)$ to be $\frac{1}{6}$ and $P(T_{1,2})$ to be $\frac{1}{3}$; then, according to axiom II (or II*), we have

$$P(T_5 \cup T_{1,2}) = P(T_5) + P(T_{1,2}) = \tfrac{1}{6} + \tfrac{1}{3} = \tfrac{1}{2}.$$

Now consider the set of throws that result in a 2, a 3, or a 4: $T_{2,3,4}$. Ordinarily we take the measure of this set to be $\frac{1}{2}$. The conditional probability of $T_{1,2}$, given $T_{2,3,4}$, is simply the probability of $T_{1,2}$ relative to the set of tosses $T_{2,3,4}$ instead of relative to the total set of tosses. It is natural to take $P(T_{1,2}|T_{2,3,4})$ to be $\frac{1}{3}$. Since $T_2 = T_{1,2} \cap T_{2,3,4}$ we have

$$P(T_{1,2} \cap T_{2,3,4}) = P(T_2) = \tfrac{1}{6}$$

and

$$P(T_{1,2} \cap T_{2,3,4}) = P(T_{2,3,4}) \times P(T_{1,2}|T_{2,3,4})$$
$$= \tfrac{1}{2} \times \tfrac{1}{3}$$
$$= \tfrac{1}{6}.$$

This illustrates the third axiom.

As another example of the multiplicative axiom, let H be the set of tosses of the die that yield a number less than 4, and let E be the set of tosses yielding an odd number. $H \cap E$ is then the set of tosses yielding an odd number less than 4, i.e., 1 or 3, and the measure of this set ($\tfrac{1}{3}$, on the conventional assignment) is the product of the measure of the first set ($\tfrac{1}{2}$), multiplied by the conditional measure of the second set, *given* the restriction to the first set, i.e., the measure of the set of odd numbers, relative to the set of numbers less than 4 ($\tfrac{2}{3}$). We have

$$P(H \cap E) = \tfrac{1}{3}$$
$$P(H \cap E) = P(H) \times P(E|H)$$
$$= \tfrac{1}{2} \times \tfrac{2}{3}$$
$$= \tfrac{1}{3}.$$

A concept which is of great importance in discussions of the interpretation of probability, and in the application of probability as well, is that of stochastic or probabilistic independence. Two events, or statements, or propositions, or sets, are said to be stochastically or probabilistically independent either if the probability of one of them is 0, or if the conditional probability of one, given the other, is the same as its unconditional probability.

○ **DEFINITION I**

H is stochastically independent of E if and only if

$$P(E) = 0, \quad \text{or} \quad P(H) = P(H|E).$$

As an illustration of stochastic independence, consider a toss of a pair of dice. Let A be the set of tosses in which the first die shows a two, and B be the set of tosses in which the second die shows a three. We usually take the two outcomes to be independent, so that we would assign the same measure to the set of tosses in which the second die shows a three as we assign to the set of tosses in which the second die shows a three, *given* that the first die shows a two. Thus,

$$P(B) = P(B|A).$$

That this is a useful concept may be seen immediately from the fact that it is the principle we use in calculating the measure of the set of throws of two dice in which the first yields a two *and* the second yields a three.

$$P(B) = P(A) = \tfrac{1}{6} \qquad \text{(depends on interpretation of } P\text{)}$$
$$P(A \cap B) = P(A) \times P(B|A) \qquad \text{(multiplication axiom)}$$
$$P(B|A) = P(B) \qquad \text{(independence)}$$
$$P(A \cap B) = P(A) \times P(B) = \tfrac{1}{36} \qquad \text{(substitution)}$$

Some elementary theorems which will come in handy later on are the following:

○ **THEOREM 1**

$$P(H \cup \bar{H}) = 1.$$

○ **THEOREM 2**

$$P(H \cap \bar{H}) = 0.$$

○ **THEOREM 3**

$$P(\bar{H}) = 1 - P(H).$$

○ **THEOREM 4**

$$P(H) \geq 0.$$

○ **THEOREM 5**

$$P(H \cup E) = P(H) + P(E) - P(H \cap E).$$

○ **THEOREM 6**

H is independent of E if and only if E is independent of H.

○ **THEOREM 7**

If H and E are independent, $P(H \cap E) = P(H) \times P(E)$.

The last theorem in the list is sometimes referred to as the special multiplication theorem.

A theorem that is no less elementary than the foregoing, but which occupies such a central place in the discussion of statistical inference that the world of statisticians has been (perhaps inaccurately) partitioned according to the importance they attach to it, is Bayes' Theorem:

○ **THEOREM 8**

$$P(H/E) = P(H)\frac{P(E|H)}{P(E)}, \qquad \textit{provided } P(E) \neq 0.$$

Under some interpretations of probability, Bayes' Theorem provides a means for calculating the conditional probabilities of hypotheses, relative to given evidence. Basically, the theorem is simply a restatement of the multiplication axiom or the definition of conditional probability.

This theorem is particularly relevant, according to some writers, to the probability of inductions. In that context it is often rewritten in the following form:

○ **THEOREM 9**

If one and only one of the hypotheses $H_1, H_2, \ldots H_n$ is true, then

$$P(H_i|E) = \frac{P(H_i) \times P(E|H_i)}{\sum_{i=1}^{n} P(H_i) \times P(E|H_i)}.$$

In this theorem it is supposed that we have a finite number of exclusive and exhaustive alternative hypotheses, each of which, prior to the availability of the evidence E, has a prior probability $P(H_i)$. If this is the case, it is easy to show that the prior probability of E, $P(E)$, may be calculated as

$$\sum_{i=1}^{n} P(H_i) \times P(E|H_i).$$

The general philosophical and scientific importance of the theorem is clearest in Theorem 9, where it is clear that we need only the prior probabilities of the alternative hypotheses, $P(H_i)$, in order to obtain the posterior probability of any hypothesis, given the evidence we have bearing on it. (There is generally no problem in calculating the probability of the evidence, given a hypothesis H_i.) There are a number of views concerning the nature of probability which take this theorem as fundamental in scientific inference, in induction, and in learning from experience generally. We shall be particularly concerned with Bayes' Theorem when we return to the discussion of particular views concerning induction. For the moment it suffices to observe that although Bayes' Theorem is indirectly the source of controversy, there is nothing controversial about its theoremhood; it is one of the standard theorems of probability calculus.

Many of the most interesting and useful theorems in probability theory involve sets that may be thought of as representing sequences of events of a certain type, trials of a given experiment, instances of a given kind of proposition, and so on. To be more precise, let V be the universal set of a certain field of sets on which there is defined a measure function. For example, let V be the set of balls in an urn, and let the field of sets $\mathscr{F}_V$ consist of the four sets, V, B, $\bar{B}$, and ϕ, where B is the set of black balls and ϕ is the empty set—i.e., the set that has no members. Now let V^2 be a new universal set consisting of all pairs of elements of V. We are immediately faced with a choice: shall we confine V^2 to pairs of *distinct* elements, or shall we allow any pair (a, b)

to belong to V^2, regardless of whether or not a and b are distinct? The former alternative is appropriate if we are considering drawing balls from the urn two at a time, or one after the other without replacing them. This situation is called 'sampling without replacement'. The latter alternative is appropriate if we are considering drawing balls from the urn, one at a time, and, after each draw, replacing the ball so that it might be drawn over again. This is called 'sampling with replacement'. The simplest thing to do is to take V^2 to be the set of *all* pairs of elements of V. If we are concerned with sampling without replacement, we can restrict our attention to that *part* of V^2 which does not contain pairs of the form (a, a) by means of conditional probabilities, $P(E|\bar{R})$, where $\bar{R}$ is the subset of V^2 that does not contain repetitions. In a similar manner, we may construct a new universal set V^3, consisting of all triples of members of V; V^4, consisting of all quadruples of members of $V; \ldots V^n$ consisting of all n-tuples of members of V.

What is the field of subsets of V^2 for which we want the probability function defined? V^2 itself; the set of pairs of balls the first of which is black, regardless of the color of the second; the set in which the first is non-black, regardless of the color of the second; the set in which the second is black, regardless of the color of the first; the set in which the second is non-black, regardless of the color of the first; the set in which the first is black and the second is black; the set in which both are non-black; the set in which the first is black and the second is non-black; the set in which the first is non-black and the second is black; and, finally, the empty set, which we must always include. It is easy to see how rapidly the number of members of the field of sets will increase. There are in general, however, only two sorts of sets that specifically concern us: first, subsets of V^n in which it is specified, for each element of the n-tuple in the subset, which element of the original field of sets it belongs to. In the example for V^2, one such set is the set of balls such that the first is black and the second non-black. Second, we are interested in the subsets of V^n consisting of n-tuples of which the ith member belongs to a given element of $\mathscr{F}_V$—e.g., elements of V^2 in which the second ball is black. Also, we are particularly interested in subsets of V^n in which the *proportion* of the elements of the n-tuple that belong to specified elements of the original probability field of sets is specified. Thus one might be interested in the subset of V^2 consisting of pairs, both elements of which are black; or the subset of V^2 consisting of pairs, in which 50% (i.e., one ball) is black.

Finally, we want to extend the probability measure from the original field of sets $\mathscr{F}_V$ to the new fields of sets $\mathscr{F}_{V^2}, \mathscr{F}_{V^3}, \ldots \mathscr{F}_{V^n}$. There is no unique way of doing this, but there are two important special cases. Consider the subset of V^n consisting of n-tuples of which the ith belongs to the set H in $\mathscr{F}_V$. It is natural to stipulate that the measure in V^n of this set should be the same as the measure in V. Indeed this treatment seems to be the only appropriate one, when we take V^n to be the set of n-fold samples drawn (with replacement) from V, or when we take V^n to be the set of sequences of n trials of the "same" experiment. Now consider the conditional measure of the set of n-tuples in which the ith belongs to the set H of $\mathscr{F}_V$, given that the first element of the n-tuple belongs to H_1, that the second belongs to $H_2, \ldots$ and the $i - 1$st belongs to H_{i-1}. We arrive at one of the two special cases by making a very strong assumption: that this conditional measure is the same as the unconditional measure of H in V^n; we express this by saying that the elements of the n-tuples are independent. This additional assumption yields a unique measure for $\mathscr{F}_{V^n}$. the other special case corresponds to a somewhat weaker assumption: that this conditional measure depends only on the sets represented and the frequency with which they are represented (H_j may be the same as H_k, of course) and not on the particular order in which they are represented. If this assumption is satisfied, we say that the elements of the n-tuples are *exchangeable*; and although the probability measure on $\mathscr{F}_{V^n}$ is not uniquely determined by the condition of exchangeability, it is subject to such constraints that it becomes possible to prove certain important theorems.

Now for some down-to-earth examples. Suppose we have an urn containing black and white balls, of which a proportion p are black. Let V be the set of draws from the urn. Under appropriate conditions of drawing (drawing blindfolded, after mixing well, ...) it seems right to take a measure of the set of draws resulting in a black ball, B, to be p. Now suppose that we draw a sample of n balls, an n-fold sample, as we shall say, in the following manner: each ball is drawn under the same conditions as earlier described. After it has been drawn, its color is noted, it is replaced, the contents of the urn are stirred, and the next ball is drawn. Let V^n be the set of such samples. Let B_i be the set of n-tuples (a subset of V^n) in which the ith ball drawn is black. Our new field of sets $\mathscr{F}_{V^n}$, may be described as consisting of the n sets B_i, together with their complements, together with all the distinct unions and intersections we can construct from these ingredients. Thus $B_1 \cap B_2 \cap \cdots \cap B_n$ is the set of n-tuples consisting of n black balls; $B_1 \cup B_2 \cup \cdots \cup B_n$ is the set of n-tuples containing at least one black ball; $\bar{B}_1 \cap B_2 \cap B_3 \cap \cdots \cap B_n$ is the set of n-tuples consisting of a white ball followed by $n - 1$ black balls, and so on. What shall the probability function on $\mathscr{F}_{V^n}$ be? Since we have set the example up so that V^n consists of n trials of the same experiment, we can impose as an initial condition that

$$P(B_i) = P(B) = p.$$

In the new field of sets, each set B_i will have the same measure as the set B in the old field of sets. Furthermore, it seems appropriate in this example to regard the element of the n-tuples as independent. Thus, for example, $P(B_1 \cap B_2 \cap \cdots B_n) = P(B_1) \times P(B_2) \cdots P(B_n) = P(B) \times \cdots P(B) = [P(B)]^n$.

Next, consider a coin of irregular appearance. Let V be the set of tosses of this coin performed under certain determinate conditions. In view of the irregularity of the coin, it is implausible to suppose that we know how often, in the long run, it will turn up heads, but we can nevertheless (depending on our interpretation of the function P!) take a function P to be defined on

$\mathscr{F}_V = \{V, H, \bar{H}, \phi\}$, where H is the subset of V resulting in heads. Let V^n now be the set of sequences of n tosses of this coin. Let H_i be the set of n-tuples (sequences of n tosses) in which the ith toss results in heads. We construct a new field of sets $\mathscr{F}_{V^n}$ as before. Since, despite the irregularity of the coin, V^n consists of n trials of the same experiment, we can take as a condition on the new probability function P, $P(H_i) = P(H) =$ some value that we may call q. In the new field of sets, each set H_i will have the same measure as the set H in the old field of sets. But if we regard the frequency of heads among the first i tosses as providing grounds for modifying what we take to be the probability of heads on the $(i + 1)$st toss, we will *not* regard the elements of the n-tuples as independent. If *all* we take as relevant is the frequency of heads in the first i tosses, and not the order in which heads and tails occur, then we are regarding the elements of the n-tuples as exchangeable. There is no neat formula, as there is in the preceding example, for deriving the new measure from the old; the condition of exchangeability does not lead to a unique new measure. What it does lead to will be discussed in more detail in Chapters 6 and 13.

There are a few theorems concerning measures of sets of n-tuples of independent elements which may be stated here for future reference.

○ THEOREM 10

Let V be a universal set, H a subset such that $P(H) = p$. Let V^n be the set of n-tuples of V, and let H_i be the set of n-tuples of which the ith element belongs to H. Let $P(H_i) = P(H)$, and let the elements of the n-tuple be independent. Let E be the set of n-tuples in which k specified elements belong to H, and the $(n - k)$ remaining elements belong to $\bar{H}$. Then $P(E) = p^k(1 - p)^{(n-k)}$.

Proof: If the k specified members of the n-tuple belong to H are the first k, then by independence,

$$P(H_1 \cap H_2 \cap \cdots \cap H_k \cap \bar{H}_{k+1} \cap \bar{H}_{k+2} \cap \cdots \cap \bar{H}_n)$$
$$= P(H_1) \times P(H_2) \times \cdots \times P(H_k) \times P(H_{k+1}) \times \cdots \times P(H_n)$$
$$= [P(H)]^k[P(\bar{H})]^{(n-k)} = p^k(1 - p)^{(n-k)}.$$

But there is nothing essential in the order of the elements of H and $\bar{H}$; in any case, by independence, the probability of the set will be a product of n terms, k of which are equal to p, and $n - k$ of which are equal to p, and $n - k$ of which are equal to $(1 - p)$.

We are more often interested in the measure of the set of n-tuples that contain a specified number k of members of H than we are in the measure of the set of n-tuples containing members of H in k specified places. In order to calculate the measure of this set, under the assumptions of Theorem 10, we require a fragment of the theory of combinations and permutations. A permutation of a set of n objects consists of those n objects arranged in some definite order. Thus Tom first, Mary second, and Susan third is a permutation of a set consisting of Tom, Mary, and Susan. Mary first, Susan second, and Tom third is another permutation of the same set. How many permutations are there of a set of n objects? There are n ways of choosing the first object. Given a first object, there are $n - 1$ ways of choosing the second object. Each of the first choices may be combined with each of the second choices, so the number of ways of choosing the first two objects is $(n) \times (n - 1)$. Each of these in turn may be combined with each of the $n - 2$ ways of choosing the third object, so the number of ways of choosing the first three objects is $(n)(n - 1)(n - 2)$. After we have chosen $n - 1$ objects, we have only one choice left. Thus the total number of permutations of n objects is $(n)(n - 1) \times (n - 2) \cdots (2)(1)$. Numbers of this form are important in mathematics, and there is a special notation for them: '$n!$', which is read 'n factorial'. We may write a formal definition simply enough:

○ **DEFINITION II**

$$0! = 1 \quad and \quad n! = n(n - 1)!$$

In order to calculate how many n-tuples there are containing k members of H and $n - k$ members of $\overline{H}$, we need to know how many ways there are of combining $n - k$ objects of one sort ($\overline{H}$) with k objects of another sort (H). Let C be the number of such combinations. A given combination is unchanged if we permute the k_H objects in any of the $k!$ possible ways, and it is also unchanged if we permute the $n - k_{\overline{H}}$ objects in any of the $(n - k)!$ possible ways. Every permutation of the H objects can be combined with every permutation of the $\overline{H}$ objects, giving $k!(n - k)!$ permutations arising from each combination. By considering all the combinations, we arrive at all the permutations of n objects. Thus, $(n - k)! k! C = n!$, and $C = n!/(n - k)! k!$. There are a number of special notations for the ratio just computed; one of the most common is $\binom{n}{k}$.

○ **THEOREM 11**

Let V be a universal set, H a subset such that $P(H) = p$. Let V^n be the set of n-tuples of V, and let H_i be the set of n-tuples of which the ith element belongs to H. Let $P(H_i) = P(H)$, and let the elements of the n-tuple be independent. Let E be the set of n-tuples of which a given number, k, are members of H. Then

$$P(E) = \binom{n}{k} p^k (1 - p)^{n-k}.$$

Proof: There are $\binom{n}{k}$ ways of combining k elements of H with $n - k$ elements of $\overline{H}$. Each combination is an n-tuple in which k specified elements belong to H, and thus the measure of the set of such n-tuples is, by the previous theorem, $p^k(1 - p)^{n-k}$.

There is one important limit theorem to which we shall have occasion to refer in the sequel, Bernoulli's theorem. It is presented here without proof; although the proof is not difficult, it involves the introduction of new terminology which would serve no other purpose.

○ THEOREM 12—BERNOULLI'S THEOREM

Let V be a universal set, H a subset such that P(H) = p. Let V^n be the set of n-tuples of V, and let H_i be the set of n-tuples of which the ith element belongs to H. Let $P(H_i) = P(H)$, and let the elements of the n-tuples be independent. Let E be the set of n-tuples in which the frequency of H, f, is such that the inequalities $|f/n - p| > \epsilon$ are satisfied. $P(E) < pq/n^2 \le 1/(4n^2)$.

The import of this theorem is that it can be made as probable as you like and that the relative frequency of H in an n-tuple will differ by as little as you like from the probability p. Put more precisely, for any ϵ that you wish to choose, no matter how small, and for any δ you wish to choose, no matter how small, it is possible to choose an n large enough so that the probability that an n-tuple will exhibit a relative frequency of H differing by more than ϵ from p will be less than δ. The theorem is a crude one; in general the n-tuples in which the inequalities are satisfied will have a measure which is less than the upper limit mentioned in the theorem.

One example will perhaps suffice to make these concepts clear. Consider a factory producing radios. On the average, one radio out of ten is defective. What is the probability that in a box of four radios, exactly one will be defective? What is the probability that three or more will be defective? What conclusions can we draw about the frequency of defective radios in a carload of ten thousand?

Let us take as our original universe V the set of radios; the subset we are interested in is the subset D of defective radios. Let V^4 be the set of quadruples of radios. A box of four radios cannot contain the same radio twice, and so strictly we should analyze this problem in terms of a problem in sampling without replacement rather than with replacement; but when the sample is small and the universe large, the difference in the numbers is small, and so we shall take V^4 as our reference set. We shall take $P(D) = \frac{1}{10}$; whether this should be construed as representing the *fact* that $\frac{1}{10}$ of the radios are defective, or whether it should be construed as a *judgement* based on that fact, or whether it should be construed in some other way, we leave for later chapters. We let D_i be the set of quadruples in which the ith radio is defective, and take $P(D_i) = P(D) = \frac{1}{10}$. Furthermore, we assume that the elements of the quadruples are independent.

By Theorem 10 we can calculate the measure of the set of quadruples in which the first and third ratios are defective:

$$P(D_1 \cap \bar{D}_2 \cap D_3 \cap \bar{D}_4) = P(D_1) \times P(\bar{D}_2) \times P(D_3) \times P(\bar{D}_4)$$
$$= p \times (1 - p) \times p \times (1 - p)$$
$$= p^2(1 - p)^2 = 0.0081.$$

The probability that exactly one radio in a box of four will be defective can be calculated by Theorem 11 to be

$$\binom{4}{1}p^1(1 - p)^3 = 0.2916.$$

The probability that three or more will be defective is the probability that three will be defective plus the probability that four will be defective (by the addition axiom); or, by Theorem 4, it will be 1 minus the probability that either none or one or two are defective; or 1 minus the probability that none will be defective, minus probability that one will be defective, minus the probability that two will be defective. We have just calculated the probability that one will be defective, so let us follow the second approach. The probability that two radios in a box of four will be defective can be calculated by Theorem 11 to be

$$\binom{4}{2}p^2(1 - p)^2 = 0.0486.$$

The probability that none will be defective is

$$\binom{4}{0}p^4(1 - p)^0 = 0.6561.$$

Therefore, the probability that zero or one or two will be defective, by the addition axiom, is 0.9963, and, by Theorem 4, the probability that three or more will be defective is $1 - 0.9963 = 0.0037$.

Turning our attention to the carload, let us take ϵ to be 0.05. The probability that the difference between 0.10 and f/n, the relative frequency of defective radios, is greater than 0.05, is less than $\frac{9}{5200}$, or less than $\frac{2}{1000}$. Let us take ϵ to be 0.01. The probability that the difference between 0.10 and f/n is greater than 0.01 is less than $\frac{9}{100}$, or, less than $\frac{1}{10}$. In other words, we can be at least 90% sure (in some sense of 'sure') that the number of defective radios in a carload will be between 900 and 1100. Recall the crudeness of the theorem, however. In point of fact, the probability of the set of carloads in which the relative frequency of defective radios lies between the limits 0.09 and 0.11 will be far greater than 0.90.

EXERCISES

1. The text dicusses probability in a field of sets; it is asserted that a similar development could be made in terms of events. What is a field of events? What is a sigma-field of events?

2. Similarly, what is a field of statements? A sigma-field of statements?
3. Prove Theorems 1 through 4.
4. Prove Theorems 5 through 8.
5. Prove Theorem 9.
6. Show that $\mathscr{F}_H$, consisting of all sets of the form $H \cap X$, where X is a member of $\mathscr{F}$, is a field when $\mathscr{F}$ is a field.
7. Let $\mathscr{F}$ be a field (sigma-field) of sets, and let P be a probability function defined on $\mathscr{F}$. Let H be a member of $\mathscr{F}$, such that $P(H) \neq 0$. Let $\mathscr{F}_H$ be the set of all sets of the form $H \cap X$, where X is a member of $\mathscr{F}$. Show that $\mathscr{F}_H$ is a field (sigma-field) of sets; and show that $P(E|H)$ is a probability function on $\mathscr{F}_H$ when $P(E)$ is a probability function on $\mathscr{F}$.

In connection with the following problems, provide an analysis of the problem *exhibiting the assumptions that are made*, as well as the answers that are arrived at.

8. What is the probability of getting four heads on ten tosses of a well-balanced coin?
9. What is the probability of getting between four and six heads (inclusive) on ten tosses of a well-balanced coin?
10. What is the probability of not getting any heads at all on ten tosses of a well-balanced coin?
11. Consider an irregular-looking coin. Suppose the probability of getting heads on a toss of this coin is p, but that the value of p is unknown. How often must we flip the coin in order to be at least 90% sure that the difference between the relative frequency of heads in our sequence of tosses, and p, is less than 0.01?
12. What is the probability of rolling a seven with a pair of ordinary dice?
13. What is the probability that two cards drawn simultaneously from a deck of cards will both be hearts? (Careful: this couple is not independent).
14. A carton contains ten pairs of shoes. If three of them contain defects, what is the probability that of two pairs taken from the box, exactly one contains defects. (Again, the couple selected is not independent).
15. A poker player holds four hearts and a club. He discards a club and draws a new card from the deck. What is the probability that the new card is a heart?

BIBLIOGRAPHICAL NOTES FOR CHAPTER 2

Standard treatments of the probability calculus from a set-theoretical point of view may be found in H. Cramér, *Introduction to Probability Theory*, John Wiley and Sons, New York, 1955; W. Feller, *An Introduction to Probability Theory and Its Applications*, John Wiley and Sons, New York, 1957; and in a large number of other common texts including Kyburg, *Probability Theory*, Prentice-Hall, Englewood Cliffs, New Jersey, 1969. An early, neat, axiomatization written from this point of view is Kolmogorov's, translated as *Foundations of the Theory of*

Probability, Chelsea, New York, 1950; first published, 1931. The first axiomatization that takes the arguments of the probability function to be propositions is J. M. Keynes, *Treatise on Probability*, Macmillan, London, 1921. A more recent and very elegant version is to be found in Rudolf Carnap's *Logical Foundations of Probability*, University of Chicago Press, Chicago, 1950. Axiomatizations of the probability calculus that do not presuppose any of the conventional logical properties (such as commutivity) of the connectives that are applied to the arguments of the probability function are provided by Karl Popper in "Two Autonomous Axiom Systems for the Calculus of Probabilities," *British Journal for the Philosophy of Science* 6, 1955–56, pp. 51–57; and in Appendices *iv and *v to *The Logic of Scientific Discovery*, Hutchinson and Co., London, 1959.

3

The Classical
Interpretation of Probability

It will be observed that the statements of the pure probability calculus are (almost) all conditional in form. In order to use the calculus we must have some way of obtaining probabilities which are not 0 or 1. Various views about the meaning of probability statements may be looked upon as ways of arriving at numbers to put into the calculus. The classical method, developed first in connection with games of chance, was to define probability as a ratio of numbers of alternatives. On this view, the reason we assign the probability $\frac{1}{6}$ to the result of getting a four on a toss of a die, is that there are six *possible* ways in which the die may turn up, only one of which is favorable to that particular result. The ratio of the number of *favorable* alternatives to the *total* number of alternatives is 1:6.

This technique of counting alternatives and taking the probability of an event (or statement) to be the ratio of the number of possibilities is a simple one, and one which leads to conventional and plausible results when we are concerned (as all the early probability theorists were) with gambling devices. But in almost any other circumstances the alternatives are hard to find. Even to calculate gambling probabilities we find that we need some principle to tell us which alternatives to count. In rolling a die, for example, we do not argue that there is a probability of $\frac{1}{2}$ of rolling a six, on the grounds that there are two possibilities, 'six' and 'not-six', just one of which is favorable to 'six'. Some further principle is required than that provided by counting any *arbitrary* set of alternatives.

The first principle that seems to have come into common use is that one should not merely count any old alternatives, but only *equipossible* alternatives. 'Six' and 'not-six' are not equipossible alternatives, because many more (five times as many) alternatives are included among the possibilities allowed by the latter as are included among the possibilities allowed by the former. On the other hand, 'one', 'two', and so on represent equally possible alternatives, in the sense that any attempt to sub-divide one of these alternatives can be paralleled by a subdivision of the other alternatives. Were someone to suggest that the alternative 'six' could be divided into 'six on a sunny day' and 'six on a rainy day', it would be pointed out that (a) these alternatives are not of interest to us, and (b) any of the other alternatives 'one', 'two', etc., could be divided in a similar irrelevant way.

This principle, without further refinement, comes a cropper, however, when we consider biased gambling equipment. With a pair of ordinary dice, we could claim, in accordance with this principle, that the probability of rolling a seven is $\frac{6}{36}$, since there are thirty-six ways in which a pair of dice may land; these constitute thirty-six equally possible alternatives; and six of these alternatives lead to the result 'seven'. But there are loaded dice as well as ordinary dice. One way of loading dice is to mark their sides in an unconventional way. If one of a pair of dice is marked with a one, a six, a four, and three threes, and if the other is marked with a one, a six, a three, and three fours, the probability of 'seven' on the classical analysis is $\frac{12}{36}$: of the thirty-six ways in which the dice may land, twelve produce the result 'seven'. But there are more subtle ways of loading dice, by changing the center of gravity; one die may be weighted on the side opposite the three, for example, and the other die may be weighted on the side opposite the four. Such a pair of dice will presumably yield 'seven' more often than a pair of unweighted dice. The *results* are just the same results we considered for the unweighted, well-balanced dice. Since they are the same set of results, why should we not regard them as being equipossible in this case as in the first case?

LaPlace provided an answer: we must interpret 'equipossible' as meaning equiprobable. This answer lies at the heart of the classical interpretation of the probability calculus. Probability is taken to be the ratio of the number of alternatives favorable to an event (such as 'seven' on the roll of a pair of dice) among a given set of *equiprobable* alternatives. With an ordinary pair of dice, the alternative ways in which they can land are designed to be, and are, equiprobable; therefore to calculate the probability of any particular way of landing, we need merely count the alternatives that produce that way of landing and divide by 36.

This technique of defining probability as a ratio of equiprobable alternatives sounds circular; it need not be, however, as long as there is some way, not involving reference to probability, for identifying the equiprobable alternatives. That is, we can avoid circularity if we can define probability in general in terms of equiprobable alternatives, and then define equiprobability of alternatives in terms of something that does not involve reference to probability. This is precisely what LaPlace attempted to do with his principle of indifference—the most notorious principle in the whole history of probability theory. According to this principle two possibilities are equiprobable if and only if there is no *ground* for choosing between them. Thus, for example, the six alternative outcomes of a throw of an ordinary die are equiprobable, since there are no grounds for choosing among them; and therefore the probability of getting a six is $\frac{1}{6}$. But the thirty-six alternative outcomes of a throw of a pair of loaded dice mentioned above are not equiprobable, because the principle of indifference does not apply to them. The alternative in which one die shows a three and the other a four is one that we have *grounds* for choosing. The grounds are, of course, that the side opposite the three is weighted in one die, and the side opposite the four is weighted in the other die. The principle of indifference as formulated by LaPlace thus not only gives us reasons for applying the ratio of alternative analysis to fair gambling equipment, but also explains why we cannot apply the same analysis to biased gambling equipment.

It should be observed that the *grounds* on the basis of which we decline to call alternatives equiprobable are not *mere* asymmetry. The unbiased die, like the biased one, is asymmetrical: It has more spots of paint on some sides than on others. What counts is a *relevant* lack of symmetry, and a lack of symmetry is relevant when it has some bearing on the frequency with which we expect a certain sort of event to happen. Notice that we cannot, tempting as it may be, say that a lack of symmetry is relevant when it affects the *probability* of a certain sort of event, for then we would be re-introducing the very word, 'probability', that we are trying to explain. There is nothing circular, however, about defining equiprobability of alternatives in terms of our lack of knowledge of characteristics which would result in unequal frequencies. Even painting one face of a die red would not introduce an asymmetry which we would have any reason to believe would turn out to be connected with an alteration in the frequency with which that side turns up, and thus would not destroy the argument for equiprobability based on the principle of indifference.

On this classical view, there is a relation between probability and frequency holding in the opposite direction, as well. Not only does knowledge or expectation of deviant frequencies destroy the applicability of the principle of indifference, but probabilities, on this classical interpretation, can be taken to give us knowledge or expectation of long-run frequencies. Theorem 12 can be applied to rolls of dice and tosses of coins, to tell us that if we regard certain alternatives as equally probable (by the principle of indifference) and *if* we regard certain alternatives (the different tosses of the coin or the different rolls of the die) as independent, *then* we may expect certain frequencies to obtain in finite sequences of trials. Consider, for example, a coin, symmetrical in relevant respects. That is, there is nothing we know about either side of the coin which would give us grounds for thinking that the coin will land more (or less) often with that side up, when tossed in an ordinary manner. We apply the principle of indifference once, and infer that the probability of heads is a half. Given that the coin has landed heads on one toss, there is still no reason to suppose that it is either more or less likely to land heads on the next toss; this is the second application of the principle of indifference: we infer in general that the tosses are independent. We may then apply Theorem 12, and infer that the probability is at least 0.99 that of 10,000 tosses, between 4,500 and 5,500 will result in heads. Thus we can argue from the probabilities of individual occurrences to the very high probability of a certain complex occurrence.

This seems suspiciously like what Nagel castigates as "a form of *a priori* rationalism." But as Nagel also points out, there is nothing wrong with the argument—indeed it is essentially a theorem of arithmetic—so long as it is kept in mind that neither of the occurrences of 'probability' are taken to entail anything about actual relative frequencies. The probability may be 0.99 that the 10,000 tosses will have the character under discussion, but that not only doesn't mean that a particular set of 10,000 tosses may not lack that character—it doesn't mean that 99% of all sets of ten-thousand tosses will have that character, as for example, they certainly will not if the coin happens (without our knowledge) to be seriously biased.

It could be maintained, however, that in the face of any extensive knowledge concerning relative frequencies, we would be obligated to use that knowledge for applying the principle of indifference, and therefore that probabilities that are arrived at by means of the principle of indifference cannot conflict too seriously with observed relative frequencies. The advantage of this gambit is dubious; to the extent that it makes probabilities always dependent on frequencies it turns the classical interpretation of the probability function into something indistinguishable from the frequency interpretation (to be discussed in the next chapter). It is probably for this reason, rather than on account of the logical arguments that follow, that the classical interpretation of the probability calculus has been virtually abandoned for forty years.

There are a number of arguments that philosophers have brought against the principle of indifference. Consider the loaded die again. If we do not know which side is weighted, then again our knowledge concerning each side is symmetrical; by the principle of indifference the probability of each side turning up is the same as the probability of any other side turning up; the probability of a two is therefore $\frac{1}{6}$. This is strange enough, considering that we know the die to be loaded. But we can carry the argument a step further. One can argue that since there is no connection between what happens on one toss of a die and what happens on another, the outcomes of a sequence of rolls of the die are independent in the sense required by Theorem 12, and that there-fore the die is practically certain, in a long run of tosses, to yield a two about a sixth of the time. Yet in another sense, knowing that the die is loaded, we should be practically certain that in the long run it will not yield two about a sixth of the time, but should yield a two either more than a sixth of the time (if it is loaded in favor of that side) or less than a sixth of the time (if it is loaded in favor of some other side).

Furthermore, suppose that we have performed a large number of rolls of our loaded die, under appropriate scientifically controlled circumstances, and suppose that a two has turned up about a third of the time. It seems inevitable that we will want to say that the probability of rolling a two under these circumstances with this die is $\frac{1}{3}$, or anyway very close to $\frac{1}{3}$. And yet what are the equiprobable alternatives, one third of which are favorable to the result 'two'? One might suppose that the alternatives are represented by certain intervals of velocity and location and spin that obtain when the die is thrown —but this already seems too complicated, too artificial, and too unnecessary. It is even more difficult to see how the definition of probability as the ratio of equiprobable alternatives can be applied to statistical probabilities of the sort with which insurance companies deal. What are the thousand equi-probable alternatives of which 945 are favorable to the survival of a thirty-nine-year-old man through the coming year? There are also probability problems in physics and mathematics which lead to irrational numbers as probabilities. These probabilities (e.g., $6/\pi^2$ for the probability that an integer selected at random is prime) cannot be regarded as ratios of numbers of alternatives for the simple reason that irrational numbers cannot be regarded as ratios of integers at all.

To look at an example in which we are led to *logically* curious conclusions by the principle of indifference, consider the problem of selecting balls of unknown composition from an urn. There seems to be no more reason to expect a given ball to be red than to expect it to be non-red; so we are led by the principle of indifference to say that the probability that it is red is $\frac{1}{2}$. But analogous reasoning applies to the proposition that it is blue, so the proba-bility that it is blue is $\frac{1}{2}$. Similarly, the probability that it is green is $\frac{1}{2}$. But now if we use the addition axiom, we are led to the *logical* absurdity that the probability that the ball is red *or* green *or* blue is $1\frac{1}{2}$, which contradicts the first axiom.

Paradoxes like this can be avoided only by demanding that the principles of indifference be applied only to alternatives about which our knowledge is symmetrical. The foregoing paradox, it is said, fails to meet this criterion, since we know that there are a large number of colors that balls in urns may have, of which the colors red and green and blue represent only a few. There

is only one way in which a ball can be red, but there are many ways in which it can be non-red. But while it is clear how to count the "ways" in which a die can fail to land with the two up, it is not clear at all how to count the "ways" in which a ball can fail to be red. One can, of course, construct a finite list of n colors, and stipulate for the purposes of a particular problem that these are the n ways in which a ball can be colored. Then it is clear that there are $n - 1$ ways in which a ball can be non-red. But while an argument can be made for doing this, the argument must construe probability as a purely logical relation. We shall discuss this interpretation of probability in a separate place. Here it should suffice to observe that setting up, for a special problem, an artificial list of n colors, is a long way from simply applying the classical principle of indifference to readymade alternatives.

Another difficulty can be seen in problems of the following sort. This is called Bertrand's Box Paradox. Consider a box with three drawers. In one drawer there are two gold coins; in another drawer there are two silver coins; and in the third drawer there is one silver coin and one gold coin. A drawer is selected at random (by a method under which each drawer is equally likely to be selected), and a coin is selected at random from the drawer. The selected coin is gold. What is the probability that the other coin is gold?

Answer I: Since the selected coin is gold, the drawer must be either the drawer with the two gold coins, or the one with a gold coin and a silver coin; it cannot be the drawer with two silver coins. Now we have no more reason to believe that it is the drawer with two gold coins than the drawer with one silver; and so we may apply the principle of indifference; there are two alternatives, one of which is favorable; the probability is $\frac{1}{2}$ that the other coin is gold.

Answer II: There are six alternatives: the drawer with two gold coins is selected, and the first coin is drawn; the same drawer is selected and the second (also gold) coin is drawn; the drawer with two silver coins is selected and the first coin is drawn; the same drawer is selected and the second coin (also silver) is drawn; the mixed drawer is selected and the first (silver) coin is drawn; the same drawer is selected and the second (gold) coin is drawn. Of these alternatives three are ruled out by having drawn a gold coin. Of the remaining three, two are favorable to the remaining coin being gold. Therefore the probability is $\frac{2}{3}$ that the second coin is gold.

Under ordinary conditions of drawing, answer II is correct, as we can see by processing the problem through Bayes' Theorem. The second coin will be gold if and only if we happen to have chosen the drawer with two gold coins in it. That probability, given that we've drawn one coin and found it gold, is $\frac{1}{3}$ (the prior probability that we will choose that drawer) multiplied by 1 (the probability that we will have gotten first a gold coin, if that is the drawer we are drawing from) divided by the total probability of getting a gold coin, which may be calculated to be $\frac{1}{2}$. But the principle of indifference seems to lead to an alternative result. Merely examining the use of the principle of indifference in answer I, it is difficult to see what went wrong.

One of the things we should like to do with probability is to argue that when we have drawn a large number of balls from an urn and found them all to be red, we are entitled to conclude that it is probable that the proportion of red balls in the urn is close to 1. We can attempt to do this with the help of Bayes' Theorem if we can, before drawing any balls, assign probabilities to the various hypotheses concerning the colors of the balls. There are two relatively natural ways in which we may call on the principle of indifference to establish these prior probabilities: we may apply it to *state descriptions* or we may apply it to *structure descriptions*. (We shall encounter these terms again when we come to discuss the logical interpretation of probability in Chapter 5.) A state description, in this context, is a statement asserting of each ball in the urn that it has one of a definite list of n colors. (For example, ball 1 is red, ball 2 is red; ball 3 is blue; etc.) A structure description, on the other hand, is a statement asserting only that the *proportion* of balls of each color in the urn has such and such a value. (For example, $\frac{3}{10}$ of the balls are blue, $\frac{1}{10}$ of the balls are red, etc.)

If we apply the principle of indifference to state descriptions, it is easy to show, as Carnap does, that Bayes' Theorem does not enable us to learn from experience in the way we expect it to. The fact that we have drawn a number of red balls from the urn is independent (in the sense of independence defined above) of any hypothesis we may consider concerning the colors of the balls remaining in the urn. It is easy to see how this is, in an example. Let the urn contain only two balls, which are either black or white. The state descriptions are:

1. The first ball is black and the second ball is black.
2. The first ball is black and the second ball is white.
3. The first ball is white and the second ball is black.
4. The first ball is white and the second ball is white.

If we suppose that these four alternatives are equally probable, it is an easy exercise to apply Bayes' Theorem to calculate:

The probability that the other ball is white, given that the first ball has been drawn and observed to be white, is $\frac{1}{2}$.

That is, the conditional probability of the hypothesis concerning the *remainder* of the balls, given data concerning a sample, is the same as the unconditional probability of that hypothesis—i.e., the initial probability that the second ball would be white.

If we apply the principle of indifference to structure descriptions (regarding each of the structure descriptions as equally probable), then we do get plausible results from the application of Bayes' Theorem. But observe that this use of the principle of indifference is perfectly analogous to the use we made of it in saying that the alternatives 'red' and 'non-red' are equally probable. We rejected the latter argument on the ground that there are more ways in which a ball can be non-red than there are in which it can be red. Similarly, here we should reject the equiprobability of structure descriptions on the ground that there are many more ways in which the proportion of red balls may be close to $1/n$, where n is the number of colors we are counting, than there are in which it can be close to 1. This may be seen by counting the number of state descriptions that correspond to each given structure description.

The principle of indifference also leads to difficulties when we deal with attributes (such as mass per unit volume) which may vary continuously. Consider an alloy of which we know that it has a mass per unit volume lying between 1 and 2. The principle of indifference might be used to argue that there is no more reason to suppose that the mass per unit volume lies in one small interval than in another of the same size, and therefore that there is a probability of $\frac{1}{2}$ that the mass per unit volume will lie between 1 and $1\frac{1}{2}$. But we may also consider, just as well, the volume per unit mass. Our sample has a volume per unit mass lying between $\frac{1}{2}$ and 1; the principle of indifference will yield the conclusion that the probability is $\frac{1}{2}$ that it is between $\frac{3}{4}$ and 1. But this is just to say that the probability is $\frac{1}{2}$ that the mass per unit volume lies between 1 and $1\frac{1}{3}$, which conflicts with our first assertion. Or we could conclude that the probability is $\frac{1}{2}$ that the mass per unit volume is greater than $1\frac{1}{2}$, and $\frac{1}{2}$ that the mass per unit volume is less than $1\frac{1}{3}$, and therefore that the probability is 0 that the mass per unit volume is between $1\frac{1}{3}$ and $1\frac{1}{2}$.

Another problem in which the application of the principle of indifference gives rise to conflicting solutions is the following, also called Bertrand's Paradox. Consider a circle of unit radius. Drop a line at random on the circle. What is the probability that the length of the chord produced by the line is greater than 1?

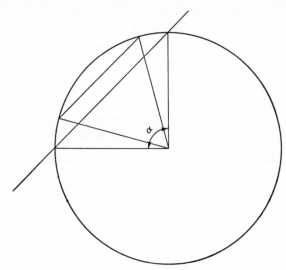

Figure 1.

Answer I: The angle α in Figure 1 may vary from 0 to 180°. There is no more reason why it should be in one interval of angles rather than another, except that interval be larger; so by applying the principle of indifference we conclude that the probability is $\frac{2}{3}$ that the angle is greater than 60°, and therefore that the probability that the chord exceed 1 is $\frac{2}{3}$.

Answer II: The line segment r in Figure 2 may vary from 0 to 1. There is no more reason why it should be in one interval than another, except that the interval be larger; so by applying the principle of indifference we conclude that the probability is $\sqrt{3}/2$ that the length of the chord will exceed 1.

The principle of indifference is the heart of the classical interpretation of the calculus of probability. Where the alternatives are clear-cut, and where we have reason to believe that each alternative will occur with approximately equal frequency under the circumstances considered, the principle of indifference has served a useful function. Under these circumstances, however, frequency interpretations of probability lead to similar results, though perhaps less directly and less simply. Many statisticians regard the classical interpretation of probability as simply a stage on the path to a modern frequency interpretation of one sort or another.

There are also logicians and mathematicians who still hope to be able to formulate a principle of indifference in such a way that it can be saved as a useful tool in the interpretation of a concept of probability which will be applicable when frequency considerations are not applicable. Some of these proposals will be considered in greater detail when we consider interpretations of probability which take it to be a logical relation similar to, but weaker than, the logical relation of entailment, for it is these interpretations which have today inherited most of the strengths, and some of the weaknesses, of the classical interpretation of probability.

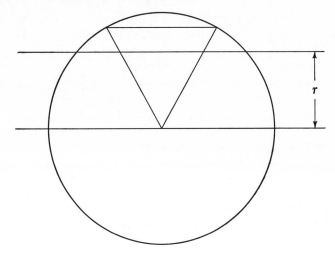

Figure 2.

In a sense the classical interpretation of probability *is* the principle of indifference, for it is only a principle of indifference that can individuate the alternatives to be counted. Some of the sound elements of the principle of indifference have been taken over by frequency or empirical theories of probability, though mostly as merely heuristic principles—rules of thumb which can always in principle be replaced by frequency analyses—and other sound elements of the principle have found their way into logical interpretations of probability, where the difficulties of the principle are avoided by circumscribing quite strictly its range of application. The classical interpretation itself, however, has been long abandoned among philosophers and reflective mathematicians.

EXERCISES

1. Does the classical interpretation of probability justify the following argument? If so, how; if not, why not?
   A pair of coins is tossed. There are three possible outcomes: a pair of heads, a pair of tails, and one of each. There is no reason to suppose one of these outcomes more probable than any other; and so the probability of a pair of heads is $\frac{1}{3}$.
2. Consider an urn containing four balls. The balls may be either black or white. List the sixteen state descriptions, and all the structure descriptions.
3. Suppose that two balls are drawn from the urn of Problem 2, and that both are black. What is the conditional probability that the remaining two balls are black, given the application of the principle of indifference to state descriptions? What is the conditional probability if the principle of indifference is applied to structure descriptions?
4. Consider a die, constructed in such a way that one half is steel, and the other half a special plastic with the same density and elasticity as steel. Should the principle of indifference apply to tosses of this die? Explain.
5. Use the principle of indifference to calculate the probability of throwing a four before throwing a seven with a pair of dice. Why is or isn't the principle of indifference appropriate here?
6. Use the principle of indifference to calculate the probability of getting a heart flush (five cards, all of which are hearts) in poker. Why is or isn't the principle of indifference appropriate here?
7. Use the principle of indifference to calculate the probability that Galloper will win a horse race against seven competitors. Why is or isn't the principle of indifference appropriate here?
8. Let a die be weighted so as to fall with one side uppermost with greater frequency than the other sides, but suppose we do not know which side it is that will turn up most often. Assuming that we may appropriately apply the principle of indifference to the first roll of the die, so that on the first roll the probability is $\frac{1}{6}$ that any given side lands uppermost; is there any way to block the application of Theorem 12, which entails that in the

long run, it is practically certain that any given side will turn up about a sixth of the time?

9. The principle of indifference of this chapter has been formulated with respect to events, or kinds of events. Provide a reformulation that will apply to statements.

10. Provide a formulation of a principle of indifference that will apply to sets.

BIBLIOGRAPHICAL NOTES FOR CHAPTER 3

Pierre Simon de LaPlace, the famous French mathematician and astronomer (1749–1827), provided the first detailed defense of the principle of indifference in his book *A Philosophical Essay on Probabilities*, Dover Publications, New York, 1951. Some of his uses of the principle lead to profound and incredible conclusions which (nowadays) tend rather to undermine than to support the principle. John Maynard Keynes, *A Treatise on Probability*, Macmillan, London and New York, 1921, gives a detailed criticism and exposition of the principle from a point of view not terribly far removed from the classical one. Ernest Nagel, in his *Principles of the Theory of Probability*, University of Chicago Press, Chicago, 1939, provides an exposition of the classical conception of probability and many penetrating criticisms of it. For the proof that applying the principle of indifference to state descriptions precludes learning from experience, see Rudolf Carnap, *Logical Foundations of Probability*, University of Chicago Press, Chicago, 1951, Section 110.

4

Empirical
Interpretations of Probability

It is clear that the classical principle of indifference was neither so clear-cut nor so compelling as to lead to universal agreement. Indeed, the more clearly was the principle formulated by its defenders, the more quickly and easily were counter-examples devised. It was also observed long ago that in many uses of probability—particularly those associated with insurance, with vital statistics, with scientific experiments in biology and agriculture, as these began to be performed in the nineteenth and twentieth centuries—the only way of arriving at probabilities was not to compute numbers of equally likely alternatives, but to count instances and to take the probability of an event to be indicated by the relative frequency with which that event occurred among the instances counted. For example, no insurance company would calculate the probability of death of an American male of the white-collar class during his thirty-ninth year in any way but by looking at the records: What proportion of the recorded cases of thirty-nine year old white-collar American males are cases in which death occurred during the thirty-ninth year?

There are three ways in which we can utilize the insight provided by the use of probability in vital statistics, agriculture, and the like, in such a way as to come up with an empirical interpretation of probability. One may literally *identify* probabilities with relative frequencies, one may take probabilities to be the *abstract counterparts* of relative frequencies, or one may take probabilities to characterize certain *kinds* of events: chance set-ups, or events exhibiting certain kinds of *propensities*.

There are many variations on the view that probabilities are to be identified with relative frequencies. Most of these interpretations of probability are more or less derivative from the views of Richard von Mises, whose influential book, *Probability, Statistics and Truth*, was published in 1928. Among mathematical statisticians there are still many who regard von Mises' view that probability should be interpreted as the limit of a relative frequency in an unending sequence as the latest (reasonable) word. There are many more people, both mathematicians and philosophers, who have views regarding the interpretation of probability that are closely related to but not identical with von Mises' views. After we have looked at von Mises' interpretation of probability, we shall look at some of the variations on it.

According to von Mises, "The theory of probability [is] a science of the same order as geometry or theoretical mechanics...just as the subject matter of geometry is the study of space phenomena, so probability theory deals with mass phenomena and repetitive events" (p. vii). To talk to the probability of an event, for von Mises, makes sense only if we have in mind some definite *collective* relative to which we have defined this probability. At first, von Mises was unclear as to whether a collective was to be understood as an actual, practically unlimited sequence of events, or whether it was to be understood as strictly infinite, so that one might speak of the existence, in such sequences, of mathematical limits in the strict sense. The current view adopted by von Mises (in *Mathematical Theory of Probability*) explicitly takes a collective to be a mathematical entity, representing an idealization of an empirical reality. The empirical reality corresponding to a collective is a sequence of events of a certain sort. This sequence may be practically unlimited, in the sense that we can (in general) always extend it a little further; we can always toss the coin a few more times, or take a few more observations on the emission of alpha particles from X.

Within the collective, we single out a certain subsequence; when we speak about probability, we are speaking about a certain subsequence in a collective. The subsequence corresponds to an event of a certain *sort* (heads on a toss of a coin, death during the thirty-ninth year, etc.). To say that the probability exists is to say that within the collective the limit of the relative frequency of members of the subsequence exists; "the probability of heads is a half" is to be interpreted as meaning that there is a certain infinite collective (representing tosses of a coin); there is a certain subsequence of that collective (representing tosses yielding heads); and that the limit of the relative frequency of elements of the subsequence in the collective exists and has the value $\frac{1}{2}$.

We demand here convergence to a limit in the strict mathematical sense. That is, if T is the infinite collective representing tosses of a coin, and H the subsequence representing tosses that result in heads, then we say that the limit of H in T exists and has the value p, if and only if: for every δ, no matter how small, it is possible to find an N with the property that for every n greater than N, if we calculate the proportion of members of H among the first n elements of the collective, that proportion will differ by less than δ from p. Let us denote the relation frequency of H among the first n elements of T by $f_n(H)$. The assertion that the limit of the relative frequency of H in T is p can then be briefly expressed symbolically:

$$(\delta)(\exists N)(n)(n > N \supset |f_n(H) - p| < \delta).$$

This is clearly an unverifiable theoretical assertion about a model which is taken to represent a certain empirically given sequence in the same sense that no set of observations will definitely verify it. It is not asserted—indeed it obviously could not be asserted—that there is some way of *calculating* N as a function of δ. Nothing is asserted but the bare existence of such an N. The assertion is therefore not refutable, either. This has been regarded as a defect of the limiting-frequency interpretation of probability. But in view of the fact that probability under this interpretation becomes a relatively high-level theoretical concept, this is not a serious shortcoming. Similar remarks concerning unverifiability and unfalsifiability could be made about such perfectly acceptable concepts as length. One could plausibly say that to assert that the length of a table is four feet is to assert that, for any δ you choose, there exists a process of measurement such that the result of applying that process of measurement to the table will yield a result that will (probably) differ from four by less than δ. It does not seem that the verification or falsification of assertions of probability are any more problematic, on the limiting-frequency interpretation, than that of many other empirical statements about which we feel no qualms at all.

There is one more requirement that von Mises imposes on collectives, and that is that they must be *random* with respect to the subsequence or type of entity under consideration. Randomness is defined as independence under place selection. This means that if we consider, instead of the whole sequence $E_1, E_2, E_3, \ldots$, the subsequence consisting of every other one of the E's, E_1, $E_3, E_5, \ldots$, or the subsequence consisting of every third or fourth of the E's, or the subsequence consisting of every E with a prime subscript, or...any other way of selecting places by subscript, then we will find the same relative frequency of H type elements in the subsequence as we found in the sequence as a whole.

It was thought for some time that the notion of randomness might lead to difficulty. In particular, of course, it is self-contradictory to demand that the limiting relative frequency be independent of *all* place selections, for there will be at least one place selection (actually, there will be an infinite number of them) which will select events in such a way that the limiting frequency of *H* type elements will be one, rather than *p*. If we cannot suppose the limiting frequency to be insensitive to all place selections, perhaps we may nevertheless suppose that it is insensitive to all of a certain set of place selections. One obviously relevant set of place selections is the set of place selections which select every second, or every third, or...or every *n*th element of the original sequence. If for every *n* it is true that the subsequence consisting of every *n*th member of the original sequence, starting from some arbitrary place, will exhibit the same limiting frequency of *H* as the original sequence, then the original sequence is called a Bernoulli sequence. It is possible to show that Bernoulli sequences exist; indeed one can give a *rule* for constructing sequences of 0's and 1's which are Bernoulli sequences. This possibility proves that there is nothing self-contradictory about the limiting-frequency model, combined with the stipulation that the limiting frequency be insensitive under all place selections of the sort just described. It can also be shown that if the limiting frequency is insensitive under all place selections of the sort just described, then it is also insensitive to place selections of the kind: take as the subsequence every element of the sequence that follows two non-*H*'s and an *H*; or take as a subsequence every element of the sequence that follows five consecutive *H*'s; and the like.

But there are still many place selections that are not taken account of by Bernoulli sequences. For example, the place selection consisting of the *E*'s with a prime subscript, already mentioned, might still, in a Bernoulli sequence, exhibit a limiting frequency different from that in the original sequence. Indeed, no matter how many place selections we think of taking account of, there will be others that we may wish to add to our list. How far can we go in extending the list of place selections that will not lead to a different limiting frequency, or to no limit at all? The strongest result that has been proved so far is this: that given a sequence, the members of which possess certain properties, the assumption that the limits of the relative frequencies of these properties exist, and that they are insensitive to any finite or denumerably infinite set of place selections, cannot lead to a contradiction. Thus although we cannot claim insensitivity to all place selections in our theoretical model, we can claim insensitivity to any arbitrary denumerable set of place selections.

Given the existence of collectives, von Mises has little trouble in showing that the limits of the relative frequencies of properties in collectives satisfy the axioms of the probability calculus. Thus if *K* is a collective, and *H* is a property defined for elements of that collective, then if the limit of the relative frequency of *H* is *p*, the limit of the relative frequency of $\overline{H}$ is $1 - p$. The general form of the multiplication rule requires the combination of two collectives; the new collective, to which the new probability of *H* and *T* refers, must be construed as a set of pairs, one member of which belongs to the collective to which the probability of *H* is referred, the other of which belongs to the collective to which the probability of *T* is referred. This kind of argument shows that limits of relative frequencies in collectives are a model of the probability calculus, and thus that the limiting frequency interpretation is an interpretation of that calculus.

Reichenbach and, more recently, Salmon offer a limiting-relative-frequency interpretation of probability in which von Mises' formal requirement of randomness is regarded as inessential. Reichenbach takes probability sequences (corresponding to von Mises' collectives) to be empirically given sequences of events, ordered, usually, by time. He admits mathematically given probability sequences as useful for formal and illustrative purposes in the probability calculus, but denies them any practical import. Furthermore, these empirically given sequences may actually be finite, as in fact most if not all empirically given sequences are. Any sequence may serve as an appropriate sequence in which to consider a relative frequency; there is no need to stipulate any form of disorder in the sequence. The formal requirement of randomness is replaced by a pragmatic or epistemological requirement concerning the choice of an appropriate empirical reference sequence for each particular application of the theory. The particular sequence which it is appropriate to consider in a given context will depend on our state of knowledge at the time (as, in fact, it also does for von Mises, despite his requirement of randomness). The formal definition of probability in a sequence is precisely the same as von Mises'—it is the standard mathematical definition of a limit. Reichenbach, unlike von Mises, applies it to finite sequences as well as infinite ones.

Salmon and Reichenbach argue that the rules for the application of probability (and they both mention such natural rules of thumb as "base your expectations on the probabilities in the smallest relevant reference class about which you have information") are not part of the meaning of probability, but part of a network of pragmatic issues that concern its use. For example, we may have grounds for believing the relative frequency of death in the thirty-ninth year among American males to be 0.012, and among American male white-collar workers to be 0.009, and we may not have enough information to make a good estimate of the corresponding death rate among American male schoolteachers. If we are going to sell insurance to an individual whom we know to be a thirty-eight-year-old American male schoolteacher, we will use the death rate 0.009. There is no formal justification for this; the relative frequency (probability) 0.012 is just as "valid" as the relative frequency 0.009, and the latter is no more valid than the unknown relative frequency *p* of death during the thirty-ninth year among American male schoolteachers. Our use of the probability 0.009 depends on a large number of pragmatic factors (such as the competitive situation among insurance companies, our feeling that this is a more appropriate number than 0.012, and the like) which Reichenbach and Salmon take to be extraneous to the scientific meaning of the probability statement. It is only the scientific meaning of probability, they argue, that enters into the probability calculus, and it is this that is captured by the concept of a limiting frequency.

In addition to this standard relative-frequency interpretation of probability, Reichenbach offers a metalinguistic interpretation of probability in terms of truth frequencies: the probability of a statement of a certain sort is taken to be the relative frequency of truth of that type of statement in a reference class consisting of an infinite (or finite) number of statements. On the basis of this interpretation of probability he constructs a probability logic of an infinite number of truth values. Nevertheless this is *not* a logical interpretation of probability; it is still empirical, for in order to estimate the truth frequency of statements of certain kinds in reference classes, we must look to the world to provide us with evidence concerning the truth or falsity of the statements that enter into the sequences. On a genuinely logical interpretation of probability, such as Carnap's, we need not look at the world at all, but need merely examine the purely logical properties of certain groups of statements.

It should be observed that in the empirical interpretations of probability which undertake to define probability in terms of the limits of relative frequencies, there is a strong element of idealization. The empirical sequences we encounter in the world are always finite, and we often have good reason to suppose that they cannot be infinite. We cannot have an infinite number of people living under given historical and social conditions; we cannot suppose in a physical experiment that we have an infinite number of helium nuclei in various stages of excitation. Furthermore any initial segment of an infinite sequence is compatible with any *limiting* frequency, or indeed with there not being a limiting frequency at all. In the case of von Mises' interpretation of probability, there is the added element of idealization involved in the supposition that the sequences are random, in his special sense. There have been two reactions to these elements of idealization in the empirical interpretations of probability. One has been to limit the idealization involved by taking the theory of probability to be concerned not with just any sequence of events, but with certain sequences encountered in the world which come close to meeting the ideal conditions; the other has been, in the best mathematical tradition, to make the sort of idealization, and to leave the applications to the applied scientists and the shopkeepers. The former reaction seems to be closer to the style of von Mises; the latter closer to the style of Reichenbach.

Most mathematicians and statisticians prefer the latter approach, in which, nowadays, one begins with an abstract axiomatic formulation, and takes 'probability' to be anything that satisfies the axioms of the probability calculus. The first to adopt this pure-mathematical approach was Kolmogorov; he was quickly followed by other mathematicians whose concern was with probability as a branch of measure theory rather than with the empirical applications of the theory. Even among those who have been concerned with the applications of probability theory, or with the interpretation of probability, this approach has often been adopted. Harald Cramér, for example, takes probability to be simply an "abstract counterpart" to observable relative frequencies in large classes of phenomena. We simply observe that the relative frequencies of certain types of events, within certain classes of experiments or trials, seem to be fairly stable; and we propose a stochastic (probabilistic) model to account for and represent this stability. The model is simply the abstract mathematical system itself. It in no fundamental way differs from other mathematical models. Sometimes one sort of model is useful and sometimes another sort. It is no more a part of the job of the pure mathematician to predict the applicability of a probability model than it is a part of his job to predict when a model involving differential equations will be useful.

One other group of writers who offer an empirical interpretation of probability, somewhat more in the direct tradition of von Mises, feel that the kind of phenomenon to which probability theory can be applied can be characterized abstractly and generally. Not just *any* large group of events may reasonably be described by probabilistic statements, but only those sequences of events which have a certain structure (or lack of structure) corresponding in an empirical way to von Mises' mathematical concept of randomness. Karl Popper, for example, takes as the most interesting and useful concept of probability one that is related to relative frequencies, but not one which is defined in terms of limiting frequencies, and not one which is simply an abstract counterpart of relative frequencies. Probability is a concept characterizing the behavior of certain entities or kinds of entities under certain conditions; it is an abstract property which can best be described as a kind of potentiality or "would-be" that may be (but need not be) expressed by mass behavior. Thus when we ascribe the probability $\frac{1}{6}$ to a one in the case of a certain die, we do not mean to say that the die has been thrown many times, or even that it will be thrown at all. We mean that the die has under the usual circumstances a certain *propensity* to land with the one uppermost; it has this propensity from the moment of its manufacture, whether or not it is thrown. Furthermore, *if* it has this propensity to land with a one up about a sixth of the time, it has it regardless of the outcome of any series of tosses. A startling sequence of ones might (or might not, if we have other and stronger evidence) constitute evidence concerning that propensity; but the finite relative frequencies we can observe do not constitute the only or even the most important evidence we have about propensities.

Another view which limits the application of probability concepts to a rather special class of events is that developed by Ian Hacking. He eschews the word 'probability' altogether, but says that statistics is concerned with a certain, presumably physical, property which, when it has a chance, expresses itself as a long-run frequency. This property is not taken to be a property of an object but a property of a *chance set-up*. A chance set-up is "a device or part of the world on which might be conducted one or more trials, experiments, or observations..." (p. 13). For Hacking the word 'chance' performs the function which the interpretations discussed in this chapter assign to the word 'probability'. "What the long-run frequency is, or was, or would have been (on the chance set-up) is to be called the *chance* of the outcome" on that chance set-up. It is an empirical concept, characteristic of certain kinds of states of affairs in the world.

The interpretation provided by each of these writers does eventually involve references to mass phenomena, repeatable experiments, and the like. There is no doubt whatever that the concept which these people have in mind and are trying to capture and characterize is an important one in the whole of science. It is central to the theory of measurement (making a measurement may be construed as making a trial on a chance set-up, sampling from a hypothetical and idealized sequence or population, etc.), and it is central to the attempt to organize and simplify any massive body of data. The concept that these writers have focused on is thus indisputably important to all of science, from pure physics to demography. The double question remains: To what extent is it appropriate to call that concept probability? And to what extent is that the concept which is involved in statements that use the word 'probability' and its cognates?

The former part of the question is largely terminological, and much less important than the latter part. To the extent that there is another prevalent concept that goes by the name 'probability', it seems appropriate to have different names for the two concepts. Carnap has proposed distinguishing them by subscripts: 'probability$_2$' for the frequency concept, and 'probability$_1$' for the logical concept corresponding to degree of confirmation. There are a number of writers, whom we shall consider in Part Two of this book, who regard probability$_1$ or degree of factual support as a concept with a completely different structure from that provided by the probability calculus, and who therefore argue that the word 'probability' should be used only for the empirical concept—at least in technical literature. On the other hand there are those who claim that close analysis reveals that the vast majority of uses of the word 'probability', even in technical literature, are uses that are not open to an empirical concept. Since there are many perfectly good terms for the empirical concept ('chance', 'relative frequency', 'proportion' [in an extended and idealized sense], and so on), it seems better to reserve the word 'probability' for the logical concept, and to use the word 'proportion', or better, 'measure' for the empirical concept. Perhaps Hacking's proposal, to do without the word 'probability', is the most rational, but it is very hard to amputate a word from the language. And it is perhaps more politic to provide analytical splints to stiffen its meaning than to let it degenerate altogether.

The main objection to any blanket empirical interpretation of probability statements, whatever particular form that empirical interpretation may take, is that it does not apply to many of the uses to which the word 'probability' is put. Reichenbach is the frequency theorist who has claimed the most for his theory of probability: "The results may be transferred to every application of the probability concept in science or daily life" (p. 10). And yet there are many probability statements that do not seem to adopt themselves comfortably to Reichenbach's analysis. In particular, when one talks about the probability of a scientific hypothesis (the quantum theory), or about the probability of a certain historical event (the probability that Caesar occupied a certain part of France), it seems very questionable indeed that one should be able to find an appropriate long probability sequence. It is even more questionable, of course, that one should know the value of the limit of the relative frequency in the sequence; but as an objection to Reichenbach's theory of probability, this observation is beside the point. Reichenbach asserts that we can never *know* the limits of relative frequencies, and that the best we can do is to make estimates of these limits. The difficulties inherent in this view we shall return to when we consider Reichenbach's contributions to inductive logic in Part Two. The point to observe here is that these difficulties are essentially difficulties of the *application* of Reichenbach's probability concept, and not difficulties in the concept itself. Reichenbach's argument for the universal applicability of his theory is that we are no worse off in making statements about the relative frequencies of truth-values in infinite sequences of statements of an historical nature than we are in making statements about the limiting relative frequency of heads in an infinite sequence of tosses of a well-tested coin.

What is a relevant objection, though, is that on an empirical interpretation, whenever we use the word 'probability' we are uttering a conjecture about a mass phenomenon. This limitation is as relevant to statements about gambling apparatus as it is to statements about historical events. To say that the probability of heads is one half is to utter a conjecture about the collective character of a set of coin tosses, or the potentialities of a chance set-up. It is not to say anything at all about any particular coin toss. Probability is applicable only to *sets* of entities or events, or sequences of events, or experimental arrangements, or chance set-ups, but never to an individual event, or the particular outcome of a particular trial.

But, as should be very clear from the instances of the use of the probability concept with which this book opened, there are many kinds of probability statements in which the general function of the probability concept is to distinguish between sound and unsound conjectures regarding *individual* events, *individual* trials, or *particular* outcomes. In particular, we make probability statements about all kinds of individual propositions: we say that the probability of rain tomorrow is high; that the constant-creation theory of cosmology is more probable than its competitors, that the probability of being killed in a particular plane flight is negligible. Reichenbach would interpret such statements as elliptical formulations of such statements as: on days following days like today, the frequency of rain is high; theories of the type of the constant-creation theory, supported by the kind of evidence that supports that theory, are more frequently true than theories of other specifiable sorts supported by their sort of evidence. It is more plausible to interpret the third statement as an ellipsis, but even here most probability theorists— even those of a frequentist persuasion—would refuse to follow Reichenbach. His formulation simply does too much violence to common usage. When I say that the probability of rain tomorrow is very low, I am not saying something about the set of days like today in some unspecified sense of 'like'. I may be implying that I know (or have reason to believe) something about that set of days, and the relative frequency with which they are followed by rainy days, but that set of days is not what I am talking *about*; I am talking about *tomorrow*. When I talk about the probability that my nervous friend Bob Wilson will survive his flight across the Atlantic next Monday, I am talking about the particular flight that Bob is planning to take, not about the whole set of first-class passenger flights across the Atlantic carried out in Boeing 707 planes.

Most of those who adopt an empirical interpretation of probability would be inclined to agree with all this as an argument against construing *all* probability statements as statistical. They would tend to follow von Mises in denying that probability statements that concern single individuals or events are always elliptical, and in asserting that they are often simply without formal meaning: "The phrase 'probability of death', when it refers to a single person, has no meaning at all for us" (p. 11). Such statements, of course, are not asserted to be without *any* sort of meaning, but only to be without the sort of meaning appropriate to the probability calculus.

Limited to statements employing the indefinite article 'a' (the probability that *a* male American will die in his thirty-ninth year; the probability that *a* roll of this die will result in a one) the empirical interpretation of probability is plausible enough, in general. But the limitation is a surprisingly serious one. In the first place the number of statements in which probability is clearly being used in a way that conflicts with the empirical interpretation is very large. It is a tough-minded empiricist indeed who will assert that "The probability of a six on the next roll of this die is $\frac{1}{6}$" is nonsense and has no empirical meaning. The same will have to be said of "The probability that applicant number 1149-A will die within the next year is 0.0017," "The probability that the first time Hume ever tossed a coin it landed heads is $\frac{1}{2}$," and so on. Nevertheless, there are a goodly number of people who are this tough-minded. Not all of these objectives (as we might call them) are so tough-minded as to see that precisely the same considerations apply also to such probability statements as: "The probability is very high that on the next thousand rolls of this well-tested die, nearly $\frac{1}{6}$ will result in a six," "It is overwhelmingly probable that not more than three out of one-thousand applicants of such and such a character will die during the coming year," and even "Given that the limiting frequency of heads is exactly one half, the probability is overwhelming that the proportion of heads on the next ten-thousand tosses will be less than three quarters." When it comes to statements of this latter category, a great number of objectivists slip into the easy practice of regarding a very high probability as a practical certainty, where *practical certainty* is the sort of concept that *does* apply to definite individual events. Von Mises himself belongs to this group. His assertion that the probability of death of a particular individual is not a subject for the probability calculus has already been quoted. But he also writes, ". . . the solution of a problem in the theory of probability can teach us something definite about the real world. It gives a prediction of the result of a long sequence of physical events; this prediction can be tested by observation" (p. 63). This statement is simply false. From statements of probability we can only derive other statements of probability, and none of them will concern the probability of any definite event, for such a probability is flatly meaningless on von Mises' theory. It is meaningless whether that event is conceptually simple like the death of a particular individual or conceptually complex like that occurrence of death for less than two-hundred of the ten-thousand individuals to whom we have issued insurance policies. Under no circumstances can we arrive at a probability statement concerning any definite experiment or observation, except by taking a high probability that applies to a characteristic in an infinite class of events of a certain sort to be a practical certainty that we can apply to each member of that class individually.

What kinds of statements do we have left, then, to which the objectivistic theory in one form or another might apply? Statements of probability that employ the indefinite article 'a' to make an assertion about an unspecified member of a class. "The probability of heads on *a* toss of this coin is $\frac{1}{2}$," "The probability that *a* birth is the birth of a boy is 0.51." But even these statements become slightly strange under the objectivistic interpretation. It does seem to be curious that a statement about a whole class of events (an imaginary class at that, generally) is offered as the *meaning* of a statement that in ordinary or scientific language appears to be about a single (though unspecified) individual.

Many of the most important uses of the probability calculus concern distributions and frequencies explicitly (How often will North–South have all the aces in Bridge? What is the distribution of shoe sizes among army recruits?). Many of the most common technical uses of the term 'probability' are adjectival: one speaks of a probability measure, of probabilistic independence, of probability distributions, and probability laws. In all of these cases the important concept is an empirical one, related to relative frequencies. Which of the various empirical interpretations seems most plausible here? The limiting-frequency interpretations of von Mises and Reichenbach seem close to the observed data (finite frequencies), but they seem to involve a surplus of idealization. It is no part of any *use* of probability theory that it refer to unending sequences; it suffices that we be able to use the mathematics that accompanies the limiting-frequency interpretation. This mathematics is available to the purely mathematical treatment of probability. By far the most prevalent empirical interpretation of probability nowadays is that which takes probability to be simply an abstract counterpart of empirically observable frequencies (but, like all mathematical abstractions, better behaved). The hope of any peculiarly intimate connection with observations is abandoned. Probabilistic or stochastic theories are theories like any other theories; it is just as hard to define empirical support for these theories as for any others. They shed no more light on their own confirmation or disconfirmation than any other theory does. As long as all of this is kept clearly in mind, the use of the word 'probability' in these contexts need not be confusing; and it is perhaps easier to keep these things in mind on the "abstract counterpart" interpretation than on a limiting-frequency interpretation or any other interpretation involving reference to a specialized model.

EXERCISES

1. Provide the details of the argument that in an infinite sequence, an assertion about a limiting frequency, '$(\delta)(\exists N)(n)(N < n \supset |f_n - p| < \delta)$', is neither definitively verifiable nor definitively refutable.
2. Show that in an infinite sequence, '$(\delta)(\exists N)(n)(n > N \supset |f_n - p| < \delta)$' is not tautologous.
3. Show that if the limit of the relative frequency of a certain property in a certain sequence exists, it has a value less than or equal to one.
4. Von Mises shows that limits of relative frequencies in collectives satisfy the axioms of the probability calculus. In order to do this, he is required to show that there are ways of operating on collectives to arrive at new collectives with new limiting frequencies related in the appropriate ways to the old limits. For example, the proof of the addition rule proceeds by applying what von Mises calls the *mixing* operation to a collective. Let a collective be given in which the limiting frequency of H is p, and in which the limiting frequency of E is q, and in which the properties H and E are exclusive. The mixing operation consists in mixing together E and H, forming, say $G = E \cup H$. We then assert (1) the limit of the relative frequency of G in the given collective exists; (2) it has the value $p + q$. Prove these assertions.
5. Another operation on collectives is that of *partition*. Given a collective and a property E, one may consider the sequence consisting of those members of the original collective that have the property E; one may take this as a new collective (being a partition of the old one), and in it consider the relative frequency of another property, H. Suppose that the limit of the relative frequency of E in a collective is p, and that the limit of the relative frequency of H in the partition of the same collective by E is q. Then, in the original collective, the limit of the relative frequency of $G = H \cap E$ exists, and has the value pq.
6. Construct (i.e., prove a rule for constructing) an infinite reference class A in which the probability of B does not exist.
7. Show that if A is a finite sequence, the limit of the relative frequency of B in A always exists.
8. Show that the probability axioms hold for Reichenbach's interpretation of probability.
9. Examine the appropriateness, pro and con, of the empirical interpretation of 'probability' in the following statements.
   (a) The probability is $\frac{1}{6}$ that a roll of this die will result in a six.

(b) The probability of rain tomorrow is 0.4.

(c) The probability of snow this Christmas is high.

(d) The probability of getting at least one head on the next ten tosses of a coin is about 999 out of 1000.

(e) The probability of getting about $\frac{1}{6}$ sixes on a thousand rolls of this die is very high.

(f) The probability that the train will be on time is high.

(g) The probability that a strong and warlike nation will be invaded by one of its weaker neighbors is rather small.

(h) It is unlikely that Russia would have been invaded by Czechoslovakia.

BIBLIOGRAPHICAL NOTES FOR CHAPTER 4

John Venn (*The Logic of Chance*, Macmillan, London, 1886) was the first to propose that probability be *identified* with the limiting frequency in an infinite reference class; Venn argued that the probability of heads on a toss of a coin was to be regarded as *p* if and only if, as the sequence of tosses was extended indefinitely, the relative frequency of heads got arbitrarily close to *p*. Venn did not work out the mathematical details of his proposals; those details were provided by von Mises in his *Wahrscheinlichkeit, Statistik, und Wahrheit*, J. Springer, Berlin, 1928. Quotations are from the most recent English version, *Probability, Statistics, and Truth*, a translation of the third revised German edition of 1951, The Macmillan Company, New York, 1957.

Hans Reichenbach's limiting-frequency interpretation of probability first appeared in German in 1934, although his ideas were talked about well before that. *The Theory of Probability*, University of California Press, Berkeley and Los Angeles, 1949, is a translation and revision of the German *Wahrscheinlichkeitslehre* of 1934. It is in that work that the most far-reaching claims for the frequency theory of probability are made, and where the attempt is made to construct an empirically interpreted probability logic. The currently most active defender of this view is Wesley Salmon; but his remarks on the subject are to be found mainly in his discussions of various problems of induction, to which reference will be made later.

The basic reference for Kolmogorov's axiomatic treatment of probability is "Grundbegriffe der Wahrscheinlichkeitsrechnung," in *Ergebnisse der Mathematik*, **2**, No. 3, Berlin, 1933. The translation is *Foundations of the Theory of Probability*, Chelsea, New York, 1950. For the current approach to these questions in mathematical statistics, see Harald Cramér, *The Elements of Probability Theory*, John Wiley and Sons, New York, 1955. Chapters I and II lead up to and present a statistician's interpretation of probability as a counterpart of relative frequencies, connected only by relatively informal and flexible criteria to actual observed frequencies.

R. B. Braithwaite, a philosopher, presents a conceptual-counterpart view in his book *Scientific Explanation*, Cambridge University Press, 1953, Chapters V and VI. Braithwaite, however, proposes to make the connections between the model and the reality of observed frequencies explicit through the use of a formal rule of rejection for statistical hypotheses.

Ian Hacking, in *The Logic of Statistical Inference*, Cambridge University Press,

1966, shows that Braithwaite's rule of rejection is not adequate as a formal rule providing the connection between model and reality; he offers instead a whole new approach to statistical inference (to which we shall recur later), and bases it on his chance set-up view of probability. Karl Popper's somewhat similar views are to be found in "The Propensity Interpretation of Probability," *British Journal for the Philosophy of Science* **10**, 1960, pp. 25–42.

Details concerning the consistency of the *collective* in which a characteristic occurs randomly and yet approaches a limit are to be found in A. H. Copeland, "Consistency of the Conditions Determining Kollektives," *Transactions of the American Mathematical Society* **42**, 1937, pp. 333–57, and Abraham Wald, "Die Widerspruchsfreiheit des Kollektivebegriffe der Wahrscheinlichkeitsrechnung," *Ergebnisse eines mathematischen Kolloquiums* **8**, 1937.

5

Degree-of-Entailment
Interpretations of Probability

A number of interpretations of probability have been offered which take probability to be a logical relation between an evidence statement (or a set of evidence statements) and a conclusion statement, in virtue of which having grounds for accepting the evidence statements constitutes partial grounds for accepting the conclusion statement, or grounds for according it a certain degree of rational belief. The first such theory to be worked out explicitly and in some symbolic detail is Keynes' theory (1921). Keynes' theory is sometimes mistakenly regarded as subjectivistic—particularly by frequency theorists—but there is a class of interpretations of probability which is subjective in a far more significant and interesting sense than Keynes' interpretation. Keynes, indeed, is at great pains to argue that the probability relation is *objective* and *logical*. Thinking so does not make something probable; it is probable only as a result of the objective logical relation it bears to its evidence.

Keynes accepts the conventional calculus of probability as holding for his probability relations, and presents it in an axiomatized form. But his probabilities are not restricted to real numbers. Probabilities are *sui generis*; although we symbolize certainty and impossibility by 1 and 0, although all other degrees of the probability relation lie between these limits, and although in many cases probabilities can be associated with real numbers, it is not by any means always the case that a probability can be associated with a real number. Although the probability of h_1, given evidence e_1, and the probability of h_2, given e_2, both lie between 0 and 1, it may not be the case that we can say either that the first probability is greater than the second, or that the second is greater than the first, or that they are equal. There are degrees of probability that are incomparable in magnitude.

For Keynes, probability is not definable. The basic probabilities must be intuited (though *what* is intuited is not subjective, but objective). Once we have an intuited stock of probabilities, however, the calculus provides us with a means of arriving at other probabilities by argument. Keynes felt that a principle of indifference was required to arrive at these basic probability intuitions. It was to be applicable only to certain special cases with a particularly simple structure. Even so, its formulation, though an improvement over earlier formulations of a principle of indifference, was not clean enough to avoid all of the classical difficulties.

Most current logical interpretations of probability are based, in one way or another, on the conception of *logical range*. This is true also of the several concepts of factual support or corroboration that play an important role in discussion of inductive logic. Carnap is the writer who has done more for and with this conception than anyone else. Like Keynes, Carnap takes probability, in many of its uses, to be a logical concept. In some contexts, he is willing to accept an empirical concept, which he calls 'probability$_2$'. But where the logical probability relation is, for Keynes, indefinable and must, at least in some cases, be intuited, Carnap regards probability$_1$, the logical concept, as at least partially definable. Carnap, in his "Replies and Expositions," develops the concept of probability$_1$ in the following way. Consider a person X at a certain time T. It is possible to discover the degree of belief that X has in a proposition h at time T. (The problems of this determination will be discussed in the next chapter.) Cr_X is the credence function of X; $Cr_X(h, T)$ is the function whose value (lying between 0 and 1) represents X's actual degree of belief in h at T. It is also equal to the highest betting quotient with which X is willing to bet on h at T, for small stakes. (We shall also postpone the discussion of betting quotients to the next chapter.)

Now if X exhibits some degree of rationality, his degree of belief in a proposition h will not depend merely on the time T, but on his body of knowledge at the time T. The function which yields the degree of belief that X *would have* in h, were e his total body of knowledge, is a *credibility function*, $Cred(h, e)$.

We now take one more step, and consider rational credibility functions.

Carnap takes the logical probability function to be a rational credibility function, but he does not assume that there can be only one such function. The technical term 'degree of confirmation' is designed as an explicatum of logical probability. This is to say that it is a term which is similar in meaning and function to 'logical probability', but free of the ambiguities and obscurities that infect 'logical probability' or 'probability$_1$'. The degree of confirmation of hypothesis h on evidence e, for example, depends entirely on the logical and semantical properties and relations of h and e. It is defined only for a particular formal language in which these logical and semantical relations can be made perfectly explicit. Carnap at one point appeared to be quite sure that only one degree of confirmation function, or c-function, would turn out to be rational, but he now prefers to leave that question open. Thus it may be that there are a number of different c-functions that may serve as equally good explicata of logical probability functions or rational credibility functions. In any event, for Carnap, the only appropriate avenue to the study of logical probability is provided by the formal development of c-functions.

In order to minimize the technical difficulties we shall consider a sample of Carnap's theory in a very simple language. Suppose the Language **L** contains two individual constants 'a' and 'b', two one-place predicates 'G' and 'F', and the usual sentential connectives including '&' for conjunction, '~' for negation, and '∨' for disjunction. We may go about constructing statements expressing possible states of the world (relative to this language) in a fairly mechanical way: does the object designated 'a' have the property designated by 'F'? the property designated by 'G'? Does the object designated by 'b' have the property designated by 'G'? the property designated by 'F'? The number of possible sets of answers to these questions is 16; there are 16 possible *states of the world* that can be described in this language, or, putting it another way, there are 16 *state descriptions* that can be expressed in this language. They are:

1. *Fa & Ga & Fb & Gb*
2. *Fa & Ga & Fb & − Gb*
3. *Fa & Ga & − Fb & Gb*
4. *Fa & Ga & − Fb & − Gb*
5. *Fa & − Ga & Fb & Gb*
6. *Fa & − Ga & Fb & − Gb*
7. *Fa & − Ga & − Fb & Gb*
8. *Fa & − Ga & − Fb & − Gb*
9. *− Fa & Ga & Fb & Gb*
10. *− Fa & Ga & Fb & − Gb*
11. *− Fa & Ga & − Fb & Gb*
12. *− Fa & Ga & − Fb & − Gb*
13. *− Fa & − Ga & Fb & Gb*
14. *− Fa & − Ga & Fb & − Gb*
15. *− Fa & − Ga & − Fb & Gb*
16. *− Fa & − Ga & − Fb & − Gb*

Given a certain language, then, a state description is a statement that describes a state of the world in as much detail as is possible in that language.

In addition to state descriptions, we shall want to consider structure descriptions. A structure description is a disjunction of state descriptions each of which can be obtained from the others by some permutation of the individual constants. For example, '*Fa* & $-Ga$ & $-Fb$ & *Gb*' and '$-Fa$ & *Ga* & *Fb* & $-Gb$' can be obtained from each other by permuting '*a*' and '*b*', and thus belong to the same structure description. In the example we are considering here there are ten structure descriptions:

1. *Fa* & *Ga* & *Fb* & *Gb*
2. (*Fa* & *Ga* & *Fb* & $-Gb$) ∨ (*Fa* & $-Ga$ & *Fb* & *Gb*)
3. (*Fa* & *Ga* & $-Fb$ & *Gb*) ∨ ($-Fa$ & *Ga* & *Fb* & *Gb*)
4. (*Fa* & *Ga* & $-Fb$ & $-Gb$) ∨ ($-Fa$ & $-Ga$ & *Fb* & *Gb*)
5. (*Fa* & $-Ga$ & *Fb* & $-Gb$)
6. (*Fa* & $-Ga$ & $-Fb$ & *Gb*) ∨ ($-Fa$ & *Ga* & *Fb* & $-Gb$)
7. (*Fa* & $-Ga$ & $-Fb$ & $-Gb$)
   ∨ ($-Fa$ & $-Ga$ & *Fb* & $-Gb$)
8. ($-Fa$ & *Ga* & $-Fb$ & *Gb*)
9. ($-Fa$ & *Ga* & $-Fb$ & $-Gb$)
   ∨ ($-Fa$ & $-Ga$ & $-Fb$ & *Gb*)
10. $-Fa$ & $-Ga$ & $-Fb$ & $-Gb$

We now assign numbers to the state descriptions in such a way that the numbers assigned to all possible state descriptions add up to one. This assignment constitutes the definition of a *measure function* for the state descriptions. We extend the definition of the measure function by stipulating that the value of the measure function for the disjunction of any two logically exclusive sentences be the sum of the values of the measure function for the two sentences: thus if S_1 and S_2 are inconsistent, the measure of their disjunction is to be the sum of the measure of S_1 and the measure of S_2. Since every consistent statement in the language can be expressed as a disjunction of state descriptions, and since every two state descriptions are inconsistent, the measure of every statement in the language is determined, and will be simply the sum of the measures of the state descriptions whose disjunction it is equivalent to. In our example, the measure of the statement '*Fa* & *Ga* & $-Gb$' will be the sum of the measures of the two state descriptions '*Fa* & *Fa* & *Fb* & $-Gb$' and '*Fa* & *Ga* & $-Fb$ & $-Gb$'. Every statement that we can form in the language now has a measure determined by the measure function for state descriptions with which we started.

Given a measure function defined for all the statements of the language, it is only a brief step to degrees of confirmation. We define the *a priori* probability of a statement to be equal to the value of the measure function for that statement (if the measure of a statement is p, its *a priori* probability will be p). Let us write 'm' for the measure function, '$m(e)$' for its value for the argument *e.* We define the degree of confirmation of a hypothesis *h* relative to evidence *e* as the conditional probability of *h* on *e*, $c(h, e)$:

$$c(h, e) = \frac{m(h \ \& \ e)}{m(e)}.$$

This is to say, we define the degree of confirmation of the hypothesis *h* on the evidence *e* to be the ratio of the *a priori* probability of the conjunction of *e* and *h* to the *a priori* probability of *e* alone. The degree of confirmation of *h* on *e* is just the conditional probability of *h*, given *e*. In this way Carnap's analysis has reduced the problem of defining degree of confirmation for the classes of languages with which he has been concerned to the problem of choosing a measure function for state descriptions.

There are two very natural functions defined by Carnap which have often been referred to in the literature. One is $m^\dagger$, which assigns to each state description the same number: if there are *N* state descriptions, then the measure of each is taken to be $1/N$. In our example the measure of each state description is $\frac{1}{16}$. This is a very natural assignment of prior probabilities; one could imagine it arising from an application of a principle of indifference to state descriptions. And yet this particular measure function leads to a concept of probability$_1$ on the basis of which it is impossible to learn from experience. In the example, if *e* is '*Fa*' and *h* is '*Fb*', the degree of confirmation of *h* on *e* is just the same as the *a priori* probability of *h*—i.e., *e* is irrelevant to *h*:

$$c(Fb, Fa) = \frac{m(Fb \ \& \ Fa)}{m(Fa)} = \frac{\frac{1}{4}}{\frac{1}{2}} = \frac{1}{2} = m(Fb).$$

In general let *e* state that of n_e individuals, m_e individuals satisfy the primitive predicate *F*. Let *h* state that of n_h individuals (not mentioned in *e*), m_h individuals satisfy the predicate *F*. Let S_h be the number of state descriptions in which *h* holds, S_e the number in which *e* holds, and $S_{e\&h}$ the number in which *h* and *e* both hold. We may calculate these numbers as follows:

The number of ways in which a specified individual may satisfy a specified primitive predicate is $2^\pi - 1$, where π is the number of primitive one-place predicates in the language; it may satisfy any of the *Q*-predicates but that one *Q*-predicate that entails that it does not satisfy that primitive predicate. The number of ways in which m_e specified individuals may satisfy *F* is $(2^\pi - 1)^{m_e}$. Similarly the number of ways in which $n_e - m_e$ individuals may fail to satisfy *F* is $(2^\pi - 1)^{(n_e - m_e)}$. The number of ways of specifying m_e out of n_e individuals is $\binom{n_e}{m_e}$. The number of ways of assigning *Q*-predicates to the remaining $N - n_e$ individuals is $(2^\pi)^{N - n_e}$. Thus the total number of state descriptions in which *e* holds is

$$S_e = \binom{n_e}{m_e} [2^\pi - 1]^{m_e} [2^\pi - 1]^{(n_e - m_e)} (2^\pi)^{(N - n_e)}.$$

Similarly

$$S_h = \binom{n_h}{m_h}[2^\pi - 1]^{m_h}[2^\pi - 1]^{(n_h - m_h)}(2^\pi)^{(N - n_e)}$$

and

$$S_{h\&e} = \binom{n_e}{m_e}\binom{n_h}{m_h}[2^\pi - 1]^{(m_e + m_h)}[2^\pi - 1]^{(n_e - m_e + n_h - m_h)}(2^\pi)^{(N - n_e - n_h)}.$$

Since the total number of state descriptions is $(2^\pi)^N$, and each is to be assigned the measure by $m^\dagger$, we have

$$m^\dagger(h) \cdot m^\dagger(e) = m^\dagger(h \& e)$$

and

$$c^\dagger(h, e) = m^\dagger(h).$$

In other words, the evidence that m_e out of n_e sampled items are F is *irrelevant* to the hypothesis that m_h out of n_h as yet unexamined items will be F. But we would hardly take the logical probability of h to be unaffected by e—we would generally suppose that the statistical makeup of the new sample would be similar to the statistical makeup of the old one.

Another natural measure function defined by Carnap is m^*. This measure function assigns numbers to the state descriptions in the following way: first, every *structure* description is assigned an equal measure; and then each state description belonging to a *given* structure description is assigned an equal part of the measure assigned to the structure description.

In the example above, we have for measure and confirmation functions on these two schemes, the following values:

$$m^\dagger(Fa \& Ga \& -Fb \& Gb) = \tfrac{1}{16}$$
$$m^\dagger((Fa \& Ga \& -Fb \& Gb) \lor (-Fa \& Ga \& Gb \& Fb)) = \tfrac{1}{8}$$
$$m^\dagger(Fa) = \tfrac{1}{2}$$
$$c^\dagger(Fa, Fb) = \tfrac{1}{2}$$
$$m^*(Fa \& Ga \& Fb \& Gb) = \tfrac{1}{10}$$
$$m^*(Fa \& Ga \& -Fb \& Gb) = \tfrac{1}{20}$$
$$m^*(Fa) = \tfrac{1}{2}$$
$$c^*(Fa, Fb) = \tfrac{3}{5}$$

Note that according to the measure function $m^\dagger$, the degree of confirmation of Fa, given Fb, is simply the same as the *a priori* probability of Fa, despite the fact that the same property is involved, while on the basis of the measure function m^*, the degree of confirmation of Fa on the evidence Fb is $\tfrac{3}{5}$, representing an increase over its *a priori* probability.

If we are dealing with a language having a large number of individual constants, even this confirmation function may lead to rather implausible values. In *The Continuum of Inductive Methods* Carnap offers a general definition of confirmation for a continuum of confirmation functions that depend on a parameter λ, which reflects the speed with which we may rationally learn from experience, neither depending too much on our *a priori* ideas, nor leaping to conclusions on insufficient evidence. The languages for which c_λ is defined are still first-order languages (comprising individual constants, predicates, and logical machinery). The value of λ may or may not be taken to depend on the number of predicates we have in the language. (It is possible to see here that the relation between probability and induction works both ways: not only is probability supposed to be our guide to induction, but we may look to our habits of induction to provide clues as to the particular function we should adopt as our probability function.)

In the initial development of his theory of probability₁ Carnap imposed severe restrictions on the languages to which his definition applied. The functions $c^\dagger$ and c^*, for example, are defined only for first-order functional calculi consisting of a finite or denumerable number of individual constants and a finite number of logically independent one-place predicates. These restrictions were all rapidly removed. In 1953 Kemeny published a system for languages subject only to the following mild restrictions:

1. The object language must be consistent.
2. It must not contain an axiom of infinity—i.e., it must not be provable that these are an infinite number of distinct individuals.
3. The number of types of individuals must be finite.
4. There must be a finite number of constants.
5. Each constant must be of finite order.

In Kemeny's system logical interdependence among the sentences of the language is handled in the following way: Let m be a measure function defined for *all* state descriptions, including those which are logically impossible. We define the measure function m' reflecting the facts of logical interdependence by the relation

$$m'(S) = \frac{m(A \ \& \ S)}{m(A)},$$

where S is an arbitrary statement, and A is the conjunction of the axioms or meaning postulates of the language.

Carnap's most recent work has been concerned with first-order languages containing a finite number of families of predicates. The confirmation functions depend on two parameters, λ and η. The special case of a language containing only one-place primitive predicates has been formulated axiomatically in "Replies and Expositions." The primitive predicates are classified into families such that to each individual exactly one member of each family applies. The axioms of this new system are as follows:

○ **A–1**

If e and e′ are logically equivalent, then c(h, e) = c(h, e′).

○ **A–2**

If h and h′ are logically equivalent, then c(h, e) = c(h′, e).

○ **A–3**

c(h & j, e) = c(h, e) × c(j, e & h).

○ **A–4**

If e & h & j is logically false, then c(h ∨ j, e) = c(h, e) + c(j, e).

○ **A–5**

If t is a tautology, and e is not logically false, c(t, e) = 1.

○ **A–6**

In a language with a finite number of models, c(h, e) = 1 only if h is a logical consequence of e.

○ **A–7**

The value of c(h, e) remains unchanged under any finite permutation of individuals.

○ **A–8**

The value of c(h, e) remains unchanged under any permutation of the predicates of any family.

○ **A–9**

The value of c(h, e) remains unchanged under any permutation of families with the same number of predicates.

○ **A–10**

The value of c(h, e) remains unchanged if the domain of individuals in language is enlarged, provided no quantifiers occur in e or h.

○ **A–11**

The value of c(h, e) remains unchanged if further families of predicates are added to the language.

The following axioms concern a single family of k predicates, $P_1, \ldots P_k$. Let e_s be a statement specifying that of s individuals, s_1 specified individuals have the property P_1, s_2 the property $P_2, \ldots$, and s_k the property P_k; h_j is the statement specifying that individual a_{s+1} has the property P_j; h'_j is the statement specifying that the individual a_{s+2} has the property P_j.

○ **A–12**

(a) $c(h_j, e_s \& h'_j) \geq c(h_j, e_s)$.
(b) $c(h_j, e_s \& h'_j) \neq c(h_j, e_s)$.

○ **A–13**

Consider a sequence $e_1, e_2, \ldots e_s, \ldots$ in which each e_i is an individual distribution for i individuals, as before, and in which e_{s+1} logically implies e_s. Then

$$\lim_{s \to \infty} \left[c(h_j, e_s) - \frac{s_j}{s} \right] = 0.$$

○ **A–14**

Let i, j, l be three distinct numbers among $1, \ldots k$. Let e'_s be like e_s except that one of the s individuals described that has the property P_j, according to e_s, has the property P_l according to e'_s, then $c(h_j, e_s) = c(h_j, e'_s)$.

The foregoing axioms yield the following theorem for a family with more than two predicates:

○ **THEOREM**

$$c(h_j, e_s) = \frac{s_j + \lambda/k}{s + \lambda},$$

where λ is a finite positive real number characterizing the function c.

To say that λ is a number characterizing the function c is to say that to choose λ is to fix the value of c for every pair of sentences in the language. The final axiom of the system presented in "Replies and Expositions" extends this theorem to the case $k = 2$.

○ **A–15**

For $k = 2$ and fixed s, $c(h_j, e_s)$ is a linear function of s_j.

Insofar as the c-function is applied to predicates belonging to only one family, it is completely specified by the choice of a value of λ. If $\lambda = k$ where k is the number of predicates in a family, we have c^*. If $\lambda = 0$, we have a rule which identifies the probability of h_j with the relative frequency of P_j among the sample of s individuals. This rule violates A-6. If we let λ approach infinity, for $k = 2$, we obtain in the limit the function $c^\dagger$; this function violates A-12.

All of the c-functions considered by Carnap in his published works have the property that the prior probability of a factual universal generalization in a language concerning an infinite number of individuals is 0, and as a consequence no amount of evidence in favor of such a generalization can change that zero probability: $c(l, e) = 0$, for any c-function belonging to the λ-continuum, for any universally quantified factual generalization l, and for any finite quantifier-free sentence e.

Some writers have found this counterintuitive, and sufficient reason for rejecting Carnap's c-functions as adequate explicata for logical probability. Among them, Jaakko Hintikka has offered an alternative confirmation function in which it is possible for laws to have nonzero probabilities. For the sake of simplicity, we shall present Hintikka's approach only in relation to a language containing k logically independent monadic predicates. As before, we define 2^k Q-predicates. To attribute a Q-predicate to an individual is to say all that can be said about it in this language. We next define constituents; a constituent is a general sentence asserting that such and such Q-predicates are exemplified in the world, and that *only* such Q-predicates are exemplified. For example, if Q_1, Q_2, and Q_3 are Q-predicates,

$$(\exists x)Q_1(x) \,\&\, (\exists x)Q_2(x) \,\&\, (\exists x)Q_3(x) \,\&\, (x)(Q_1(x) \lor Q_2(x) \lor Q_3(x))$$

is a constituent. There are $(2)^{2^k}$ subsets of the Q-predicates, but since one of these is the empty subset, and at least one Q-predicate must be exemplified, there are only $(2)^{2^k} - 1$ consistent constituents that can be formed. Hintikka's new assignment of *a priori* probabilities, which leads to the result that universal generalizations can have nonzero probabilities, consists in first assigning probabilities to the constituents. The probabilities thus assigned are independent of the number of individuals to which the language is to be applied. In "On a Combined System of Inductive Logic," Hintikka proposed assigning to each constituent the same probability, $1/[(2)^{2^k} - 1]$; in "A Two-dimensional Continuum of Inductive Methods," he proposes the assignment $[(\alpha + w - 1)!]/[(w - 1)!]$, where w is the number of components in the constituent, and α is a free parameter, like Carnap's λ. In both of the papers mentioned, Hintikka then proceeds to divide the probability of a constituent evenly among the structure descriptions that make it true, and then to divide the probability of each structure description among the state descriptions that make it true, thus proceeding at the lower levels in precisely the way Carnap proceeds in developing c^*.

There are two kinds of questions that may be raised about such systems: one concerns the justification for the assumption that probability$_1$ should obey the usual probability axioms; the other concerns the question, *which* confirmation function? On the first question, definite answers have been forthcoming, in two ways. First, a number of writers (Shimony, Lehman, Kemeny) have shown that *if* probability$_1$ is to be taken as a guide to action—e.g., in making bets or in choosing between uncertain alternatives—*then* it must obey the usual probability axioms. (The first arguments establishing the relation between behavior under circumstances of uncertainty and the probability axioms were set forth by F. P. Ramsey; his work will be referred to in the next chapter.) This kind of defense of the usual probability axioms is characteristic of the subjectivistic theorists, but is also welcomed by those who accept a logical interpretation of probability. Abner Shimony, for example, has presented careful arguments in favor of the axioms of the probability calculus, but so far from being a subjectivist, he hopes to find a version of the principle of indifference which can be certified on *a priori* grounds.

In a very different way, the physicist R. T. Cox has offered arguments in favor of the axioms of the conventional probability calculus. His method is functional analysis. He begins by assuming that the probability is a functional relationship whose domain is pairs of propositions (evidence; hypothesis) and whose range is included in the set of real numbers in the closed interval (0, 1). He shows that a very few, very innocuous and natural, conditions suffice to ensure that the probability function will satisfy the axioms of the probability calculus. The arguments employed by Cox are both beautiful and sophisticated.

Given that we have decided to accept a probability$_1$ function satisfying the usual probability calculus, we must face the question, *which* probability$_1$ function? It was Carnap's original belief that there was one and only one probability function that could plausibly be accepted as yielding the appropriate meaning of probability$_1$. Since that time, he has begun to have his doubts. The continuum of inductive methods proposed a continuum of probability functions, any one of which might with some degree of plausibility, be regarded as giving the meaning of probability$_1$. In his most recent work, he intends to provide a two-dimensional continuum of inductive methods (*The Basic Systems of Inductive Logic*, forthcoming). The extent to which that two-dimensional continuum of inductive methods can be narrowed down, he now regards as an open question. Hintikka and others are exploring the results of adopting various different ways of choosing c-functions.

We shall return to this question of the arbitrariness of probability$_1$ functions in Part Two when we consider the inductive logics that can be based on these functions. For the moment, we merely observe that *given* a measure on the statements of a language, which is additive and has a maximum value of 1, we can in a natural and obvious way derive a probability$_1$ function that satisfies the laws of the probability calculus. On the other hand, there is no general agreement about which of the possible measures that satisfy these conditions should be adopted.

In the following chapter we shall see that this element of arbitrariness may be regarded as a virtue rather than a shortcoming. The subjectivistic interpretation of probability is offered on the basis that there is an ineradicable element of arbitrariness in the assessment of evidence and that an adequate formalization of the probability relation must reflect that arbitrariness.

EXERCISES

1. Consider a language L_2^2 containing two individual constants ('a', 'b') and two logically independent one-place predicates ('P', 'Q'). Compute $c^\dagger(Pa, t)$ and $c^*(Pa, t)$, where t represents a tautology, such as '$Pa \vee \sim Pa$'. Show that it does not matter what tautology of L you choose. Compute $c^\dagger(Pa, Pb)$ and $c^*(Pa, Pb)$. In a finite language, a universal generalization, '$(x) \phi(x)$' may be represented as a conjunction, '$\phi(a) \& \phi(b) \& \cdots \phi(n)$', where $a, b, \ldots n$ are the individuals referred to in that language. Compute (for L_2^2), $c^\dagger((x)(P(x) \supset Q(x)))$, $P(a) \& Q(a)$, and $c^*((x)P(x) \supset Q(x))$, $P(a) \& Q(a))$.

2. Repeat the calculation of problem 1 for a language L_3^2 containing three individual constants ('a', 'b', 'c') and the same two predicates.

3. Repeat the calculations of problem 1 for a language L_2^3 containing three predicates, 'P', 'Q', 'R', and two individual constants.

4. What is the effect on $c^\dagger$, on c^*, on confirmation functions of this sort, of the addition to the language of new individual constants? What is the effect of the addition of new predicates?

5. Show that Axiom A–6 is equivalent (given the other axioms) to the following convention from Carnap's *Logical Foundations of Probability*:
   For any state description S in a language concerning only a finite number of individuals, $c(S, t) > 0$.

6. Explain in words, and give a justifying argument for each of Carnap's axioms A47, A–8, and A–9.

7. What is the point of Axiom A–10? Of Axiom A–11?

8. Explain Axiom A–12 in words.

9. How does $\lambda = 0$ violate A–6?

10. How does $\lambda = \infty$ conflict with A–12?

11. Let L be a language concerning an infinite number of individuals, and l a universal factual generalization in that language. Let e be any finite statement not containing quantifiers. Show that if c satisfies Carnap's axioms, $c(l, e) = 0$.

12. In Hintikka's system, show that a law can have a nonzero probability.

13. What are the constituents of the language L_2^3 of problem 2? What is the effect of adding more individual constants to the language?

14. If '$(x)(Px \supset Qx)$' has been observed to hold for five individuals, what is the degree of confirmation of each of the constituents of problem 13? (Assign equal weight to each constituent.)

BIBLIOGRAPHICAL NOTES FOR CHAPTER 5

The first explicit treatment of probability as a logical relation between evidence and conclusion is John Maynard Keynes' *Treatise on Probability*, Macmillan, London and New York, 1921. The system of Harold Jeffreys, a down-to-earth and practical adaptation of Keynes' ideas, is to be found in his *Scientific Inference* (second edition), Cambridge University Press, New York, 1957. B. O. Koopman's work on systems of probability which, following Keynes' suggestion, take degrees of probability to be partially ordered rather than simply ordered, and thus to form a lattice, is to be found in three articles: "The Axioms and Algebra of Intuitive Probability," *Annals of Mathematics* **41**, 1940, pp. 269–92; "Intuitive Probabilities and Sequences," *Annals of Mathematics* **42**, 1941, pp. 169–87; and "The Bases of Probability," *Bulletin of the American Mathematical Society* **46**, 1940, pp. 763–74. The last article is reprinted in Kyburg and Smokler, *Studies in Subjective Probability*, John Wiley and Sons, New York, 1964.

Rudolf Carnap's *magnum opus* on probability, to date, is *The Logical Foundations of Probability* (second edition), University of Chicago Press, Chicago, 1962 (first edition, 1950). Two works have appeared extending the system of *Logical Foundations*, and a third is promised soon. The two that have appeared are, *The Continuum of Inductive Methods*, University of Chicago Press, Chicago, 1952, and Rudolf Carnap and Wolfgang Stegmüller, *Induktive Logik und Wahrscheinlichkeit*, Springer, Vienna, 1959; the third in his projected *Basic System of Inductive Logic*. The axioms appearing in this chapter come from "Replies and Expositions," in *The Philosophy of Rudolf Carnap* (P. A. Schilpp, ed.), Open Court, La Salle, Illinois, 1963, pp. 859–1013.

Developments that have followed the lines suggested by Carnap's work include John G. Kemeny, "A Logical Measure Function," *Journal of Symbolic Logic* **18**, 1953, pp. 289–308, in which Carnap's techniques are extended to a large class of object languages, and Hilary Putnam, "A Definition of Degree of Confirmation for Very Rich Languages," *Philosophy of Science* **23**, 1956, pp. 8–62, which extends the technique still further. A further development of Carnap's original system is provided by Richard Martin, "A Formalization of Inductive Logic," *Journal of Symbolic Logic* **23**, 1958, pp. 251–56. A clear exposition of the Carnapian point of view will be found in John Kemeny's "Carnap's Theory of Probability and Induction," in *The Philosophy of Rudolf Carnap* (P. A. Schilpp, ed.), Open Court, La Salle, Illinois, 1963, pp. 711–38.

Jaakko Hintikka's work is fairly recent. The basic logical framework is provided by "Distributive Normal Forms in First-Order Logic," in *Formal Systems and Recursive Functions* (Crossley and Dummett, eds.), North-Holland, Amsterdam, 1965, pp. 47–90. Developments of the system are to be found in "Towards a Theory of Inductive Generalization," in *Proceedings of the 1964 International Congress for Logic, Methodology, and Philosophy of Science*, North-Holland, Amsterdam, 1965, pp. 274–88; "On a Combined System of Inductive Logic," in *Studia Logico-Mathematica et Philosophica in Honorem Rolf Nevalinna,*

Acta Philosophica Fennica **18**, 1965, pp. 21–30; and "A Two-Dimensional Continuum of Inductive Methods," in *Aspects of Inductive Logic* (Hintikka and Suppes, eds.), North-Holland, Amsterdam, 1966, pp. 113–32.

Arguments justifying the usual probability axioms have been presented (independently and almost simultaneously) by Abner Shimony, "Coherence and the Axioms of Confirmation," *Journal of Symbolic Logic* **20**, 1955, pp. 644–60; John G. Kemeny, "Fair Bets and Inductive Probabilities," *Journal of Symbolic Logic* **20**, 1955, pp. 263–73; and R. Sherman Lehman, "On Confirmation and Rational Betting," *Journal of Symbolic Logic* **20**, 1955, pp. 251–62. The rather different argument of Richard T. Cox is to be found in his book *The Algebra of Probable Inference*, Johns Hopkins University Press, Baltimore, 1961.

6

Subjectivistic
Interpretations of Probability

The most recent and one of the most interesting interpretations of probability is the subjectivistic one: According to the subjectivistic point of view probabilities concern actual degrees of belief. Although this interpretation of probability was presented for the first time in 1926 by F. P. Ramsey, and was first claimed to be important for statistics in 1937 by Bruno de Finetti, the subjectivistic interpretation of probability had no great effects on English-speaking statisticians until the publication, in 1954, of L. J. Savage's book *The Foundations of Statistics*. Since that time the interpretation has had a considerable impact on statistical practice, though it does not by any means outweigh or replace the classical frequentist orientation of most statisticians.

The degrees of belief with which probability is concerned, according to the subjectivistic interpretation, are the actual subjective degrees of belief of people: the starting point is just the set of degrees of belief that they have.

Degrees of belief are to be interpreted behavioristically. Ramsey first proposed that degrees of belief be measured by betting odds: if one is willing to bet at odds of $1:5$ on the occurrence of a three on the roll of a die, but at no higher odds, then one's degree of belief is $1/(1 + 5) = \frac{1}{6}$. As Ramsey also pointed out, there are ways of avoiding the difficulties (e.g., of decreasing marginal utility) of money bets. In fact Ramsey devised an ingenious technique by means of which both the evaluation of utilities and the evaluation of probabilities could be carried out simultaneously on the basis of a single proposition believed to the degree $\frac{1}{2}$. In a more formal style, Savage has worked out a whole system of subjective probability on the basis of the simple relation of *preference* between acts. For example, if a person prefers to stake a possible gain on the occurrence of an event E, rather than to stake a possible gain on the occurrence of an event F, then, for that person, the event E is more probable than the event F.

Although the subjectivistic theory takes as its starting point people's actual degrees of belief, it is not held that all degrees of belief in a group of propositions are equally acceptable. Some distributions of belief allow a book to be made against the holder of the beliefs. For a person to have a book against him is for him to accept a set of bets such that he cannot win, whatever happens. For example, if a person had a degree of belief equal to $\frac{4}{5}$ in the event E, he would, on our behavioristic interpretation, be willing to bet at odds of $4:1$ in favor of the occurrence of E. On the other hand, if he had a degree of belief equal to $\frac{2}{5}$ in the non-occurrence of E, he would be willing to bet at odds of $2:3$ against the occurrence of E. Now let him make both of these bets in dollars. Then if E does not occur, he wins the second bet (receiving three dollars) and loses the first bet (paying out four dollars); and if E does occur, he wins the first bet (receiving one dollar) but loses the second bet (paying out two dollars). In either case, then, he loses one dollar. In gambling parlance, he has had a book made against him.

Now it is possible to show that in these circumstances the person can avoid being in a position to have a book made against him by apportioning his degrees of belief in the occurrence of E and in the occurrence of not-E so that the sum of these degrees of belief is 1. A necessary and sufficient condition of not being in a position to have a book made against you on a single event E, is that your degree of belief in E and in the denial of E, as reflected in the least betting odds you will accept, add up to 1. In general it can be shown that a necessary and sufficient condition of not being in a position to have a book made against you is that your degrees of belief in any set of statements satisfy the axioms of the probability calculus. (This has been called the *Dutch Book Theorem* by Isaac Levi.)

A set of degrees of belief in a set of propositions (or statements, or events) is called *coherent* if and only if those degrees satisfy the axioms of the probability calculus. We may now express the Dutch Book Theorem as follows: a necessary and sufficient condition of not being in a position to have a book made against one is that one's degrees of belief be coherent.

Since not everybody's body of beliefs is coherent, the theory of probability cannot be regarded simply as a description of the way people do in fact distribute their degrees of belief. It represents an ideal of rationality: people *ought* to distribute their beliefs in accordance with the rules of the probability calculus. There is thus a close kinship between the logical view and the subjectivistic view of probability; but on the latter view there are no conditions of rationality that are to be imposed on people's degrees of belief above and beyond those embodied in the calculus of probability itself.

Savage, indeed, argues that the calculus of probability is simply a complex criterion of consistency. The person who finds himself in the position of violating theorems of the calculus is in roughly the same situation as the person whose beliefs have been shown to be logically inconsistent. He must modify his beliefs, but in neither case does the standard (the calculus of probability in the former case; the deductive calculus of logic in the latter) tell him the specific manner in which he should modify his beliefs. He must make some adjustment; but logic cannot tell him which.

In "The Aim of Inductive Logic," Carnap discusses the matter in more detail. He distinguishes between an *actual* credence function which is a theoretical property of an individual that, together with his utility function (also a theoretical property), provides a psychological explanation for his actions and decisions, and a *rational* credence function, which is taken to be the credence function of a perfectly rational being. A perfectly rational being will not have a book made against him; therefore his credence function at a given time will be coherent. Furthermore, if E is the observational data received by a perfectly rational being between time T_n and time T_{n+1}, then his credence functions Cr_n and Cr_{n+1} will be related by the relation that for any H,

$$\mathrm{Cr}_{n+1}(H) = \frac{\mathrm{Cr}_n(E \cap H)}{\mathrm{Cr}_n(E)} = \mathrm{Cr}_n(H|E).$$

It is but a step from this consideration to the supposition that there is a credence function for time zero, Cr_0 such that, if A represents the perfectly rational beings's total observational knowledge up to time n, his credence function at time n for any H will be $\mathrm{Cr}_0(H|A)$. A credibility function, for Carnap, is simply a generalized conditional credence function: $\mathrm{Cred}(H|A)$ is defined for an H and all consistent A, while $\mathrm{Cr}_0(H|A)$ merely represents the perfectly rational being's credence when in fact his knowledge is A. Then, as we saw in the last chapter, Carnap goes on to impose further conditions (invariance conditions, for example) of the formal counterparts of the credibility function. But the serious subjectivist will not follow him in imposing any more conditions on the credence function than are imposed by the axioms of probability themselves.

One of the most attractive things about the subjectivistic interpretation of probability is that it provides a complete rationale for induction, or, more specifically, for statistical inference. In this regard the crucial theorem of subjectivistic approach is Bayes' Theorem; indeed, among statisticians the subjectivistic theory is often called 'Bayesian'. This is slightly misleading, since even frequentists are often, in virtue of statistical background knowledge, in a position to use Bayes' Theorem.

As an example of the kind of inference that admits of a subjectivistic interpretation, but only in the most strained way a frequentist interpretation, consider the following: Let H be the statement that a certain holograph manuscript, newly come to light in the attic of an old house in Provence, is a hitherto undiscovered poem by Dante Alighieri. Let E be the statement that Dante was well known to the family that lived in that house at the time that Dante was in Provence. A person might well take the credibility of H, to be quite small, say 0.2; and similarly the probability of E might be quite small, say 0.2. The conditional credibility of E, given H, however, might quite justifiably be large: say 0.7. Thus, as subjectivists, we can calculate the conditional credibility of H, given E: it is

$$\mathrm{Cr}(H|E) = \frac{\mathrm{Cr}(H)\mathrm{Cr}(E|H)}{\mathrm{Cr}(E)} = \frac{0.2 \times 0.7}{0.2} = 0.7.$$

Now suppose we find that E is true. The subjectivist will say that we should assign a credibility of 0.7 to it. The frequentist will say that the whole analysis is nonsense, and that we might just as well admit flat out that our beliefs have changed, and not pretend to give reasons for the change.

And indeed there is a problem in the use of Bayes' Theorem, for the true subjectivist. If one coherent credence function is as good as another, a single person at two different times has as much right to two credence functions as two people at the same time. At time T_1 my credence function may be Cr_1, and my conditional credence function for the hypothesis H on the evidence E may be $\mathrm{Cr}_1(H|E) = \mathrm{Cr}_1(H \cap E)/\mathrm{Cr}_1(E)$. But suppose at T_2 I have observed E (and that that is all I have observed since T_1); the value of my new credence function for the hypothesis H will be $\mathrm{Cr}_2(H)$. The subjectivist would like to say that $\mathrm{Cr}_2(H)$ *ought* to be equal to $\mathrm{Cr}_1(H|E)$. Carnap says this, but Carnap is no true subjectivist; in the back of his mind he still entertains the belief that there is only one rational credibility function. The true subjectivist, however, can say no more than that most people feel uncomfortable about switching their credibility functions in midstream, as it were, and that his intent is to provide guidance for those who wish to remain consistent through time, as well as coherent at a given time.

Richard Jeffrey, in *The Logic of Decision*, has offered a more general approach to the problem of changing beliefs. One of the problems with the standard subjectivistic (and also the logical) approach is that experience is taken to render evidence statements completely certain: $\mathrm{Cr}_2(E)$ is taken to be $\mathrm{Cr}_1(E|E) = 1$. But often we should take account of evidence which is uncertain. When $\mathrm{Cr}_2(E)$ merely differs from $\mathrm{Cr}_1(E)$, Jeffrey suggests we compute our new credence function as follows:

$$\mathrm{Cr}_2(H) = \mathrm{Cr}_1(H|E)\, \mathrm{Cr}_2(E) + \mathrm{Cr}_1(H|\bar{E})\, \mathrm{Cr}_2(\bar{E}).$$

Again, the conditional probabilities are supposed not to change. It is hard to see what rules that possibility out. The difference between $Cr_1(E)$ and $Cr_2(E)$ is supposed to be a result of experience. But it might also result from a change in blood sugar. And it is perfectly possible that certain physiological changes —or perhaps mere reflection—should change the value of the credence function for H—say, a general hypothesis—instead of its value for an 'observation' such as E. It is one thing to take the Dutch Book Theorem as an argument for having a credence function which is coherent at any given time; it is quite another thing to use either Bayes' Theorem of Jeffrey's Theorem to change beliefs.

Much of the appeal of Bayesian statistics to statisticians stems from the fact that *a priori* probabilities or distributions that are fed into Bayes' Theorem, which represent the most subjective element of the theory, often turn out to be less and less important as the empirical evidence provided by observed frequencies or observed distributions increases. The subjective element is out in the open, they say, but the actual results of the statistical inference often do not depend in any quantitatively significant way on that subjective element.

This phenomenon—the swamping of the influence of prior probabilities by that of empirical observations—has not gone unnoticed. Even an extreme frequency theorist, von Mises, makes a point of remarking on it, in order to argue that Bayes' Theorem is useful in statistics. He makes much of the fact, which is central to all of statistical inference from the subjectivist's point of view, that often whatever probability assessments or estimates you start with are very quickly overwhelmed by the importance of empirical evidence. Reichenbach, too, makes important use of Bayes' Theorem. But most frequency-oriented statisticians in recent years have eschewed the use of Bayes' Theorem, except where there are available known prior probabilities that can be interpreted empirically, primarily on the ground that lacking this sort of prior information one could only assign prior probabilities subjectively, and that this subjectivity would therefore infect all of their results. (Here is a particularly clear example of the utter lack of communication between members of opposing camps, even when they use the same words.)

Three kinds of objections have been brought against the subjectivistic interpretation of probability; in view of the fact that there are those who accept the subjectivistic interpretation, it may be inferred that these objections are not decisive. The first two objections apply as well to the logical theories of the preceding chapter; the third applies only to the subjectivistic theory.

One thing which has been held to be implausible about either the subjectivistic theory or the logical program for a theory is that degrees of belief are regarded as being completely precise, like betting ratios. The logical theory has the difficulty that it legislates (or intends to legislate) in complete detail about degrees of belief in the absence of any evidence at all. The subjectivistic theory has the difficulty that any such degree of belief is permissible, so long as it does not conflict with other degrees of belief. On either theory, we must suppose that the probability of any event—such as that of finding furry animals on Mars, or that of experiencing rain in Detroit on Tuesday—can be evaluated to any desired number of decimal places. On neither theory is there any intrinsic distinction between probabilities that are based on the careful assessment of extensive evidence and probabilities that are (logically or psychologically) *a priori*. I take the probability of heads on the first toss of a coin that you casually pull out of your pocket to be one-half; and after performing extensive mechanical tests, static and dynamic, and after running a long series of trials, and subjecting them to extensive statistical tests, I conclude that the probability of heads on the next toss of that coin is one-half. On either the logical or the subjectivistic theory, this means that the net effect of all that work is zero; the probability is unchanged. A probability of one-half is just a probability of one-half.

This objection has to some extent been met by recent developments in the foundations of the theory (formalism plus interpretation) of probability. I. J. Good and C. A. B. Smith have both proposed generalizations of the subjectivistic theory in which one speaks of upper and lower probabilities.

A second objection, also applicable both to the logical and to the subjectivistic interpretation, is that both interpretations allow the derivation, on the basis of purely *a priori* probabilities, of very high probabilities concerning long sequences of future events. For example, let us consider a sequence of balls drawn with replacement from an urn. Let the probability that the first ball is purple be 0.01, on either logical or subjectivistic grounds, and similarly, let the probability that the second ball is purple, given that the first one is purple, be 0.02. Given the usual conditions regarding draws from urns, it is then possible to show that the probability is 0.99 that an arbitrarily long sequence of draws will produce less than 10% purple balls, and to show this, furthermore, on *a priori* grounds alone. The probability is 0.9996 that less than half the balls will be purple. One does not expect to obtain such high probabilities concerning such generalizations on no evidence at all; something seems to have gone wrong.

The subjectivist's answer is a shrug of the shoulders: "All this shows is that your original dispositions (degrees of belief), consistently carried out, lead to some surprising conclusions. But there is nothing unusual in that state of affairs in mathematics or in philosophy. If you find the conclusions intolerable, change the premises." The logical theorist will have much the same answer; he may regard the conclusion simply as a surprising consequence of initial statements that he takes to be incontrovertible; or else he will take the surprising conclusion to throw doubt on the initial measure function which led to that conclusion.

The third objection, which applies only to the subjectivist theory, is already suggested by the subjectivist's answer to the second objection: if you find the conclusion intolerable, change the premises. Since on the subjectivistic interpretation of probability I can adjust my probabilities in any way that I want to, provided only that they satisfy the rules of the calculus, there is nothing in principle that precludes my arranging my degrees of belief in such a way that I attribute a high degree of belief to the things that fit in with my preconceptions, and a low degree of belief to the things that don't fit in. That is: The relation of evidence to conclusion itself depends on the probability assignments that I make; I can in principle adjust these assignments so that the evidence supports (or does not badly undermine) the hypotheses that I want it to support, rather than those I don't want it to support. As Savage has observed, the probability calculus may show that we should modify some of our beliefs, but cannot show *which* of our beliefs should be modified.

Now it seems absurd that we should be able, so to speak, to change our beliefs retroactively after seeing to what further beliefs they lead. It is certainly poor science to decide which hypothesis to accept first and to evaluate the evidence concerning that hypothesis in the light of the hypothesis itself. The defense is that people just don't do that with their beliefs; people don't decide what to believe first and then calculate backwards, using the probability calculus, to find out what their prior beliefs must (should) have been. On the contrary, the way the probability calculus does generally function is to lead us to modify our beliefs in accordance with the evidence, rather than to modify the impact of the evidence in accordance with our beliefs. From an abstract point of view this may seem like no more than a fortunate accident. From the point of view of the subjectivist it is simply a fact, a datum, and for the subjectivist that is sufficient. For the epistemologist or the scientist, however, this is the way probability calculus *ought* to function, and indeed it is the whole point of having a probability calculus.

EXERCISES

1. The text contains an informal demonstration that the holder of a set of degrees of belief that violated the theorem $P(H) = 1 - P(\overline{H})$ could have a book made against him. Construct a similar demonstration for the necessity of the addition axiom.
2. Construct a similar demonstration for the multiplication axiom.
3. Construct a similar demonstration for the axiom of total probability.
4. Give a proof of the assertion on page 73 that the probability is 0.99 that in an arbitrarily long sequence of draws, there will be less than 10% purple balls. (Use the fact that

$$P\left[|f - P_1| > K\left(\frac{P_1}{H_1} + \frac{h-1}{h} P_1 P_2 - P^2\right)^{1/2}\right] < \frac{1}{K^2},$$

   where P_1 is the prior probability of a purple ball, P_2 is the conditional probability of getting a purple ball on the second draw, given that a purple ball resulted on the first draw, and f is the relative frequency of purple balls among h draws; K is arbitrary).
5. There are two urns, urn 1 and urn 2. One has ten white balls and five black balls; the other has ten black balls and five white balls. Suppose that I

believe to the degree 0.75 that I have urn 1. What is the conditional probability that I should attach to the hypothesis that I have urn 1, given that I draw four balls (with replacement) and that they are all black? I now draw four balls, with careful mixing and replacement; all of them turn out to be black. What degree of belief should I now attach to the hypothesis that I have urn 1, according to Bayes' Theorem? Suppose in spite of this recommendation, my belief remains of degree 0.75 that I have urn 1; how can this be explained?

6. Suppose that the subjective probability for you that the Yankees will win the first game of the coming World Series is 0.4, and that the probability for you that they will win the Series is 0.6. Suppose the conditional probability that if they will have won the first game is 0.5. What is the conditional probability that they will win the Series, given that they win the first game? Suppose they win the first game and your belief that they will go on to win the Series is 0.3. How can this be explained?

7. Let H be the statement that the football team will win their game this afternoon, and E the statement that the field will be wet. My current credence function has the values

$$\text{Cr}(H) = 0.4, \qquad \text{Cr}(H|E) = 0.2, \qquad \text{Cr}(H|\bar{E}) = 0.5.$$

What does coherence require of my belief in E? Suppose I look out the window and my belief in E becomes 0.7, because it is drizzling lightly. How should my other beliefs change, according to Jeffrey? Suppose my eggs are overdone and my coffee is cold and this causes my belief in H to change to 0.2. How should my other beliefs change?

BIBLIOGRAPHICAL NOTES FOR CHAPTER 6

A general source book on subjective probability is Kyburg and Smokler (eds.) *Studies in Subjective Probability*, John Wiley and Sons, New York, 1964. It includes reprints and translations of some of the items mentioned below.

F. P. Ramsey's original penetrating discussion of subjectivistic (the word is not his) probability was written in 1926 but did not appear in print until 1931 in the posthumous collection of essays, *The Foundations of Mathematics*, Humanities Press, London, 1931, 1950. This essay is reprinted in Kyburg and Smokler.

The work of Bruno de Finetti is altogether independent of that of Ramsey, and appears in a number of publications from 1930 onward. An early philosophically oriented essay is "Probabilismo: Saggio critico sulla teoria delle probabilità e sul valore della scienze," *Biblioteca di Filosofia diretta da Antonio Aliota*, Perrella, Naples, 1931. The most influential of de Finetti's works is "La Prévision: ses lois logiques; ses source subjectives," *Annales de l'Institute Henri Poincaré*, Volume 7, 1937, pp. 1–68; a translation of the latter article, with new (1964) footnotes by de Finetti, appears in Kyburg and Smokler.

The big book of subjective probability theory, including both logical foundations and statistical applications, is L. J. Savage, *The Foundations of Statistics*, John Wiley and Sons, New York, 1954.

The best book for the philosophy student, presenting both the general theory of subjectivistic probability and a detailed and comprehensive treatment of utilities, probabilities, and coherence, is Richard Jeffrey's *The Logic of Decision*, McGraw-Hill, New York, 1965. This book also contains Jeffrey's substitute for Bayes' Theorem.

Carnap's discussion of the relationships between credence functions, rational credence functions, conditional rational credence functions, and credibility functions is to be found in "The Aim of Inductive Logic," in *Logic Methodology and Philosophy of Science* (Nagel, Suppes, and Tarski, eds.) Stanford University Press, Stanford, California, 1962, pp. 303–18. The same volume also contains a presentation of I. J. Good's ideas concerning upper and lower probabilities, in "Subjective Probability as the Measure of a Non-Measureable Set," pp. 319–29. A similar approach is to be found in C. A. B. Smith, "Personal Probability and Statistical Analysis," *Journal of the Royal Statistical Society*, Series A, **128**, 1965, pp. 469–99.

7

The Epistemological
Interpretation of Probability

An epistemological interpretation of probability is an interpretation which takes as the fundamental clue to the nature of probability the role it plays, both formally and informally, in scientific inference. Any of the preceding theories of probability can be understood in this way: in the cases of several of the authors whose views we have considered, epistemological considerations were uppermost. This is most clearcut for Keynes and Carnap. Each of them is explicitly concerned with the relation that obtains between evidence and conclusion when the evidence does not entail the conclusion, but when the evidence does provide strong support for the conclusion. As the words 'evidence' and 'conclusion' suggest, the importance of the relation in question lies in its relevance to the grounds we have for believing that quinine is a specific for malaria or that the present forms of life on the earth evolved from earlier forms, on the evidence we do in fact have for these hypotheses. What may we properly claim to know or what may we believe to what degree, on the basis of what we may call evidence? This is the question that the logical theorists have taken most seriously.

But other points of view can be brought to bear on the same question. Reichenbach, for example, is very much concerned with general epistemological questions in his *Theory of Probability*, though he regards them as purely *pragmatic* questions, and rejects all forms of rational belief; and Reichenbach is the most thoroughgoing frequentist there is. Some subjectivists are concerned (or claim to be concerned) only with such questions as choosing among a set of available actions under conditions of uncertainty, but others are as concerned as Carnap with questions of an epistemological nature; preeminent among those concerned with these questions is Isaac Levi.

Any view of probability can thus be coaxed into shedding light of a certain sort on epistemological questions. Why then should the interpretation of probability under discussion be called "the" epistemological view? Partly because it is an interpretation of probability which takes epistemological questions even more seriously than the interpretations of Keynes or Carnap do; partly because the view entails that certain questions about probability and certain questions about epistemology be answered simultaneously; and partly because no other name seems appropriate. This interpretation takes probability to be a logical relation between evidence and conclusion, in a certain sense, but it takes that relation to reflect *known* frequencies; it thus conflicts with both the conventional logical interpretation and (by being non-empirical) with frequency or dispositional interpretations.

On this view, the probability relation holds between a statement (in a given language) constituting a rational corpus or body of knowledge. Statements concerning frequencies are essential ingredients of that body of knowledge. A situation in which there is a clear and simple relation between probability and measure (to use a better term than 'frequency') is this: when we *know* that the proportion of A's that are B's is p; when we know that a is an A; and when we know nothing else about a; then we say that the probability that a is a B, relative to that body of knowledge, is p.

What has just been described is not only an idealization; it is an idealization that is unattainable in several respects. We never *know* of a class A that the measure of its members that are members of B is precisely p, except in those uninteresting cases in which A and B are logically related, as when A is the set of unmarried men and B is the set of men. In real life the situation generally is that we have *reason to believe* that the proportion or measure of B in A is *close to* (differs by less than δ from) p. Furthermore there is no situation in which we know of an object *only* that it belongs to a single class A: we can never know of a particular man only that he belongs to the class of white-collar workers. To say that he is a particular man is already to say that we know so much about him that he can be differentiated from all other men. This knowledge may not amount to much (as when a subject in an experiment is identified simply as subject 1862548), or it may amount to a great deal (as when a policyholder is identified by his dossier in an insurance company). The point is that the only knowledge we have of a that is *relevant* to its being a B, is that it is an A. Finally, as in the case of the measure statement, it is sometimes asking too much to demand that we *know* that a is an A; it will suffice if we have *reason to believe* that a is an A in the same sense what we have *reason to believe* that the measure of B in A is about p.

When the only knowledge we have of a that is relevant to its being a B is that it is a member of A, let us say that a is a random member of A with respect to belonging to B, relative to a certain body of knowledge. We can then put the matter this way: We say that the probability that a is a B is about p, when, relative to our body of knowledge, a is a random member of some class A, with respect to belonging to B, and we know, in that same body of knowledge, that the proportion of A's that are B's is about p.

Randomness (or relevance) needs to be more precisely defined. Randomness is a four-termed relation; we can only sensibly talk about the *object a* being a random member of the *class A*, with respect to belonging to the *class B*, relative to a given *rational corpus* or body of knowledge. By a body of knowledge, I mean here a collection of statements we have *good reason* to believe. In this body of knowledge we will of course have the statement '$a \in A$', for if a is a random member of A, a must be a member of A. Furthermore we must have an acceptable measure statement connecting the sets A and B in our rational corpus; it will not assert that the measure of B in A is exactly p, but that it is *about p*, or that it lies in an interval (p, q). To say that this statement is "acceptable" is to say that we have adequate evidence for it, and that adequate evidence in turn will be explicated with the help of the concept of probability. But, for reasons that will be apparent shortly, there need be no circularity.

What else is required in order that we may say that a is a random member of A, with respect to belonging to B, relative to a certain body of knowledge—say K? When we are concerned only with precise statistical statements of the form, 'The measure of B in A is exactly p', there is no difficulty. We need merely stipulate that there be no subclass C of A such that (1) we know that a belongs to C, and (2) we know the measure of B in C, where that measure differs from the known measure of B in A. Put more compactly, we stipulate that there be no subclass C of A such that (1')'$a \in C$' belongs to our body of knowledge K and (2') '$\%(C, B, q)$' belongs to K, where $q \neq p$. ('$\%(C, B, q)$' is to be understood as a statement asserting that the measure of B in C is q.) This is roughly what is done in the practical application of statistical knowledge. In calculating the premium that John Doe will have to pay for his insurance, the insurance company takes the class of which he is a random member with respect to dying to be the smallest class to which he is known to belong about which the company has mortality data.

There are already difficulties with this approach to randomness. For suppose that a is known to belong to both A and A'; and suppose we know that the measure of B in A is p, and that the measure of B in A' is p', where $p \neq p'$.

If we happen to know the measure of B in the intersection of A and A', we are all set; but there is no reason at all why we cannot know the former measure statements without knowing the latter. The difficulties already apparent become vastly multiplied if we begin to be concerned, as it is obvious we must, with proportions that are only known within limits.

There are certain expressions which, although they denote classes about which we have statistical knowledge, do not denote classes that are appropriate as reference classes for probabilities. For example, let '$\{n\}$' denote the unit class of the next toss of a certain coin, and let 'T' denote the set of its tosses and 'H' the set of tosses resulting in heads. We know that n belongs to $(T \cap H) \cup \{n\}$. We know that the measure of heads among $(T \cap H) \cup \{n\}$ is 1. There is not even any unlimited subclass of $(T \cap H) \cup \{n\}$ in which the measure of H differs from 1. And yet we would not on this account ever want to say that the probability of heads on the next toss was 1. The fact that we have mentioned n explicitly is irrelevant; we can always substitute some relatively small class to which n is known to belong. For example, if n happens to be the twenty-third toss, we can consider the union of $T \cap H$ with the set of tosses whose ordinal number is prime; in this set, too, the measure of the set of heads will be 1.

Another kind of expression that leads to difficulties is the kind invented by Nelson Goodman, which he calls 'nonprojectible'. Let us define 'grue (x)' to mean that x is green at any time before the year 2000, and x is blue at any time after the year 2000. The classical problem of nonprojectible predicates lies in the fact that we feel quite comfortable about arguing from the premise that all the emeralds we have ever seen have been green to the conclusion that an emerald which is examined after the year 2000 will also be green, but quite uncomfortable about arguing from the premise that all the emeralds we have ever seen have been grue to the conclusion that an emerald which is examined after the year 2000 will turn out to be grue. This problem will be discussed later on in connection with various other paradoxes of confirmation. But it is obvious that a similar problem can arise in statistical projections. For example, the fact that 80% of the parrots of a certain species are grue doesn't mean that the probability is 0.8 that the first one to be examined after New Year's of the year 2000 will be grue.

What seems to be the best way of defining randomness so far depends on our having a reasonable list of classes–expressions or predicates to start with. One might start with a primitive list including such predicates as 'black', 'green', 'round', 'square', 'longer than', 'hotter than', 'cow', 'dog', etc. To the original list, we then add negations of the predicates of the original list: 'not-black', 'not-green', etc. Finally we add conjunctions of members of the new list: 'green and square', 'round and not-black', etc. Observe that the process described does not in general give rise to unions, which seem to be the source of the difficulty both in case of '$(T \cap H) \cup \{n\}$' and in the case of 'grue'. To characterize this set of plausible predicates in general appears to be quite a difficult task; but given a language appropriate to a specific branch of scientific inquiry, it does not seem as though it would be too difficult. Relativity to a specific language is something which must be built in, in any case, as it must be for the "degree-of-entailment" interpretations of probability.

Let us suppose that we have a list of names of classes which seem appropriate candidates as reference classes. Let the classes in the list be referred to as *rational classes*. Given such a list, we can define randomness as follows:

○ **D–1**

a is a random member of A, with respect to membership in B, relative to the body of knowledge or rational corpus **K** *if and only if*
1. *'a ∈ A' belongs to* **K**.
2. *'%(A, B, p, q)' belongs to* **K**, *for some fractions p and q*.
3. *A and B are rational classes*.
4. *For every rational class C such that for some p' and q" 'a ∈ C' and '%(C, B, p', q')' belong to* **K**, *either (a) 'A is included in C' belongs to* **K**, *or (b) (p, q) is a sub-interval of (p', q')*.

To this formal definition of randomness, we add one principle, the *equivalence principle*:

○ **P–1**

If two statements are reasonably believed to be equivalent, they should have the same probability; i.e., if 'S is equivalent to T' belongs to **K**, *and the probability of S is (p, q), then the probability of T should be (p, q)*.

With the help of this principle, we can set out a formal definition of probability.

○ **D–2**

The probability of the statement S is the interval (p, q), relative to the rational corpus **K** *if and only if*
1. *There are terms 'a', 'A', and 'B', such that a is a random member of A, with respect to membership in B, relative to* **K**; *and '%(A, B, p, q)' belongs to* **K**; *and 'S is equivalent to a B' belongs to* **K**,
2. *For every triple of terms a', A', B', if 'S is equivalent to a' ∈ B'' belongs to* **K**, *and a' is a random member of A' with respect to B', relative to* **K**, *then '%(A', B', p, q)' belongs to* **K**.

Under D–1, P–1, and D–2, it is obvious that no statement has more than one probability (some statement may have no probability at all, relative to a given rational corpus **K**); and furthermore that all equivalent statements have the same probability.

This definition of 'probability' is only complete when we have specified the contents of **K**, our body of knowledge. Here is where the connection between probability and epistemology comes to the fore. One natural and useful approach is to take the contents of **K** to be the set of statements that, in a given context, are accepted as practically certain. In turn, one may take that "practical certainty" to be explicated by reference to probability. We may do this without circularity; we may suppose that there is a highest level of rational corpus containing logical truths and those certainties of sense that would be regarded as practically certain in any context. A rational corpus of level $1 - \delta$ will then consist of those statements whose probability, relative to this highest-level rational corpus, is an interval whose lower limit exceeds $1 - \delta$. The highest rational corpus will contain measure statements which are logically true; the rational corpus of level $1 - \delta$ will contain empirical measure statements as well. One may then speak of probabilities relative to this lower-level rational corpus, as well as relative to the highest-level rational corpus. This suffices to show that we can speak of probabilities relative to rational corpora that are in turn defined in terms of probabilities without circularity. There are still problems to be discussed bearing on the contents of rational corpora, as well as on the construction of the list of rational classes, but since they are related to problems of induction which are common to a number of different approaches, that discussion will be postponed to Part Two.

We must now consider the connection between probability as it has been defined above and the interpretations of probability we considered earlier. Let us begin with degree-of-belief interpretations of probability. When probability is defined as in D–2, the probability interval is taken to be legislative for degree of rational belief in the following way: A person has a certain rational corpus—a body of rational beliefs—containing a set of statements that are regarded in a given context as practically certain. Relative to this set of statements the probability of a statement S is the probability interval (p, q). This ought to determine his degree of belief; that is, if he is rational, he will have a degree of belief corresponding to this interval. This "degree of belief" will have some behavioristic correlates—the person will make bets only at odds ranging from p to $1 - p$, to q to $1 - q$—but we need not suppose that the very meaning of the phrase 'degree of belief' is given by these correlates.

The subjectivists point out that the better can offer only one set of odds, and argue that therefore the degree of his belief must be representable by some real number p^0. If he were to bet at odds of p to $1 - p$ in favor of the truth of S, and at odds of $1 - q$ to q against S, he could have a book made against him unless $q = p$. But we need not stipulate anything about his degree of belief in order to ensure that he (as a rational man) will not have a book made against him. That he avoids having a book made against him is something characteristic of a given set of bets, and is a purely behavioristic matter. That he could, on different occasions but on the same evidence, accept bets at different odds is acknowledged by the subjectivists. The difference in this respect is merely that, given a certain rational corpus, certain evidence, there is only a certain limited range of betting ratios that it is possible for him, with rationality, to accept.

On the Carnapian or logical view, as on the subjectivist view, it is supposed that degrees of belief are representable by real numbers. But while with respect to a single statement S the subjectivist will accept any betting ratio as rational, one who takes probability to represent a degree of entailment will accept only *one* betting ratio as rational, given a certain body of evidence. In allowing a range of betting ratios to be rational, the view sketched above embodies a more generous notion of rationality than that embraced by the Carnapian; in taking that range to be limited, its concept of rationality is more restrictive than that accepted by the subjectivists.

In the view under discussion as in Carnap's view, probability is taken to be a logical relation, and probability statements to be logically or analytically true, if true at all. That the probability of a statement is such-and-such relative to this particular body of evidence is to be construed as a logical truth, not a truth about the world at all. It is to be true in all possible worlds; how, then, can we take it as a guide to action in this particular world?

The answer is straightforward enough: it is because the probability for *us*, that to which *our* degree of belief ought to conform, is determined by the rational corpus that we in fact have, and that in turn is determined by the empirical evidence that we in fact possess. What is rational for me to believe to a high degree is what the evidence supports. If another person's evidence is different, what he should believe may not be the same as what I should believe. Perfect rationality consists in having beliefs that are in accord with the (empirical) evidence, not in having beliefs that merely *happen* in fact to be true. The latter corresponds to clairvoyance rather than to rationality; logic pertains to rationality only; and rationality itself suggests that human beings should not aspire to clairvoyance.

But what of the argument, most often presented by frequentists (for so let us lump together all those who interpret probabilities as frequencies or limiting frequencies or dispositions to exhibit frequencies or abstract measures or ...) that it would be absurd to say that the probability of something was high if it were not something that happened "for the most part"? The answer is that the absurdity lies in supposing *both* that we attribute a high probability to something, *and* that we know that it does not often happen. On the other hand, for one who interprets probability as a logical relation, there is nothing absurd at all about supposing that on the evidence one might properly attribute a high probability to something, even though in fact (as *more* evidence would indeed show) it is a rare sort of thing.

On the interpretation of probability offered in this chapter, one can make an even stronger answer. On that interpretation every probability is based on a frequency or measure statement. To say that, relative to a certain rational corpus, the probability of a statement is about p is simply to say, among other things, that the truth of that statement corresponds to an occurrence that we have reason to believe happens roughly p of the time. Events may in due course lead us to abandon or modify the measure statement on which we have based our probability; but on my view we can never assert that the probability that an A is also a B is about p, unless we have grounds for including in our rational corpus a measure statement to the effect that the measure of B in A is about p.

There need be no conflict between the frequency interpretation of probability and the epistemological view. The statements with which the frequentist is concerned represent in the object language one ingredient of the metalinguistic concept of probability. For Carnap the case is similar; it will be recalled that Carnap distinguished two senses of probability, probability$_1$, which he took to be a logical concept, and probability$_2$, which he took to be an empirical concept. The distinction between the epistemological view and Carnap's, in this respect, is that in the former view the connection between the two concepts is taken to be more intimate than in the latter.

Finally, there is the question of the probability calculus. Since under this interpretation probabilities are represented by intervals, it is clear that the conventional probability calculus does not hold; it is not possible to calculate in the usual way with the probabilities provided by definition D–2. On the other hand, there is no problem at all about calculating with the empirical object-language statements on which these probabilities are based. Thus, for example, it is possible to prove that if the probability of S is (p, q), then the probability of the denial of S is $(1 - q, 1 - p)$. It is also possible to show that there exists a real-valued function R (in fact infinitely many of them) such that (1) for every S, if the probability of S, on definition D–2, is (p, q), then $p \leq R(S) < q$, and (2) R is a probability function in the sense that it satisfies the axioms of the probability calculus.

I would claim that the epistemological interpretation of probability makes sense in very nearly all those contexts in which the word and its cognates are used, including many of those contexts that even Carnapians ordinarily agree to be reserved for empirical interpretations. Whether that claim is justified or not, it will be worthwhile to look once more at the list of probability contexts with which we started and to see how well each of the interpretations we have considered fits each context. We shall leave out of account only the simple classical interpretation; whatever truths it may once have contained are now incorporated in one or another of the other interpretations.

1. Empirical generalizations are rendered probable by the evidence in their favor; and generally can be no more than probable.

(a) Most frequentists deny that the word 'probable' can be given any technical meaning here at all. In itself a generalization is simply true or false; no more than any other particular can it be given a probability measure. Nor can we profitably consider a sequence of empirical generalizations, for all the generalizations whose truth values we know are false.

(b) On some logical theories, such as Carnap's in its present state, the prior probability of any generalization, and therefore also its posterior probability, is 0. There are other theories, such as Hintikka's, for which this is not true and for which (1) may hold in the intended sense.

(c) On the subjectivistic theory, (1) is simply and naturally true; plausible hypotheses are hypotheses that we regard as having some finite chance of being true; such a hypothesis may become more and more probable as evidence for it increases.

(d) According to the epistemological view, (1) is also generally true. Occasions may arise in which the body of evidence in a rational corpus renders a generalization as "practically certain" as other items in that rational corpus, in which case one will say, not that the generalization is probable, but that it is simply true.

2. The probability of getting a six with a throw of a die is $\frac{1}{6}$.

(a) Frequency interpretation: a die has a disposition to yield a six about a sixth of the time in the long run.

(b) Most Carnapians would agree that there is no call to apply a degree-of-entailment interpretation in such statements.

(c) Some subjectivists would say that we simply have no use for such a statement; others that it amounts to the claim that the set of tosses are considered independent with constant probability $\frac{1}{6}$ of getting a six on each toss. 'Independence' for the subjectivist, remember, represents a strong claim: it means that after a run of a million sixes, he would still bet at odds of five to one against the next six.

(d) On the epistemological interpretation such a statement would be true for a rational speaker if and only if he had *reason to believe* that about one-sixth of the tosses of a die landed with the six uppermost. The indefinite article 'a' in 'a toss' is plausibly interpreted as "any random toss, with respect to yielding a six, relative to the speaker's rational corpus." The content of (2) is thus: My rational corpus is such as to make the measure statement "about one sixth of the tosses yield a six" acceptable, which in turn has a content close to (a) above.

3. If there is any probability that God exists, you should believe that He does.

(a), (b), (d) Any of these interpretations render (3) true, and all for the same reason: vacuity of the antecedent.

(c) On the subjectivist theory only, (3) makes perfectly good sense, and everyone is free to assign his own probability, from 0 to 1 including the end-points 0 and 1 themselves. On this interpretation (3) becomes a perfectly straightforward, if dubious, assertion in applied morals.

4. If there is any probability that this mushroom is poisonous, you should believe that it is.

Despite the superficial similarity between (4) and (3), (4) admits an interpretation on each of the views of probability under discussion.

(a) On the frequency view, (4) must be understood elliptically as a conditional statement about a certain class of mushrooms. It is to be taken as meaning that if, in this class of mushrooms (say, a certain general species), the measure of the set of those that are poisonous is not zero, then you should treat each individual mushroom of that class as though it were poisonous. The statement is justified by the claim that the ratio of the utility of eating a nonpoisonous mushroom to the disutility of eating a poisonous one is essentially zero. The only problem in this interpretation of (4) is the problem of identifying the class implicitly referred to. We cannot say that it means: If there is *any* class of mushrooms..., because every mushroom belongs to a class of mushrooms in which the measure of poisonous individuals is not zero—namely the class of all mushrooms. Although (4) can be interpreted elliptically in such a way as to make sense on this view, it is difficult to know in any particular case what ellipsis has been made. We cannot tell just by looking at the mushroom.

(b) The logical interpretation of (4) is better off, though it is still elliptical. Let h be the statement that the mushroom is poisonous; e a statement expressing our observational data concerning that particular mushroom (e.g., "it has gills, no veil, a purple spore deposit,..."), and b our general mycological knowledge. The interpretation of (4) is then: If the degree of confirmation of h on e and b is greater than zero, act as if h were true. The supporting argument in terms of utilities is the same as in (a). Observe, however, that the degree of belief one should have in h, if one is rational, should be the same as the degree of confirmation of h on e and b; the injunction to believe h must be taken as a roundabout way of saying, "Act as if you believed h." Note that on this interpretation, in the presence of a given body of knowledge and a given mushroom, there is no difficulty in principle in filling in the ellipsis.

(c) On the subjectivistic interpretation, (4) turns out to be empty. Given the utilities presupposed in each of the other elucidations of (4), it is true by the subjectivistic meaning of probability alone that for any person, his subjective degree of belief that the mushroom is poisonous is significantly different from zero if and only if he is willing to act as if it were nonpoisonous.

(d) On the epistemological interpretation, (4) says that if the particular mushroom we are confronted with is not a random member of some class of mushrooms in which the measure of poisonous individuals is known to be zero (with respect to being poisonous), then we should act as if it were poisonous. In general, on the epistemological interpretation, given any body of background knowledge **K**, there will be some class C of which the mushroom is a random member, with respect to being poisonous. The degree of precision of our information concerning the measure of poisonous mushrooms in that class will vary with the extent of our mycological knowledge: if we know practically nothing about mushrooms, we will know only that the frequency of poisonous mushrooms lies somewhere in the interval (0, 1); if we know a great deal about mushrooms, we may know that it lies between 0.5 and 0.6, say, or in the interval (1, 1) or in the interval (0, 0). Only in the last case should we act as if the mushroom were nonpoisonous. In a practical sense the problem of filling in the ellipsis is even easier on this interpretation than on the logical interpretation.

5. The probability that a white American male white-collar worker will survive his fortieth birthday, given that he has survived his thirty-ninth birthday, is 0.994.

(a) The empirical interpretation of (5) will follow the plan of the empirical interpretation of (2).

(b) There would be no logical interpretation; most logicists would say that (5) is a clear-cut instance of statistical probability.

(c) The subjectivist would interpret (5) in the same way as (2), or else would take it to mean "0.994 is a parameter in a certain descriptive theory..."

(d) From the epistemological point of view, the interpretation would be the same as that of (2), as signaled by the indefinite article 'a' in the phrase 'a white American male...'

6. I will probably be late meeting the train.

(a) It is difficult to see how any empirical interpretation can be offered for (6), even an elliptical one, except by such extreme procedures as Reichenbach's.

(b) As the logicist interprets (6), the speaker has a certain body of evidence, concerning the time of arrival of the train, the state of the speaker's car, and so on. Relative to this body of factual knowledge the hypothesis "the speaker will be late for the train" has a certain probability which is in fact greater than one-half.

(c) The subjectivist need make no reference to evidence; he may interpret (6) merely as a datum, as merely expressing the speaker's preference for staking a possible gain, for example, on the event of being late for the train, rather than on the event of being on time for the train.

(d) On the epistemological interpretation we need an underlying frequency or measure statement; for example, we must suppose that there is some class of occasions—of meeting trains, or of keeping appointments, or of meeting the 5:34 on Tuesdays—in which the speaker has adequate evidence to assign a measure greater than one-half to the set of occasions on which lateness occurs. This class of occasions may be actual or hypothetical; the evidence on the basis of which a parameter greater than one-half may be assigned to it may be straightforwardly statistical, or it may be deviously theoretical and complex (e.g., it might be that the person whom the speaker is to meet on the train wears a beard reminiscent of the speaker's father, that the speaker still suffers the effects of his severe Oedipus complex, even though he acknowledges its existence, and so on). Furthermore, this particular meeting of a train is a random member of that class of occasions, with respect to being an occasion of lateness, relative to the speaker's body of knowledge.

7. The quantum theory is probably true, in its broad outlines.

(a) As in the case of (1), no frequency interpretation seems to be possible.

(b) No current logical interpretation would be able to provide an interpretation of the word 'probably' under which (7) could turn out to be true.

(c) Assuming that some precise sense could be made of the phrase 'in its broad outlines', there would be no difficulty in principle in assigning a finite probability in the subjectivist's sense to the hypothesis in question.

(d) It is difficult to see how any direct sense could be made of this on the epistemological interpretation of probability. Two possibilities suggest themselves: first, that the import of (7) is that quantum theory in its broad outlines is to be accepted in a high-level rational corpus, and the word 'probably' is applied, by assocation, to the quantum theory, because it is properly applied to other ingredients of that rational corpus; and second, that the import of (7) is that any given consequence of the general quantum theory has a high probability of being true, this latter being then treated as tantamount to a statistical assertion, like (2) and (5). Both of these possibilities will be discussed further in Part Two; neither takes the word 'probability' to have a literal sense in this context.

8. If all the crows anyone has seen are black, then probably all crows are black.

(a) Obviously no direct empirical interpretation is possible, but one might try to give the statement some meaning by a kind of contraposition: If a significant proportion of crows are *not* black, then it is very *im*probable that all the crows anyone has seen should happen to be black, therefore (8). But this principle of inference is highly questionable.

(b) The logical interpretation fits perfectly: the degree of confirmation of 'all crows are black', relative to the evidence consisting of the observation of a lot of black crows by a lot of people, is high. None of Carnap's confirmation functions happen to render (8) true, but that is accidental; there are other logical confirmation functions, such as Hintikka's, which do make (8) true.

(c) The subjective interpretation also fits well. If all the crows anyone has seen are black, then it seems reasonable to offer high odds that all crows are black.

(d) The epistemological interpretation is more complicated. The hypothesis must be padded out; not only must all the crows anyone has seen be black, but that set of crows must be a random one, with respect to showing up variations in color, relative to the speaker's rational corpus. Under these circumstances the probability may be high that *practically* all crows are black. If this 'practically' is as large as the "practical certainty" we are concerned with, and if no counter-examples are known of, we often replace 'practically all' by 'all'.

9. Crows are probably black.

(a) The empirical interpretation: The measure of the set of black crows among the set of crows is near 1.

(b) The logical interpretation: Relative to the evidence we in fact have, the probability that a given crow is black is high. This is true for *any* crow.

(c) the subjectivist interpretation: I'll give you better-than-even odds that crows (as a species) are black (rather than some other color).

(d) The epistemological interpretation: The species crow is a random member of the set of species of birds (or northern birds, or some other set of species of birds) with respect to having uniform coloration, and a high proportion of these species have uniform coloration. Thus the species crow is probably uniform in color, and since we know that some crows are black we may say that crows are probably black. Observe that an interpretation similar to this might be offered for (8).

10. The probability distribution of the quantity Q is given by the probability distribution function $F_Q(x)$; i.e., for every real number x, the probability that Q is less than x is $F_Q(x)$.

(a) The empirical interpretation of (10) is the most natural one.

(b) No logical interpretation would be offered for (10).

(c) Some subjectivists would regard (10) as an assertion about the limiting form of a distribution function $P_Q(x)$ giving subjective probabilities, as the body of evidence concerning the quantities Q is increased, provided the initial probability function $P_Q^0(x)$ is not extreme in certain specifiable ways.

(d) From the epistemological point of view, the interpretation of (10) is analogous to the interpretation of (2) or (5). One would assert (10) only when one's rational corpus contained the assertion that the distribution of Q was adequately described by the function F_Q. For example, the measure of the set of instances in which the quantity Q is less than x is given by $F_Q(x)$; and the probability, relative to that rational corpus, that a *random* instance of Q will be less than x is that same function of x, $F_Q(x)$.

11. The tales told by Marco Polo when he returned from the Orient were improbable but true.

(a) No empirical interpretation of (11) is possible.

(b), (c), (d) The idea behind (11) is taken to be the same on each of the other interpretations of probability; namely, that relative to the body of beliefs of the people of Marco Polo's time, the things he told them were not rationally credible, but relative to our body of beliefs they are credible.

The truth value of (11) is another matter; on the subjectivistic interpretation it is obviously true; on either the logical or the epistemological interpretation its truth value depends on the contents of the rational corpora of Marco Polo's contemporaries, and that, of course, is highly conjectural.

12. If the probability of heads on one toss of a coin is one-half, then the probability of two heads on two independent tosses is one-fourth.

(a), (b), (c) On each of the empirical, the logical, and the subjectivist interpretations of probability, (12) is necessarily true.

(d) On this view precise probabilities are an idealized figment. What might plausibly be taken to correspond to (12) is this: If, relative to my rational corpus, the probability of a random member of the set of coin tosses yielding heads is $\frac{1}{2} + \epsilon$, then, relative to my rational corpus, the probability that a random member of the set of *pairs* of coin tosses will be a member of the set of pairs of coin tosses that both yield heads is $\frac{1}{4} \pm 2\epsilon + \epsilon^2$.

13. Induction is probable inference.

(a) Most frequentists would deny that the word 'probable' is used in (13) in their technical sense. However, there are those who would even in (13) interpret it as an empirical term; one might say that just as deductive inference is inference that yields truth 100 per cent of the time when it starts from true premises, so inductive inference is inference that yields truth *for the most part* when it starts from true premises. It is this *truth frequency* that is signified by 'probable' in this context. But although this interpretation of (13) makes sense, it is hard to see how anyone could maintain that (13) under this interpretation is true.

(b) The logicist will say that a need for a clear understanding of induction is the greater part of the motivation behind his explication of probability as degree of confirmation. On his view, the equation (13) is trivially true; the problem is the explication of its two terms.

(c) For the subjectivist, too, (13) offers no problems. By 'probable inference' he understands demonstrative inference in the calculus of probability and in particular, in one way or another, the application of Bayes' Theorem.

(d) One may also interpret (13) as asserting that induction is inference according to (epistemological) probability. In this sense (13) is false, for much of scientific or inductive inference proceeds according to purely deductive patterns. But it is also true that on a relatively detailed epistemological analysis of a bit of scientific reasoning, it will always turn out that if the inference does not proceed in accord with epistemological probability, but according to a deductive pattern, then at least some of the ultimate premises will have been supported by directly probabilistic arguments.

14. The probability of heads on the next toss of this particular well-tested coin is one-half.

(a) According to most empirical interpretations of probability, (14) must be understood elliptically as referring to the chance set-up, or the coin together with the flipping arrangement. Although it seems to be about the *next* toss, on this view, it isn't really.

(b) Relative to the evidence which I have, to which I refer in an abbreviated fashion when I call the coin 'well tested', the degree of confirmation of the hypothesis 'the coin will land heads on the next toss' is one-half.

(c) According to the subjectivist view, the content of (14) is nothing more or less than that I am willing to offer no more than even odds that heads will occur on the next toss. The reference to testing is so much window dressing, except insofar as it indicates that it will take many tosses to make me change my degree of belief.

(d) According to the epistemological view, (14) requires that the speaker have enough evidence ("well-tested") to have grounds for believing that the measure of heads in trials on the chance set-up in question will be close to one-half, and also requires that the "next toss" be a random member of the set of trials on that chance set-up, with respect to resulting in heads, relative to the speaker's rational corpus. If we deny that the probability on a particular toss (the "next", the fifteenth, or whatever) is one-half, it may be for either of two reasons: either we do not have reason to accept the hypothesis that the measure of heads in the set of trials under consideration will be close to one-half, or else it is because we know something about the particular toss in question which will prevent it from being a random member of that set.

15. I do not know what the probability of heads for this coin may be.

(a) On the empirical view, we would have a coin and a chance set-up in mind; I utter (15) because I do not know the value of the parameter which characterizes that chance set-up.

(b), (c) On either the logicist or the subjectivist view, (15) is no more than a testimonial of laziness or lack of insight. To be ignorant of a probability on the logical view is to be too lazy to calculate; to be ignorant of a probability on the subjectivistic view is to be too muddled to know one's own mind.

(d) On the epistemological view, in one sense, to be ignorant of a probability is impossible, for at the very least one will be able to say that the probability is the interval (0, 1). But in many circumstances only a rather narrow probability interval will be of use to us, and we are likely to deny modestly having any probabilistic knowledge at all where our knowledge is vague. This is particularly true in cases in which we could obtain the required statistical knowledge in a straightforward way, less true in the case, say, of historical conjectures where there is no obvious procedure for obtaining a useful statistical statement.

EXERCISES

1. Let one card be drawn, under the usual circumstances obtaining in parlor games, from an ordinary well-shuffled deck of cards. Suppose that we know that it is drawn from the top half of the deck of cards, by a man

named John in the early afternoon. Is it a random member, relative to what we know about it so far, of the set of cards in the deck with respect to being a spade? Is it a random member, relative to what we know about it so far, of the set of cards drawn from decks of cards, with respect to being a spade? How can it be a random member of both these sets? Why is it not a random member of the set of cards in the top half of the deck? Why is it not a random member of the set of cards drawn by John in the afternoon? What is the probability that it is a spade? What is the probability that it is drawn from the top half of the deck?

2. Let (a, b) be an ordered pair of cards drawn, one at a time, with replacement, from a standard deck under the standard conditions. Apply definitions D–1 and D–2 to arrive at the probability that a and b are both hearts; to arrive at the probability that a is a heart or b is a heart or both.

3. Let (c, d) be an ordered pair of cards drawn, one at a time, *without* replacement, from a standard deck under standard conditions. Use definitions D–1 and D–2 to arrive at the probability that c is a heart, that d is a heart, that both c and d are hearts, and that either c or d or both are hearts.

4. Let B be a class in which we know that the measure of C is p. Let B^n be the set of all ordered sets of n objects, each of which belongs to B. Let $(a_1 \cdots a_n)$ be, relative to our body of knowledge, a random member of B^n. What is the probability that exactly r of the n a's will belong to C?

5. Let B be as in problem 4, but let it contain only N objects, N_C of which belong to C. (Thus $p = N_C/N$.) Let $a_1, a_2, \ldots a_n$ be selected from B, but without replacement. Of what class is the ordered n-tuple $(a_1 \ldots a_n)$ a random member, with respect to exhibiting a certain distribution of C's; and what is the probability that it will contain exactly r C's?

6. Let B be as in problem 4, but suppose that all we know about the measure of B in C is that it lies between $p + \epsilon$ and $p - \epsilon$. Let $n = 2$. What is the probability that *both* a_1 and a_2 belong to C? That either a_1 or a_2 or both belong to C? That exactly one of a_1 and a_2 belongs to C? (State explicitly what you assume about randomness.)

7. Let the circumstances be as in problem 6. What is the probability that of the n a's exactly r will belong to C?

8. In the general population the measure of the set of people with I.Q.'s of 100 or less is 0.5. What considerations might be adduced as relevant to the *logical* question of whether or not it is reasonable for us to assign a probability of about $\frac{1}{2}$ to the proposition that John Smith has an I.Q. of less than 100? That is, what kinds of things might we know which would prevent him from being a random member of the population in general in this respect?

BIBLIOGRAPHICAL NOTES FOR CHAPTER 7

The epistemological interpretation of probability presented here is my own. A systematic and strictly formal presentation is contained in *Probability and the*

THE EPISTEMOLOGICAL INTERPRETATION OF PROBABILITY **93**

Logic of Rational Belief, Wesleyan University Press, Middletown, Connecticut, 1961. Difficulties with that system were pointed out by Frederick Schick, "Rationality and Consistency," *Journal of Philosophy* **60**, 1963, pp. 5–19. Those difficulties are avoided (but not, in a certain sense, dealt with) in the form presented here, as well as in the two papers "Probability and Randomness," *Theoria* **29**, 1963, pp. 27–55, and "Probability, Rationality, and a Rule of Detachment," *Proceedings of the Second International Congress for the Logic, History, and Philosophy of Science*, North-Holland, Amsterdam, 1965, pp. 301–10. Further discussion of the problems created by this point of view, and of their tentative solutions, will be found in Chapter 14.

PART TWO: INDUCTIVE LOGIC

8

Ordinary Language
and Inductive Argument

Arguments lead from premises to conclusions, and are designed to compel a rational person who accepts the premises also to accept the conclusion, or to compel a rational person who has certain degrees of belief in the premises also to have a corresponding degree of belief in the conclusion. We shall be concerned here only with arguments whose force depends on rational relations between the premises and the conclusion.

Traditionally, rational arguments are divided into deductive and inductive. Valid deductive arguments are those in which the conclusion follows necessarily from the premises, in the sense that the conjunction of all the premises and the denial of the conclusion is self-contradictory. For example, "Socrates is mortal" follows deductively from the premises "Socrates is a man" and "All men are mortal," because the conjunction of the premises and the denial of the conclusion, "Socrates is a man, and all men are mortal, and Socrates is not mortal," is self-contradictory, or logically false. Another way of stating the matter is to say that a valid deductive argument is an argument such that the conditional whose antecedent is the conjunction of the premises of the argument, and whose consequent is the conclusion of the argument, is logically true.

Valid inductive arguments are then easy to define: They are the other ones.

There are two respects in which this characterization of deductive, and thus indirectly of inductive, argument is seriously defective. For one thing, logical truth is a more slippery concept than it appears to be; for another, most arguments encountered in their natural state appear as enthymemes, with one or more premises suppressed.

One notion of logical truth that is fairly easy to get at is the following: a certain statement is a logical truth if it can be obtained from a theorem of a system of formal logic by substituting the names of individuals for individual constants, predicates for predicate variables, relation expressions for relation variables, etc. Thus in the earlier example, we can take the theorem '$[Fa \& (x)(Fx \supset Gx)] \supset Ga$' and turn it into a valid conditional representing the argument about Socrates by substituting 'Socrates' for 'a', 'is a man' for 'F', and 'is mortal' for 'G'. This notion of logical truth will not suffice to reflect the validity of the following argument, however: "John is a bachelor, therefore John is unmarried." Although the conjunction of the premise and the denial of the conclusion, "John is a bachelor and John is not unmarried," is contradictory, it is not contradictory in virtue of the meanings of the purely logical particles such as 'all', 'and', 'not', etc. It is contradictory in virtue of the relation between the meaning of the word 'bachelor' and the meaning of the word 'unmarried'. Thus although the conditional "If John is a bachelor then John is unmarried" is always and necessarily true, regardless of John's marital status, we can see that it is true only by analyzing the term 'bachelor'. Such truths are called 'analytic'. Analyticity itself is a slippery notion, and one whose usefulness has been and is being questioned by many. For our purposes here, however, it will suffice to indicate a broad, general distinction between deductive and inductive argument. In explicit deductive arguments, the premises analytically imply the conclusions.

The enthymematic character of most real argument creates more serious obstacles in the way of a clear-cut distinction between inductive and deductive argument. When I argue that Socrates is a man, and therefore Socrates is mortal, I am obviously suppressing the premise "all men are mortal." But when I argue that all the crows I've seen have been black, and therefore all crows are black, it is not at all clear whether there are premises I am suppressing, whether, if the premises were provided, they would be as acceptable as "all men are mortal," or even whether, if the premises were provided, and were acceptable, they would be such as to render the argument deductive in the sense just characterized.

Rather than to attempt a clean distinction between deductive argument and inductive argument, it seems more fruitful at this stage merely to attempt a rather informal characterization of inductive argument. It is an argument that is not explicitly deductive. Often the conclusion of an inductive argument appears to be a simple generalization of its premise: All the crows I've seen have been black; therefore (probably) all crows are black. Sometimes the conclusion is particular, but does not merely repeat the particulars of the premises: All the Irish setters I've known have been wild, so (probably) the next Irish setter I meet will be wild too. It is characteristic that the conclusion is asserted only with probability or plausibility, but this is by no means universal. It is characteristic that the conclusion goes beyond the premises, or has more content, or says more; but this is true of many enthymematic deductive arguments as well. Some inductive arguments are quite complex in structure: the argument from the data of particle physics to the general plausibility of quantum mechanics is exceedingly complex.

The problem of induction stems from the fact that the premises cited explicitly do not entail the conclusion. Put one way, there is nothing inconsistent in the conjunction of the premises and the denial of the conclusion; put another, there is nothing analytic about the conditional whose antecedent is the conjunction of the premises, and whose consequent is the conclusion.

There are a number of ways of dealing with this problem. One way is to dismiss the problem by saying that induction is a fact of human existence; people make inductions; some do it better than others; good inductive arguments are simply the arguments that people who are good at making inductions use, and there is nothing more to be said. Another way is to seek to uncover implicit premises, such that from the cited evidence, conjoined with these implicit premises, the inductive conclusions do follow deductively. Another way is to seek, rather than a relation of entailment between premises and conclusion, a probability relation of *partial* entailment between premises and conclusion. Both of these approaches may be followed together: perhaps we need to have auxiliary premises in order to ensure that a probability relation will hold between premises and conclusion. Yet another approach consists in taking induction to be the process of selecting the best of a number of alternative hypotheses, perhaps the one that explains the evidence best. For the subjectivist, the problem is that of showing how Bayes' Theorem, or Jeffrey's more general theorem, can be used to control the modification of our degrees of belief in various propositions, in response to sensory stimulation and its consequent modification of our beliefs in certain elementary propositions.

We shall discuss all of these approaches in subsequent chapters. In this chapter we shall be primarily concerned with the first approach, according to which induction is simply one characteristically human way of responding to the world, which admits of analysis, but no form of justification. One of the leading proponents of this view is Stephen Toulmin.

Toulmin, in *The Uses of Argument*, denies that significant arguments of any sort are analytic. Arguments may use either deductive or inductive *warrants* to get from their premises to their conclusions, but there is no real difference, for neither type of warrant yields a conclusive argument; neither type of warrant (with the exception of the type of warrant used in mathematics) is strictly analytic. Consider, for example,

Socrates is a man, therefore Socrates is mortal.

This argument uses a deductive warrant: from '*x* is a man', one may deduce '*x* is mortal', but the argument is obviously not analytic, since 'Socrates is mortal' does not follow analytically from 'Socrates is a man'. Nor is the argument conclusive, because the warrant itself is not altogether certain, and is certainly not analytic. As an example of an argument using an inductive warrant consider,

A sample of 500 telephone receivers out of a population of 10,000 has been drawn by careful techniques involving stratification and randomization, and 10 have been found defective; therefore less than 5% of the original population are defective.

The warrant here is somewhat more complex: it is to the effect that premises of the kind considered here are adequate grounds for the kind of conclusion considered here. The warrant itself allows for the possibility of error in a particular application: that is why it is called 'inductive'.

An argument may be warrant establishing as well as warrant using. The argument

All the men born over 150 years ago are dead; therefore all men are mortal,

is warrant-using—it uses the simple inductive warrant, from 'all observed *A*'s are *B*'s', conclude that all *A*'s are *B*'s—and it is also warrant-establishing, because 'all men are mortal' is just another way of expressing the warrant used in the first argument: from *x* is a man, one may infer that *x* is mortal. Some inductive arguments, such as the last, are warrant-establishing as well as warrant-using, while, according to Toulmin, deductive arguments are not warrant-establishing.

What are the consequences for inductive logic of looking at argument in this light? The most immediate and important consequence is that the principles of inductive argument are, if Toulmin is correct, to be found in the examination of the arguments that scientists use to support their conclusions, and not in abstract considerations. To find out what forms of argument are acceptable in physics, we must look at the ways flesh-and-blood physicists argue. "There is no explanation of the fact that one sort of argument works in physics, for instance, except a deeper argument also within physics. (Practical logic has no escape route...into the *a priori*.)" (p. 258). The other major consequence, for Toulmin, is that no analysis of the relative strength or relative goodness of arguments is possible, because of his interpretation of probability. It will be recalled that he regards 'probably' as a term which indicates the speaker's attitude toward the statement he is uttering. To say that it will probably rain is simply to say that it will rain, but to say it guardedly.

Criticism of Toulmin's interpretation of probability has already been offered. In part, it was that it precluded the possibility of a more quantitative, more constructive treatment. It was a counsel of despair. Few writers have adopted positions like Toulmin's on probability, but several have followed him with varying degrees of conformation in asserting that the source of information about inductive rules of inference is the study of the actual arguments used by scientists. Often this position is coupled with the claim that there can be no *formal* inductive logic (another counsel of despair?), and often it is also coupled with the claim that since the only standard for inductive arguments is to be found in the inductive arguments that are actually used, it is analytic to say that these arguments are reasonable.

Peter F. Strawson adopted both of these auxiliary positions. He argues explicitly against the existence of a formal quantitative inductive logic: "In fact, we can never describe the strength of evidence more exactly than by the use of such words as 'slender', 'good', 'conclusive',..." (*Introduction to Logical Theory*, p. 247). It is possible to answer the question "Will induction continue to be successful?" in the affirmative, because we have good evidence for this; but that induction is *reasonable* is simply analytic. Like Toulmin, he feels that the way to find out how inferences *should* be made in a particular field is to look at the way in which inferences *are* made in that field. Inductive logic, if there is such a thing, contains no normative element above and beyond those embodied in the rules of evidence of each particular area of scientific study. Strawson argues that there is no way of justifying induction in general, although there are ways of justifying particular inductions ("On Justifying Induction"). Further, he regards the problem of finding a general justification of induction unreal: It is sufficient that inductive beliefs, as Hume pointed out, are natural. Strawson challenges his critics to *try* to choose a counterinductive policy. "If it is said that there is a problem of induction, and that Hume posed it, it must be added that he solved it" (*Ibid.* p. 21).

R. Harré follows the trail blazed by Strawson and Toulmin. Like Strawson, he regards sensible questions about induction to be of the form "How is this particular procedure justified?," and the request for a general justification of inductive standards to be misconceived. "There are no general standards of reasonableness everywhere appealed to." ("Dissolving the 'Problem' of Induction.") Like Toulmin, he takes many of the statements of science to formulate principles of inference, which do not, according to him, require inductive justification. The seeds of this curious doctrine of inference tickets, which suggests that if we call something a principle of inference we don't care whether or not it will lead us astray, while if we consider the corresponding statement, we must take seriously the chance that it might be in error, are to be found in Gilbert Ryle's "Predicting and Inferring," and "'If', 'So', and 'Because'." Ryle is there attempting to provide a pragmatic justification for induction: The question of induction is settled when we *see* that induction works. On Ryle's view, we do not establish the general statement 'all *A*'s are *B*'s' by observing *A*'s and *B*'s. Rather we adopt the rule of inference: from the fact that something is an *A*, infer that it is a *B*; and then we see from the success of the inferences made in accordance with this rule of inference that the rule *works*.

The claim that it is profitable to look at certain classes of general statements as rules of inference has been examined carefully by H. G. Alexander in "General Statements as Rules of Inference." He concludes that nothing is added to the traditional account in terms of enthymeme (suppressed premises) by talking instead of "material rules of inference" or "inference tickets". Alexander suggests that both deductive and inductive arguments be reconstructed in the traditional way, including all the material premises explicitly as premises. In the second place, as Peter Achinstein has argued, the problem is not to show that the rule (if that is how you wish to reconstruct the inference) has worked in the *past*; the problem is to show that it will continue to work in the future. "The scientist not only points to the past successes of his theory, but he infers to its future successes as well" ("From Success to Truth," p. 8). He charges that Ryle is playing on the ambiguity of 'it works'. Ryle denies the charge. A general law or theory, he says, is like a design or a recipe: it is tenseless. There is no inference from successful inference to the truth of the *basis* of that inference, any more than there is an *inference* from a successful soufflé to the validity of the recipe in accordance with which it was made. We *learn* the merits and demerits of a design or recipe by testing it— but to learn is not to infer. The dispute is settled, I think, by Harry V. Stopes-Roe, who says, "... the fact is that, when one shows the goodness of a recipe or a theory by means of successful instances, there is a gap between what is literally shown—namely the successes to date—and the goodness of the recipe or theory." Whatever be the nature of the gap—and many would be happy to withhold the term 'inference' from the process that leads us across it—it is that gap which an inductive logic or an examination of scientific method is called upon to fill.

N. R. Hanson also takes a pragmatic and descriptive approach to scientific inference. "'That *F* obtains is a good reason for *G*' is necessarily true, if it is true at all. Nothing but reflection is needed to discover the goodness of reasons ..." ("Good Inductive Reasons," p. 123). Hanson, too, distinguishes between the problem (he admits that it *is* a problem) of justifying inference permits and the problem of justifying general statements. "'All *F*'s are *G*'s' does not by itself, disclose whether it is up for scrutiny *qua* inference-permit or *qua* the factual support for that permit" (p. 123).

The temptation to disregard completely the normative element that can be discerned in the appraisal of inductive arguments has been succumbed to by a number of writers. Strawson, Toulmin, and Harré—and to some extent

Hanson—have all said that to evaluate inductive arguments we must look no further than the inductive arguments that are actually regarded as valid in the relevant fields. But far more extreme views of this sort have been held by other writers.

There is certainly a sound instinct underlying these far-fetched claims; we would rightly suspect that there was something seriously wrong with an inductive logic that came into conflict with too many of the patterns of inference that can be discerned in the sciences. Just as the touchstone of formalizations of deductive logic may be taken to be the agreement between the formalization and patterns of acceptable deductive argument, so a helpful guide to the general principles of inductive logic might well be the study of actual scientific inferences. The more is the pity, then, that those who claim that all there is to inductive logic is the examination of accepted patterns of inference have not spent more effort reporting and analyzing those patterns. (N. R. Hanson was an important exception to the general principle that those who spent the most time exhorting others to look at *real* inductive arguments themselves were the most ignorant of the actual inferential procedures of the sciences.)

We have just examined a number of approaches according to which the inductive arguments encountered in the sciences themselves provide (express) the standards of cogency for argument in those sciences. A related approach to inductive logic seeks to find a small number of principles which pervade all the sciences, and to construct an inductive logic on the basis of those principles. Max Black and Nelson Goodman both fall into this category. Black, although he states flatly that he rejects "the view that induction needs any 'justification' or 'vindication' in the sense which philosophers have usually attached to these words" (*Models and Metaphors*, p. 262), is perfectly willing to talk of the "unsolved problem of a satisfactory formulation of canons of inductive inference..." (p. 211). Goodman writes, "An argument that [conforms to the general rules of deductive inference] is justified or valid, even if its conclusion happens to be false.... Analogously, the basic task in justifying an inductive inference is to show that it conforms to the general rules of induction" (*Fact, Fiction, and Forecast*, p. 66). Goodman shows that the solution to the problem of spelling out these rules depends on the prior solution of the problem of *projectibility*, to which we shall return in a later chapter. The justification for accepting a scientific conclusion, in any event, is the conformity of the argument from the evidence for the conclusion to the conclusion, to the general rules or canons of inductive inference. And in any event, the justification for those rules or canons is that they embody the concept we have in mind when we speak of *good* inductive arguments or *sound* scientific inferences.

One might hope that a canon of inductive procedures would be unnecessary —that all inductive argument in science depends ultimately, on only a single principle of induction. Some of the principles that have been offered as fulfilling this hope have been defended as analytic. It has been maintained by

G. S. Brown, for example, that the uniformity of nature is a tautology, on the ground that if things started acting very oddly we would not decide that nature was no longer uniform, but simply that we were dreaming and no longer observing nature. This gambit, like that of K. Campbell, who calls our attention to the fact that continuing concomitances are *presupposed* in our language and thought, simply won't do what is expected of it. Even if the existence of uniformities were enough to enable us to justify specific scientific inferences—which it is not, since we can only justify induction through uniformity when we have some further indication as to where the uniformities are and how far they extend—the analyticity of the uniformity principle would prevent us from using it to justify extrapolations into the future. If the uniformity of nature is made analytic, the continuing *existence* of nature cannot be regarded as analytic, but becomes contingent, and is precisely what inductive justification would have to depend on.

It is more plausible to maintain that the principle of induction itself is analytic, and at the same stroke to justify the belief that past uniformities will continue and that nature, as we know it, will continue to exist. The first explicit statement of the thesis that the principle of induction is analytic is by Asher Moore, in "The Principle of Induction." The principle of induction which he formulates is "It is more probable than not that uniformities, either universal or statistical, which have been observed to hold uniformly in past experience will continue to hold uniformly in the future" (p. 741). This principle, he says, is analytic; it is analytic of what we mean by 'probable' or 'reasonable'. It goes without saying that the word 'probable' here does not carry any commitment concerning future frequencies; nor does it seem that any underlying logical structure is being suggested. Against this view, May Brodbeck argues that by making the principle of induction analytic, we find ourselves with no basis on which to construct an inductive logic. What is the basis for preferring large samples to small ones? Highly varied ones to homogeneous ones? According to her, all such knowledge concerning the superiority of certain kinds of samples over others is itself based on induction. Furthermore, the real problem of justification is untouched: to say that we have observed uniformity in the past and that this analytically implies that it is reasonable to expect uniformity in the future is to *say* no more than that we have observed uniformity in the past. "Yet if there is any problem of induction, it is about the relationship between the observed and the unobserved . . ." ("An Analytic Principle of Induction?" p. 750), which is not touched at all by an analytic principle of induction. Moore answers that the rules of induction concerning mixing, large samples, varied data, and so on, "constitute the full expansion of the Principle of Induction itself" (p. 572). But the "full expansion" of the principle of induction would involve more than this—indeed it would constitute a full inductive logic, or set of canons for induction, of the sort that Black and Goodman have taken as the "real" problem of induction. Moore neither develops an inductive logic nor discusses in any detail Brodbeck's most serious contention, that the problem of induction concerns the relationship between the observed and the unobserved, and that an analytic principle can have nothing to contribute to the elucidation of this relationship.

Grover Maxwell does attack that problem, maintaining that "It is necessarily true that the future will to some extent resemble the past" (An Analytic Vindication of Induction, p. 43). His argument for this is that we can ask questions only within a conceptual framework; to doubt that crows will be black in the future as they have been in the past presupposes that crows will remain an identifiable species, and that there will be this much uniformity in the future at least. "... unless it is presupposed that the future will to some extent resemble the past, we cannot meaningfully ask questions about the future at all" (p. 44). It does not seem to me that this follows at all: we are, after all, asking the questions now; that the questions will not be meaningless in the future is still open to question; and what is even more relevant from the point of view of inductive logic is that even an answer to this question would not lead us to any principles of inductive logic which we could use to justify particular conclusions on the basis of actual evidence. The important question remains, "In *what respects* will the future resemble the past?" Observe that in this respect Maxwell's thesis is only a slightly attenuated form of Campbell's.

H. A. Nielsen, in "Sampling and the Problem of Induction," develops a similar principle for statistical inference, arguing that arguments proceed, not from a *subclass* to a population, but from a *sample* to a population. The latter inference is sound, because *fairness* is a logical requirement of a sample. Thus, according to Nielsen, a sample *must* be like the population from which it was drawn. He is wrong here, however. A certain proportion of fair samples—i.e., samples drawn by a method which will produce each possible sample equally often in the long run—will in the general case be *unlike* the population from which they are drawn. Most of the fair samples will be representative of the population, however, and this would suffice to confer a statistical probability on the conclusion of such an argument. The problem remains, of course, that it is difficult to tell when a particular subclass that we happen to have observed is a *sample* in Nielsen's technical sense. As C. D. Broad pointed out long ago, in "The Principles of Problematic Induction," we cannot base our science on a "fair" sample of the universe, because everything we can observe is close to us in time and space; we cannot include space–time points in our sample that are far removed from us.

There are two general problems concerning induction on which the analysis of ordinary inductive argument has been alleged to throw light. One is the problem of justification; the other the problem of clarification. The justification of particular inductive arguments can in one sense be uncovered by looking at those arguments: to find out how certain scientific hypotheses are justified, one must look at the arguments and the bodies of evidence which are offered in their support. Whether one can obtain a general justification of induction in this way is another matter. The arguments of those who claim to have dissolved, rather than solved, the general philosophical problem of inductive justification seem to be very strong. On the other hand, what is involved in the analysis of actual scientific arguments is more in the nature of clarification than justification. What is being clarified is a particular instance of justification, but what is offered is clarification rather than justification.

The next question is whether the clarification that can be provided by this sort of analysis is the best that can be hoped for. Many writers feel that a deeper analysis of inductive arguments is possible, which will ultimately lead to a small number of very general principles in terms of which the canon of inductive procedures can be developed. Some writers feel that these principles are empirical in nature; these views will be examined in the next chapter. Other writers find these principles in one interpretation or another of probability, or in a general methodological principle; these views will be the subject of later chapters.

EXERCISES

1. Reconstruct the argument in two ways:

   . Polly is a crow, so Polly is black.

2. Reconstruct the following argument in two ways:

   Johnson is an American, so Johnson is part of a family with an income of over three thousand dollars a year.

3. Reconstruct this argument in several different ways:

   In this sample of smokers, we find twice as much lung cancer as in this other sample of nonsmokers. Therefore smoking is a causal factor in lung cancer.

4. A standard sort of inference ticket is one which allows the passage from a statement concerning the composition of a sample (e.g., 75% of the observed B's have been C's) to the composition of the population sampled (about 75% of the B's are C's). How might one criticize the use of this ticket in a *particular* case?

5. Show that every inductive argument whatever can be reconstructed (though perhaps implausibly) as an enthymematic deductive argument.

6. Show that every enthymematic deductive argument can be construed as an inductive argument.

7. Give an example of an inductive argument in the form in which it is familiar to you from your study of some elementary science, and reconstruct it (a) as a deductive enthymeme, (b) as an inductive enthymeme, (c) as an argument employing an inference ticket. What is the nature of

the ticket? (Is it something that in turn needs to be supported by evidence? Is it a presupposition of that science? Is it analytic?)

8. Read carefully one of the articles mentioned in the bibliographical notes to this chapter (or a group of related articles); present its arguments carefully and sympathetically; and present the objections to the arguments. (Coming to a conclusion is allowable, but inessential in this exercise.)

BIBLIOGRAPHICAL NOTES FOR CHAPTER 8

Stephen Toulmin's book, *The Uses of Argument*, Cambridge University Press, 1958, contains the most extensive presentation of his views on both deductive and inductive argument. This point of view has been roundly criticized, not only by H. G. Alexander, in "General Statements as Rules of Inference" (Feigle, ed.), *Minnesota Studies in the Philosophy of Science* Vol. II, University of Minnesota Press, Minneapolis, 1958, but specifically by Hector Castañeda, "Are Conditionals Principles of Inference?" *Analysis* **18**, 1957–58, pp. 77–82, and John C. Cooley, "Toulmin's Revolution in Logic," *Journal of Philosophy* **56**, 1959, pp. 297–319. The roots of Toulmin's views are to be found in two articles by Gilbert Ryle, "Predicting and Inferring" (Korner, ed.), *The Colston Papers* **9**, 1957, pp. 165–70, and "'If', 'So', and 'Because'" (Black, ed.), *Philosophical Analysis*, Cornell University Press, Ithaca, 1950 and 1963, pp. 302–18.

Peter F. Strawson's similar viewpoint is expressed in *Introduction to Logical Theory*, New York, John Wiley and Sons, 1952. His note on induction, "On Justifying Induction," is in *Philosophical Studies* **9**, 1958, pp. 20–21. R. Harré's contribution, "Dissolving the 'Problem' of Induction," is in *Philosophy* **26**, 1957, pp. 58–64.

Additional contributions on the subject of inference tickets are Peter Achinstein's "From Success to Truth," *Analysis* **21**, 1960–61, pp. 6–9, Ryle's reply, "Comment on Mr. Achinstein's Paper," *Analysis* **21**, 1960–61, pp. 9–11, and Harry V. Stopes-Roe's finale, "Recipes and Induction: Ryle v. Achinstein," *Analysis* **21**, 1960–61, pp. 115–20.

The work of N. R. Hanson is *sui generis*; his thesis is that there is a constructive logic of discovery and that finding the right scientific hypothesis to explain a body of data is not a matter of luck, but of a kind of plausible reasoning which is not demonstrative and perhaps not formal at all, but which is nevertheless *reasoning* and not *guessing*. The defense of his thesis requires the careful study and analysis of historically important scientific discoveries. This work is reported mainly in *Patterns of Discovery*, Cambridge University Press, 1958. The quotation in the text is from "Good Inductive Reasons," *The Philosophical Quarterly* **11**, 1961, pp. 123–24.

The extremists who take inductive logic to be a purely empirical psychological study of what scientists do and the reasons which they claim to have for doing it are: D. G. C. McNabb, "Hume on Induction," *Revue Internationale de Philosophie* **6**, 1952, pp. 184–98; Jerry J. Katz, *The Problem of Induction and Its Solution*, University of Chicago Press, Chicago, 1962; and Edward Gross, "Toward a Rationale for Science," *Journal of Philosophy* **54**, 1957, pp. 829–38.

Max Black's views are to be found in a number of articles and books; the quotations come from a collection of his papers, *Models and Metaphors*, Cornell

University Press, Ithaca, New York, 1962. The quotation from Nelson Goodman comes from his book, *Fact, Fiction, and Forecast*, Harvard University Press, Cambridge, Massachusetts, 1955.

On the analyticity of the uniformity of nature, we have G. Spencer Brown's interesting little book, *Probability and Scientific Inference*, Longmans Green, London, 1957; Keith Campbell, "One Form of Scepticism about Induction," *Analysis* **23**, 1962–63, pp. 80–83; Asher Moore, "The Principle of Induction," and "The Principle of Induction (II): A Reply to Miss Brodbeck," *Journal of Philosophy* **49**, 1952, pp. 741–47 and pp. 750–58; May Brodbeck, "An Analytic Principle of Induction?" *Journal of Philosophy* **49**, 1952, pp. 747–50; and Grover Maxwell, "An 'Analytic' Vindication of Induction," *Philosophical Studies* **12**, 1961, pp. 43–45.

On samples and subclasses, we have H. A. Nielsen, "Sampling and the Problem of Induction," *Mind* **68**, 1959, pp. 474–81; and C. D. Broad, "The Principles of Problematic Induction," *Proceedings of the Aristotelian Society* (Sup. Vol. **28**), 1927–28, pp. 1–46.

9

Demonstrative Induction

In popular parlance one may speak of scientific certainty without being contradicted, and indeed scientists themselves often speak as if their reasoning were all demonstrative and their conclusions all certain. One reads that a new theory has been proved by a certain experiment. This attitude finds expression among philosophers, too. There exist still some holders of traditional rationalist views, according to which everything that is true is necessarily true, and furthermore accessible to the rational intellect. W. I. Matson, for example, in "Against Induction and Empiricism," claims that we achieve mathematical necessity in science. He neglects to say how we do this. Ordinary Discourse Analysts provide more plausible arguments for the necessity of scientific conclusions. Thus J. O. Nelson, in "The Confirmation of Hypotheses," writes, "... scientists all the time conclusively establish hypotheses." For example, we may speculate about the existence of life on Mars; when scientists have amassed enough evidence of the right sort, they do not say that it is "highly probable" that there is life on Mars, but that it is now certain, it has now been conclusively established, that there is life on Mars, because "It has been conclusively established by spectrographs that the green spots are lichen." To talk in any other way, according to Nelson, is to abuse language. But it is clear that the issue here can no more be settled by taking a poll of common usage than can the issue of whether a whale is to be regarded as a fish or a mammal. As L. Resnick points out in his comments on Nelson's article, 'probably' and 'certainly' are used in philosophy as technical terms.

In another article, "Are Inductive Generalizations Quantifiable?" Nelson tries an ingenious device for achieving certainty for inductive conclusions: that of leaving off a universal quantifier. Thus he claims that we do not argue from 'some crows are black' to 'all crows are black', but merely from 'this crow is black' and 'that crow is black' to 'crows are black'. This inductive conclusion is in a somewhat ambiguous sense *conclusively* verified by the earlier observations, "... it is precisely because their ordinary mode of expression is characterized by ambiguity that inductive generalizations can possess (conclusive) verification and evidence" (p. 61). If it were not for this fortunate ambiguity, we could never have evidence relevant to future actions and commitments, for in the future we are concerned with unobserved crows; we have never observed one of them, and thus we have no evidence concerning them. Again Nelson quickly finds an antagonist, J. E. Llewelyn, who accuses him of abusing technical language. He points out that 'Crows are black' is not a proposition at all, for when some crows are black and some are not, it is true and false at the same time. The very least a logician has a right to demand is that the statements of science lack this kind of ambiguity.

William Kneale has defended a rather more plausible doctrine according to which certain general synthetic propositions of a certain sort could be considered certain, although they cannot be known *a priori*. J. P. Day, who follows Kneale's lead in interpreting 'probably', follows him in this as well. He argues that not all ampliative induction is probable, "For we do often call generalizations true or certain" (p. 256).

It can more plausibly be maintained that certainty in a strict philosophical sense is a liability to scientific conclusions than that it is an asset. As long as we can regard a counterinstance to our generalization as conceivable, the generalization is not absolutely certain; and to regard a counterinstance as inconceivable or *really* impossible is just to commit oneself to explaining it away, come what may—i.e., it is to regard the generalization as analytic and uninformative.

These writers do call our attention to something important, however; the idea of *practical certainty* as a level of confirmation at which we can detach scientific conclusions from the data that support them. It should also be noticed, however, that practical certainty is a flexible concept. In Nelson's example, were one to fix the astronomer with a beady philosophical eye and say, "Are you *absolutely certain* that there is life on Mars? Has no one ever misread a spectrograph?" he would of course say "Well, it is at any rate overwhelmingly probable that there is life on Mars." It is in representing a body of knowledge composed of practical certainties which are nonetheless in an absolute sense merely probable, that the concept of a rational corpus is very useful. Within the framework of a rational corpus we can treat statements that are only *practically certain* as acceptable, and thus (as we shall see) treat much inductive argument as deductive in form. This is appropriate, for analysis of scientific argument reveals that much of it is deductive, in the sense that the conclusion follows deductively from the premises—general as well as particular—that we accept in a given inquiry. At the same time, we cannot *accept*, in a given inquiry, just anything we feel like accepting; in science we are responsible not only for the cogency of our arguments but for the acceptability of our premises. For the time being, however, we shall leave to one side the problem of criteria for rational corpora, and concentrate on the deductive arguments most often encountered in the sciences (excluding, of course, purely mathematical arguments).

The analysis of these arguments is the analysis of *demonstrative induction*. The most extensive piece of work on demonstrative induction is that of G. H. von Wright, in *A Treatise On Induction and Probability*. In this book he is mainly concerned with the logical problem of analyzing the inferential mechanism of induction rather than either the psychological problem of discovery or the specifically philosophical problem of justification. Chapters 4, 5, and 6 are on the logic of necessary, sufficient, and necessary and sufficient conditions. The other chapters are concerned with nondemonstrative induction, but that is considered from the same point of view as consisting essentially in the *probable* eliminations of causal laws by observed instances. In the main portion of the book, devoted to the logic of conditions, we have an elaborated, precise, and explicit version of Mill's canons of induction.

The concepts basic to this reconstruction of demonstrative inductive argument are three: *Necessary condition, sufficient condition,* and *necessary-and-sufficient condition*. We begin by defining these concepts. A condition in general is interpreted as a property or characteristic or anything that can be predicted of the kinds of entities we are concerned with, which may be physical individuals, abstract individuals, events occupying a significant portion of space–time, or point events. A sufficient condition of something is a condition which will suffice to bring it about: a sufficient condition of death (of an individual) is dismemberment (of the individual); a sufficient condition of a tie-game is that no one team have more points than any other team; a sufficient condition of combustion is the presence of sufficient oxygen, sufficient heat, and methane gas. In symbolic notation, writing '(x)' for the universal quantifications, for all x, and '$\supset$' for the conditional 'if ... then ...', we may say that F is a sufficient condition for G, when everything that has F also has G, or when

$$(x)\,(Fx \supset Gx)$$

is true.

A necessary condition of something is a condition the lack of which precludes the occurrence of the something. A necessary condition of combustion is the presence of oxygen, for if there is no oxygen present, combustion cannot occur. The presence of methane, on the other hand, is not a necessary condition of combustion, since butane, oxygen, and sufficient heat will produce combustion in the absence of methane. One necessary condition of death is the cessation of respiration, another is the cessation of circulation. Using the same symbolic notation as before, and using '$\sim$' for negation, we may say in general that F is a *necessary condition* of G when everything that lacks F also lacks G, or when

$$(x)\,(\sim\! Fx \supset\, \sim\! Gx)$$

is true. Since '$(x)\,(\sim\! Fx \supset\, \sim\! Gx)$' is logically equivalent to '$(x)\,(Gx \supset Fx)$', we may also take the latter universal conditional as expressing 'F is a necessary condition of G'.

A necessary and sufficient condition is a condition which is both necessary and sufficient; no one team having more points than any other team is a necessary and sufficient condition for the existence of a tie. Using '$\equiv$' for the biconditional ('if and only if'), we may say in general that F is a necessary and sufficient condition of G if everything that is F is also G and everything that lacks F also lacks G, or if

$$(x)\,(Fx \equiv Gx)$$

is true.

In each case considered by von Wright, we begin with the knowledge that the necessary, or sufficient, or necessary and sufficient condition is to be found in a list of combinations of possible conditioning properties, we will also consider conjunctions and disjunctions of them to be possible conditioning properties. Thus if we consider F_1, and F_2, and F_3 to be possible conditioning properties, we will also consider conjunctions and disjunctions of them to be possible conditioning properties. Note that if F_1 is a sufficient condition of G, so is F_1 & F_2, since from

$$(x)\,(F_1 x \supset Gx),$$

which expresses the first fact,

$$(x)\,((F_1 x \,\&\, F_2 x) \supset Gx)$$

follows. Thus, in general, if F is a sufficient condition of G, so is the conjunction of F with any other property. Similarly, if F_3 is a necessary condition of G, so is $F_2 \vee F_3$, since from

$$(x)\,(Gx \supset F_3x)$$

the statement

$$(x)\,(Gx \supset (F_3x \vee F_2x))$$

follows. In general, if F is a necessary condition of G, so will the disjunction of F with any other property be a necessary condition of G.

The mechanism of elimination is simple, straightforward, and familiar. It depends on the fact that '$(x)\,(Hx \supset Kx)$' and 'Ha and $\sim Ka$' are contraries. Thus to eliminate F as a possible sufficient condition of G, it suffices to observe an entity a that has the property F but lacks the property G. We then have grounds for accepting the statement '$Fa\ \&\ \sim Ga$', and therefore on pain of inconsistency cannot also accept '$(x)\,(Fx \supset Gx)$' which expresses the fact that F is a necessary condition of G.

Suppose, for example, we are attempting to discover the cause of the common cold. (We leave aside, for now, the question of the relation between causes and conditions.) Among the list of possible sufficient conditions for coming down with a cold is being chilled. We can express the hypothesis in question as follows:

$$(x)\,(x \text{ is chilled} \supset x \text{ comes down with a cold}).$$

We may eliminate being chilled as a sufficient condition of coming down with a cold by finding a counterexample, i.e., finding an individual who has been chilled but who has not come down with a cold. Thus the fact that brother John has been chilled while out hunting but has not come down with a cold suffices to refute the hypothesis that being chilled is a sufficient condition of coming down with a cold. 'John is chilled and John does not come down with a cold' contradicts the generalization displayed above.

Similarly, to eliminate F as a possible necessary condition of G, it suffices to observe an instance of G in which F is lacking: '$\sim Fb\ \&\ Gb$' is a contrary of '$(x)\,(Gx \supset Fx)$', which, as we observed earlier, is logically equivalent to '$(x)\,(\sim Fx \supset \sim Gx)$'. To continue the previous example, we might suppose that although one might not always get a cold from being chilled, one sometimes gets a cold after being chilled and never gets a cold without being chilled. This is to suggest that being chilled is a necessary condition of coming down with a cold. This hypothesis would be expressed:

$$(x)\,(x \text{ has a cold} \supset x \text{ has previously been chilled}).$$

Again the hypothesis can be refuted by a single counterexample. We notice that Great Aunt Ellen, though she has hardly been out of her overheated apartment for months, has come down with a cold. We can be sure that Aunt Ellen has not been chilled; and it is obvious that she has a cold. This fact refutes the hypothesis that chilling is a necessary condition of coming down with a cold.

If all the possible combinations of conditioning properties are allowed, von Wright shows, it is still possible for inductive elimination to lead to certainty: when all the possible sufficient conditions but one are eliminated, the one that remains will be the conjunction of all the possible conditioning properties; and when all the possible necessary conditions but one are eliminated, the one that remains will be the disjunction of all the conditioning properties.

As an illustration, let us consider again the conditions for having a cold. Let us suppose that the conditions related to having a cold are to be found in the following list:

C_1x x has been exposed to very dry air.
C_2x x has been exposed to chills.
C_3x x has been exposed to virus X.

We follow tradition in supposing that the lack of a certain property is not efficacious; there is no loss of generality in this; if it is felt, for example, that *not* having been exposed to dry air might be relevant to coming down with a cold, we may introduce this as a fourth possible condition, C_4, keeping track of the fact that then C_1 and C_4 are contradictory properties. Furthermore, a sufficient condition that is a disjunction (such as $C_1x \lor C_2x$) is regarded (also traditionally) as *two* sufficient conditions (namely, C_1x and C_2x). The list of possible sufficient conditions for coming down with a cold thus contains these three basic conditions, and all possible conjunctions of them:

$$C_1x$$
$$C_2x$$
$$C_3x$$
$$C_1x \ \& \ C_2x$$
$$C_1x \ \& \ C_3x$$
$$C_2x \ \& \ C_3x$$
$$C_1x \ \& \ C_2x \ \& \ C_3x$$

A similar analysis leads to the following list of necessary conditions:

$$C_1x$$
$$C_2x$$
$$C_3x$$
$$C_1x \lor C_2x$$
$$C_2x \lor C_3x$$
$$C_1x \lor C_3x$$
$$C_1x \lor C_2x \lor C_3x$$

Possible laws stating sufficient conditions are eliminated by discovering individuals who satisfy the conditions, but who do not come down with colds. Thus C_3x is eliminated as a sufficient condition by the example of John. C_2x & C_3x is eliminated as a sufficient condition by finding someone who has been chilled, and who is found to harbor virus X bodies, but who has no cold. Clearly if C_2x & C_3x has been eliminated as a sufficient condition of coming down with a cold, so have C_2x & C_3x. The only way in which every possible sufficient condition but one can be eliminated is for every condition in the list but the last to have been eliminated by a counterexample. At that point, we can say that *the* sufficient condition of coming down with a cold is a combination of excess dryness, being chilled, and being exposed to virus X. Of course the argument is no better than the list of conditions with which we start; having eliminated all the sufficient conditions but one, we may go on and find a counterexample that will eliminate that one, too: a man Peter who is exposed to virus X every day, who is often chilled when hunting, and who lives in a dry, overheated apartment, and who doesn't come down with colds. What we learn from Peter is that the list of possible sufficient conditions with which we started was incomplete.

Possible laws stating necessary conditions are eliminated by finding individuals who have colds but who lack the corresponding necessary condition. Thus Great Aunt Ellen eliminates C_2x as a sufficient condition. Again, if all necessary conditions but one are eliminated, it is the most complex one. Again, if our list of possible necessary conditions is inadequate, we may end up eliminating all of the possible necessary conditions.

It is obvious that this is not a very interesting result. Indeed, given a finite list of possible conditioning properties, one could in a purely mechanical way construct a list of all the possible causal laws (concerning necessary conditions, sufficient conditions, or necessary and sufficient conditions) relating the conditioning properties or combinations of them to the conditioned property. We may thus avoid all talk of conditions by talking about the laws directly.

If there is a single necessary and sufficient condition, it will generally give rise to a number of necessary conditions and a number of sufficient conditions. If the true state of affairs is expressed by the generalization

$$(x)\,((C_1x \ \& \ C_3x) \equiv Cx),$$

where 'Cx' is short for 'x has a cold', then C_1x & C_2x & C_3x, as well as C_1x & C_3x will be a sufficient condition; and C_1x, C_3x, $C_1x \lor C_2x$, etc., will all be necessary conditions. We may nevertheless construct a list of possible necessary and sufficient conditions, and proceed to eliminate all but one of them. We may do this by taking the list of possible sufficient conditions, and considering as possible necessary and sufficient conditions all disjunctions of one of more members of that list. Thus in this case, the list of possible necessary and sufficient conditions, containing 127 members, is as follows:

C_1x
C_2x
C_3x
$C_1x \mathbin{\&} C_2x$
$C_1x \mathbin{\&} C_3x$
$C_2x \mathbin{\&} C_3x$
$C_1x \mathbin{\&} C_2x \mathbin{\&} C_3x$
$C_3x \lor (C_1x \mathbin{\&} C_2x)$
$C_3x \lor (C_1x \mathbin{\&} C_3x)$
$C_3x \lor (C_2x \mathbin{\&} C_3x)$
$C_3x \lor (C_1x \mathbin{\&} C_2x \mathbin{\&} C_3x)$

$(C_1x \mathbin{\&} C_2x) \lor (C_1x \mathbin{\&} C_3x)$
$(C_1x \mathbin{\&} C_2x) \lor (C_2x \mathbin{\&} C_3x)$
$(C_1x \mathbin{\&} C_2x) \lor (C_1x \mathbin{\&} C_2x \mathbin{\&} C_3x)$
$(C_1x \mathbin{\&} C_3x) \lor (C_2x \mathbin{\&} C_3x)$
$(C_1x \mathbin{\&} C_3x) \lor (C_1x \mathbin{\&} C_2x \mathbin{\&} C_3x)$
$(C_2x \mathbin{\&} C_3x) \lor (C_1x \mathbin{\&} C_2x \mathbin{\&} C_3x)$

$C_1x \lor C_2x$
$C_1x \lor C_3x$
$C_1x \lor (C_1x \mathbin{\&} C_2x)$
$C_1x \lor (C_2x \mathbin{\&} C_3x)$
$C_1x \lor (C_1x \mathbin{\&} C_3x)$
$C_1x \lor (C_1x \mathbin{\&} C_2x \mathbin{\&} C_3x)$

$C_2x \lor C_3x$
$C_2x \lor (C_1x \mathbin{\&} C_2x)$
$C_2x \lor (C_1x \mathbin{\&} C_3x)$
$C_2x \lor (C_2x \mathbin{\&} C_3x)$
$C_2x \lor (C_1x \mathbin{\&} C_2x \mathbin{\&} C_3x)$

$C_1x \lor C_2x \lor C_3x$
$C_1x \lor C_2x \lor (C_1x \mathbin{\&} C_2x)$
$C_1x \lor C_2x \lor (C_1x \mathbin{\&} C_3x)$
$C_1x \lor C_2x \lor (C_2x \mathbin{\&} C_3x)$
$C_1x \lor C_2x \lor (C_1x \mathbin{\&} C_2x \mathbin{\&} C_3x)$
$C_1x \lor C_3x \lor (C_1x \mathbin{\&} C_2x)$
$C_1x \lor C_3x \lor (C_1x \mathbin{\&} C_3x)$
$C_1x \lor C_3x \lor (C_2x \mathbin{\&} C_3x)$
$C_1x \lor C_3x \lor (C_1x \mathbin{\&} C_2x \mathbin{\&} C_3x)$

$C_1x \lor (C_1x \mathbin{\&} C_2x) \lor (C_1x \mathbin{\&} C_3x)$
$C_1x \lor (C_1x \mathbin{\&} C_2x) \lor (C_2x \mathbin{\&} C_3x)$
$C_1x \lor (C_1x \mathbin{\&} C_2x) \lor (C_1x \mathbin{\&} C_2x \mathbin{\&} C_3x)$

$C_1x \lor (C_1x \mathbin{\&} C_3x) \lor (C_2x \mathbin{\&} C_3x)$
$C_1x \lor (C_1x \mathbin{\&} C_3x) \lor (C_1x \mathbin{\&} C_2x \mathbin{\&} C_3x)$
$C_1x \lor (C_2x \mathbin{\&} C_3x) \lor (C_1x \mathbin{\&} C_2x \mathbin{\&} C_3x)$
$C_2x \lor C_3x \lor (C_1x \mathbin{\&} C_2x)$
$C_2x \lor C_3x \lor (C_1x \mathbin{\&} C_3x)$
$C_2x \lor C_3x \lor (C_2x \mathbin{\&} C_3x)$
$C_2x \lor C_3x \lor (C_1x \mathbin{\&} C_2x \mathbin{\&} C_3x)$

$C_2x \lor (C_1x \mathbin{\&} C_2x) \lor (C_1x \mathbin{\&} C_3x)$
$C_2x \lor (C_1x \mathbin{\&} C_2x) \lor (C_2x \mathbin{\&} C_3x)$
$C_2x \lor (C_1x \mathbin{\&} C_2x) \lor (C_1x \mathbin{\&} C_2x \mathbin{\&} C_3x)$
$C_2x \lor (C_1x \mathbin{\&} C_3x) \lor (C_2x \mathbin{\&} C_3x)$
$C_2x \lor (C_1x \mathbin{\&} C_3x) \lor (C_1x \mathbin{\&} C_2x \mathbin{\&} C_3x)$
$C_2x \lor (C_2x \mathbin{\&} C_3x) \lor (C_1x \mathbin{\&} C_2x \mathbin{\&} C_3x)$

$C_3x \lor (C_1x \mathbin{\&} C_2x) \lor (C_1x \mathbin{\&} C_3x)$
$C_3x \lor (C_1x \mathbin{\&} C_2x) \lor (C_2x \mathbin{\&} C_3x)$
$C_3x \lor (C_1x \mathbin{\&} C_2x) \lor (C_1x \mathbin{\&} C_2x \mathbin{\&} C_3x)$
$C_3x \lor (C_1x \mathbin{\&} C_3x) \lor (C_2x \mathbin{\&} C_3x)$
$C_3x \lor (C_1x \mathbin{\&} C_3x) \lor (C_1x \mathbin{\&} C_2x \mathbin{\&} C_3x)$
$C_3x \lor (C_2x \mathbin{\&} C_3x) \lor (C_1x \mathbin{\&} C_2x \mathbin{\&} C_3x)$
$(C_1x \mathbin{\&} C_2x) \lor (C_1x \mathbin{\&} C_3x) \lor (C_2x \mathbin{\&} C_3x)$
$(C_1x \mathbin{\&} C_2x) \lor (C_1x \mathbin{\&} C_3x) \lor (C_1x \mathbin{\&} C_2x \mathbin{\&} C_3x)$
$(C_1x \mathbin{\&} C_2x) \lor (C_2x \mathbin{\&} C_3x) \lor (C_1x \mathbin{\&} C_2x \mathbin{\&} C_3x)$
$(C_1x \mathbin{\&} C_3x) \lor (C_2x \mathbin{\&} C_3x) \lor (C_1x \mathbin{\&} C_2x \mathbin{\&} C_3x)$

$C_1x \lor C_2x \lor C_3x \lor (C_1x \mathbin{\&} C_2x)$
$C_1x \lor C_2x \lor C_3x \lor (C_1x \mathbin{\&} C_3x)$
$C_1x \lor C_2x \lor C_3x \lor (C_2x \mathbin{\&} C_3x)$
$C_1x \lor C_2x \lor C_3x \lor (C_1x \mathbin{\&} C_2x \mathbin{\&} C_3x)$
$C_1x \lor C_2x \lor (C_1x \mathbin{\&} C_2x) \lor (C_1x \mathbin{\&} C_3x)$
$C_1x \lor C_2x \lor (C_1x \mathbin{\&} C_2x) \lor (C_2x \mathbin{\&} C_3x)$
$C_1x \lor C_2x \lor (C_1x \mathbin{\&} C_2x) \lor (C_1x \mathbin{\&} C_2x \mathbin{\&} C_3x)$
$C_1x \lor C_2x \lor (C_1x \mathbin{\&} C_3x) \lor (C_2x \mathbin{\&} C_3x)$
$C_1x \lor C_2x \lor (C_1x \mathbin{\&} C_3x) \lor (C_1x \mathbin{\&} C_2x \mathbin{\&} C_3x)$
$C_1x \lor C_2x \lor (C_2x \mathbin{\&} C_3x) \lor (C_1x \mathbin{\&} C_2x \mathbin{\&} C_3x)$
$C_1x \lor C_3x \lor (C_1x \mathbin{\&} C_2x) \lor (C_1x \mathbin{\&} C_3x)$
$C_1x \lor C_3x \lor (C_1x \mathbin{\&} C_2x) \lor (C_2x \mathbin{\&} C_3x)$
$C_1x \lor C_3x \lor (C_1x \mathbin{\&} C_2x) \lor (C_1x \mathbin{\&} C_2x \mathbin{\&} C_3x)$
$C_1x \lor (C_1x \mathbin{\&} C_2x) \lor (C_1x \mathbin{\&} C_3x) \lor (C_2x \mathbin{\&} C_3x)$
$C_1x \lor (C_1x \mathbin{\&} C_2x) \lor (C_1x \mathbin{\&} C_3x) \lor (C_1x \mathbin{\&} C_2x \mathbin{\&} C_3x)$
$C_1x \lor (C_1x \mathbin{\&} C_2x) \lor (C_2x \mathbin{\&} C_3x) \lor (C_1x \mathbin{\&} C_2x \mathbin{\&} C_3x)$
$C_1x \lor (C_1x \mathbin{\&} C_3x) \lor (C_2x \mathbin{\&} C_3x) \lor (C_1x \mathbin{\&} C_2x \mathbin{\&} C_3x)$
$C_2x \lor C_3x \lor (C_1x \mathbin{\&} C_2x) \lor (C_1x \mathbin{\&} C_3x)$
$C_2x \lor C_3x \lor (C_1x \mathbin{\&} C_2x) \lor (C_2x \mathbin{\&} C_3x)$

$C_2x \lor C_3x \lor (C_1x \,\&\, C_2x) \lor (C_1x \,\&\, C_2x \,\&\, C_3x)$
$C_2x \lor C_3x \lor (C_1x \,\&\, C_3x) \lor (C_2x \,\&\, C_3x)$
$C_2x \lor C_3x \lor (C_1x \,\&\, C_3x) \lor (C_1x \,\&\, C_2x \,\&\, C_3x)$
$C_2x \lor C_3x \lor (C_2x \,\&\, C_3x) \lor (C_1x \,\&\, C_2x \,\&\, C_3x)$
$C_2x \lor (C_1x \,\&\, C_2x) \lor (C_1x \,\&\, C_3x) \lor (C_2x \,\&\, C_3x)$
$C_2x \lor (C_1x \,\&\, C_2x) \lor (C_1x \,\&\, C_3x) \lor (C_1x \,\&\, C_2x \,\&\, C_3x)$
$C_2x \lor (C_1x \,\&\, C_2x) \lor (C_2x \,\&\, C_3x) \lor (C_1x \,\&\, C_2x \,\&\, C_3x)$
$C_2x \lor (C_1x \,\&\, C_3x) \lor (C_2x \,\&\, C_3x) \lor (C_1x \,\&\, C_2x \,\&\, C_3x)$
$C_3x \lor (C_1x \,\&\, C_2x) \lor (C_1x \,\&\, C_3x) \lor (C_2x \,\&\, C_3x)$
$C_3x \lor (C_1x \,\&\, C_2x) \lor (C_1x \,\&\, C_3x) \lor (C_1x \,\&\, C_2x \,\&\, C_3x)$
$C_3x \lor (C_1x \,\&\, C_2x) \lor (C_2x \,\&\, C_3x) \lor (C_1x \,\&\, C_2x \,\&\, C_3x)$
$C_3x \lor (C_1x \,\&\, C_3x) \lor (C_2x \,\&\, C_3x) \lor (C_1x \,\&\, C_2x \,\&\, C_3x)$
$(C_1x \,\&\, C_2x) \lor (C_1x \,\&\, C_3x) \lor (C_2x \,\&\, C_3x) \lor (C_1x \,\&\, C_2x \,\&\, C_3x)$

$C_1x \lor C_3x \lor (C_1x \,\&\, C_3x) \lor (C_2x \,\&\, C_3x)$
$C_1x \lor C_3x \lor (C_1x \,\&\, C_3x) \lor (C_1x \,\&\, C_2x \,\&\, C_3x)$
$C_1x \lor C_3x \lor (C_2x \,\&\, C_3x) \lor (C_1x \,\&\, C_2x \,\&\, C_3x)$

$C_1x \lor C_2x \lor C_3x \lor (C_1x \,\&\, C_2x) \lor (C_1x \,\&\, C_3x)$
$C_1x \lor C_2x \lor C_3x \lor (C_1x \,\&\, C_2x) \lor (C_2x \,\&\, C_3x)$
$C_1x \lor C_2x \lor C_3x \lor (C_1x \,\&\, C_2x) \lor (C_1x \,\&\, C_2x \,\&\, C_3x)$
$C_1x \lor C_2x \lor C_3x \lor (C_1x \,\&\, C_3x) \lor (C_2x \,\&\, C_3x)$
$C_1x \lor C_2x \lor C_3x \lor (C_1x \,\&\, C_3x) \lor (C_1x \,\&\, C_2x \,\&\, C_3x)$
$C_1x \lor C_2x \lor C_3x \lor (C_2x \,\&\, C_3x) \lor (C_1x \,\&\, C_2x \,\&\, C_3x)$

$C_2x \lor C_3x \lor (C_1x \,\&\, C_2x) \lor (C_1x \,\&\, C_3x) \lor (C_1x \,\&\, C_2x \,\&\, C_3x)$
$C_2x \lor C_3x \lor (C_1x \,\&\, C_2x) \lor (C_1x \,\&\, C_3x) \lor (C_2x \,\&\, C_3x)$
$C_2x \lor C_3x \lor (C_1x \,\&\, C_2x) \lor (C_2x \,\&\, C_3x) \lor (C_1x \,\&\, C_2x \,\&\, C_3x)$
$C_3x \lor (C_1x \,\&\, C_2x) \lor (C_1x \,\&\, C_3x) \lor (C_2x \,\&\, C_3x) \lor (C_1x \,\&\, C_2x \,\&\, C_3x)$
$C_1x \lor C_2x \lor C_3x \lor (C_1x \,\&\, C_2x) \lor (C_1x \,\&\, C_3x) \lor (C_2x \,\&\, C_3x)$
$C_1x \lor C_2x \lor C_3x \lor (C_1x \,\&\, C_2x) \lor (C_1x \,\&\, C_3x) \lor (C_1x \,\&\, C_2x \,\&\, C_3x)$
$C_1x \lor C_2x \lor C_3x \lor (C_1x \,\&\, C_2x) \lor (C_2x \,\&\, C_3x) \lor (C_1x \,\&\, C_2x \,\&\, C_3x)$
$C_1x \lor C_2x \lor C_3x \lor (C_1x \,\&\, C_3x) \lor (C_2x \,\&\, C_3x) \lor (C_1x \,\&\, C_2x \,\&\, C_3x)$

$C_1x \lor C_2x \lor (C_1x \,\&\, C_2x) \lor (C_1x \,\&\, C_3x)$
$\qquad\qquad\qquad\qquad \lor (C_2x \,\&\, C_3x) \lor (C_1x \,\&\, C_2x \,\&\, C_3x)$
$C_1x \lor C_3x \lor (C_1x \,\&\, C_2x) \lor (C_1x \,\&\, C_3x)$
$\qquad\qquad\qquad\qquad \lor (C_2x \,\&\, C_3x) \lor (C_1x \,\&\, C_2x \,\&\, C_3x)$
$C_2x \lor C_3x \lor (C_1x \,\&\, C_2x) \lor (C_1x \,\&\, C_3x)$
$\qquad\qquad\qquad\qquad \lor (C_2x \,\&\, C_3x) \lor (C_1x \,\&\, C_2x \,\&\, C_3x)$
$C_1x \lor C_2x \lor C_3x \lor (C_1x \,\&\, C_2x) \lor (C_1x \,\&\, C_3x)$
$\qquad\qquad\qquad\qquad \lor (C_2x \,\&\, C_3x) \lor (C_1x \,\&\, C_2x \,\&\, C_3x)$

$C_1x \lor C_2x \lor (C_1x \,\&\, C_2x) \lor (C_1x \,\&\, C_3x) \lor (C_2x \,\&\, C_3x)$
$C_1x \lor C_2x \lor (C_1x \,\&\, C_2x) \lor (C_1x \,\&\, C_3x) \lor (C_1x \,\&\, C_2x \,\&\, C_3x)$

$C_1x \lor C_2x \lor (C_1x \ \& \ C_2x) \lor (C_2x \ \& \ C_3x) \lor (C_1x \ \& \ C_2x \ \& \ C_3x)$
$C_1x \lor C_2x \lor (C_1x \ \& \ C_3x) \lor (C_2x \ \& \ C_3x) \lor (C_1x \ \& \ C_2x \ \& \ C_3x)$
$C_1x \lor C_3x \lor (C_1x \ \& \ C_2x) \lor (C_1x \ \& \ C_3x) \lor (C_1x \ \& \ C_2x \ \& \ C_3x)$
$C_1x \lor C_3x \lor (C_1x \ \& \ C_2x) \lor (C_1x \ \& \ C_3x) \lor (C_2x \ \& \ C_3x)$
$C_1x \lor C_3x \lor (C_1x \ \& \ C_2x) \lor (C_2x \ \& \ C_3x) \lor (C_1x \ \& \ C_2x \ \& \ C_3x)$
$C_1x \lor C_3x \lor (C_1x \ \& \ C_3x) \lor (C_2x \ \& \ C_3x) \lor (C_1x \ \& \ C_2x \ \& \ C_3x)$
$C_1x \lor (C_1x \ \& \ C_2x) \lor (C_1x \ \& \ C_3x) \lor (C_2x \ \& \ C_3x) \lor (C_1x \ \& \ C_2x \ \& \ C_3x)$
$C_2x \lor (C_1x \ \& \ C_2x) \lor (C_1x \ \& \ C_3x) \lor (C_2x \ \& \ C_3x) \lor (C_1x \ \& \ C_2x \ \& \ C_3x)$
$C_2x \lor C_3x \lor (C_1x \ \& \ C_3x) \lor (C_2x \ \& \ C_3x) \lor (C_1x \ \& \ C_2x \ \& \ C_3x)$

This enormous list results from the consideration of all the possible universal laws relating three properties as conditions to another property. Obviously, if one were to attempt to take account of other things in the etiology of colds besides dryness, chills, and virus X, the sheer computational problems would be overwhelming. No piece of scientific inference actually proceeds this way; there are always legitimate grounds for cutting down on the number of generalizations to be considered. In the example at hand, if it were plausible to regard C_1x, C_2x, and C_3x as the only relevant conditions, we would probably content ourselves with considering the following laws:

$$(x)\,(C_1x \equiv Cx)$$
$$(x)\,(C_2x \equiv Cx)$$
$$(x)\,(C_3x \equiv Cx)$$
$$(x)\,(C_1x \ \& \ C_3x \equiv Cx)$$
$$(x)\,(C_2x \ \& \ C_3x \equiv Cx)$$

We might wonder, of each of the conditions by itself, whether it is necessary and sufficient; or we might suppose that if more than one thing is involved, it is a virus acting under conditions of organic stress. Of course we might refute each of these five laws by experiment; and then we might consider more complex laws; or we might consider new possible conditions, such as diet, hereditary resistance to disease, and so on.

By imposing special conditions on the form of the properties we are interested in, von Wright's logic of conditions may lead us to more interesting results than those mentioned above, but it is clear that in any event we can get no results which we could not get by composing a list of possible laws compatible with our body of presupposed knowledge, and attempting to eliminate all but one. Indeed, if the interest of constructing an inductive logic is to throw light on the sort of thing scientists actually do, the latter procedure is far more realistic than the former. It is far more sensible to suppose that in a particular inquiry we have narrowed the plausible possibilities down to three or four (or at most ten or twelve) specific laws, and that we then try to eliminate *all* of them as best we can, coming to conclusion only when there is one law remaining which resists our best efforts to falsify it, than it is to suppose that we write down a list of the properties that might in some combination or other be conditioning properties, and that we then try to eliminate all but one of the much larger list of possible laws that we can construct on the basis of this list of possibly conditioning properties. If we could construct a finite list of all properties whatsoever, the general eliminative procedure might be interesting; but von Wright is perfectly clear that we must start with some factual knowledge. When we can be pretty sure, before making any observations, that one or another or some combination of a list of conditioning properties is relevant, then we can generally also be pretty sure that the conditioning property will be one of a relatively small number of possibilities. Many purely formal possibilities can be ruled out in advance by our background knowledge.

In principle, at any rate, there is nothing problematic about the logic of elimination at work here: the law is a general statement, and the observation report can be a singular statement that contradicts the law. But something might well be written about the construction of the sets of laws of which we are (hopefully) to eliminate all but one. This might be a contribution to the actual practice of science as well as to the logic of induction. Where does a useful set of possible laws come from? On what kinds of grounds do we accept the empirical hypothesis that one of these laws will be found to hold? Do such sets of hypotheses exhibit an internal structure? They clearly do not exhibit the complex and exhaustive structure that Mill and von Wright have supposed they do. But so far as I know, very little has been done to answer these questions, least of all by those whose maxim is: Examine usage and discover the concept.

Some very interesting work has been done by S. Nowak, in "Some Problems of Causal Interpretation of Statistical Relationships," who carries the analysis of necessary and sufficient conditions into the field of statistics and derives some very interesting results. As an example, suppose that $A \& S$ is necessary and sufficient for B; if S_1 is an essential component of S (i.e., if S is composed of S_1 and S_2), then the probability of B given A, $P(B|A)$, will be the product of the probability of S_1 given A, $P(S_1|A)$, and the probability of B given A and S_1, $P(B|AS_1)$. If these probabilities are interpreted as empirical frequencies, this relationship is empirically testable (by means of statistical inference—but that is a question for another chapter), and we may thus be able to throw light on a possible causal relationship between B and S_1. Results like this, Nowak shows, are of considerable practical and theoretical importance in actual statistical work in the constructing and testing of statistical hypotheses. They enable us, he says, to discuss such things as spurious correlation and spurious independence more carefully and rigorously than we could without the analysis into necessary and sufficient conditions.

The most difficult philosophical question that arises in connection with the logic of conditions and the logic of causal relations concerns the character of the causal relation. In our discussion so far we have spoken only about general conditionals of the form '$(x)(Fx \supset Gx)$', for example, '$(x)(x$ is chilled $\supset x$ comes down with a cold)', or '$(x)(x$ is a plant that has not been watered for several days $\supset x$ is a plant with wilting leaves)'. But there are general conditionals of the form in question that seem irrelevant to science, even if they happen to be true: '(x) (x is a coin in my pocket $\supset$ x is made of copper)'. The former conditionals, if true, seem to be appropriately called natural laws; the latter, even if true, seems accidental. By contrast with the latter, the former conditionals are often said to embody necessity. Many writers wish to represent this causal necessity notationally by replacing the conditional sign '$\supset$' by a new connective '$\supset_N$' which is to represent "nomological implication". Thus if Fx is a lawful sufficient condition for Gx, they would write

$$(x)\,(Fx \supset_N Gx)$$

in place of '$(x)\,(Fx \supset Gx)$'. The connective '$\supset_N$' is not truth-functional: one cannot determine the truth value of '$S \supset_N T$' merely by knowing the truth values of S and T. Precisely what *does* determine the truth of statements of the form '$S \supset_N T$' is the subject of considerable debate, even among those who believe that sufficient and necessary conditions or causal relations should be represented by means of this sign.

Other writers find the introduction of a new connective unnecessary. For them, what makes certain general conditions natural laws is their generality and the role they play in a body of knowledge. It is not, as on the other view, that the statement properly called a natural law expresses a special relation between its antecedent and its consequent.

Both views can be made plausible. But we need not enter into the debate here, because the logical mechanism of eliminative induction, with which we are here concerned, is the same on either view. The general conditional '$(x)\,(Fx \supset Gx)$' is always a logical consequence of the corresponding nomological implication '$(x)\,(Fx \supset_N Gx)$'; thus the particular observations that refute (eliminate) the general conditional also refute the corresponding nomological implication. Either statement is refuted by the observation of an F that is not a G.

It has been suggested by some writers (e.g., A. C. Ewing) that it is through the concept of causality that the justification of induction must be sought. But it is important here to distinguish between the logic of inductive inference and the justification of induction. The logic of eliminative induction which we have seen applied to general conditionals applies as well to nomological implications. To the extent that the claim that inductive justification depends on a presupposition of causality is clearcut, it is more appropriate to discuss it in the following chapter, where we will be concerned with various presuppositions that have been claimed to underlie inductive logic.

There are demonstrative inductive arguments which do not have the eliminative structure we have been considering so far. These are arguments in which a key concept is that of a *natural kind*. This is a very common form of scientific argument. A species S falls under a certain genus G; a property P belongs to a certain class of properties K. On the basis of previous knowledge,

we know (with adequate empirical evidence) that all the species of that genus G are such that if one member of that species has a given property belonging to that class of properties, then all members of that species have that same property. The inductive argument proceeds from the empirical generalization about G and K, together with an observation of a member of S, and proceeds to a general conclusion: All the members of S have the property P which one member of S was observed to have. This kind of demonstrative inductive argument has not been much discussed in the literature.

Every naturalist, biologist, and psychologist knows that the mating behavior of a species of fish, say, is inborn, and subject to only minor fluctuations from individual to individual in ordinary environments. Let us take the properties belonging to K to be descriptions of the mating behavior of individuals. To be sure, such descriptions must not be too precise (or we would know in advance that they would not apply to all members of a species), but they need not be too general either. How precise they may be without leading to the falsification of our overriding generalization is something we have learned from experience; but there is no particular problem here—the generalization itself is one which we have learned from experience, and which is supported perhaps by various theoretical structures as well as by the observations of particular species. The generalization may be expressed this way: Any species falling under the general genus fish is such that if one normal pair in its natural habitat exhibits a certain mating pattern, then all normal pairs of that species, under natural conditions, will exhibit that same behavior. 'Normality' and 'natural habitat', like the degree of precision involved in the descriptions P belonging to K, are to be interpreted on the basis of experience. We now make detailed observations of the mating behavior of a pair of fish of a certain species. We conclude that the description which results from our observations applies to *all* pairs of fish of this species. This conclusion is a demonstrative consequence of the large generalization with which we started, taken in conjunction with particular statements comprising the description of our single pair of fish. Observe that the large generalization need not be based on extensive observations of other species of fish—it may be a consequence of general biological or physiological theories. What counts is not the *kind* of support it has, but that it does have empirical support—that it be acceptable into a rational corpus as practically certain. Similarly, our complex observation report may be accepted; and from the conjunction of the two our general inductive conclusion follows.

As an example of a different sort, consider the generalization that chemical compounds are such that if one sample of a given (pure) compound melts at a certain temperature, under standard pressure, then all samples of that compound will exhibit the same melting point under standard pressure. We make an experiment consisting of testing the melting points of a couple of samples of compound X, and find that it melts at about $T°C$. The inductive conclusion that all samples of this compound will melt at $T°C$ follows from the general premise (which may have various kinds of support), together with the particular observation statements. Though the conclusion follows deductively from its premises, it admits of some degree of doubt, and in fact it admits of doubt on two scores. First, the general premise, which we have called 'practically certain' and which we have regarded simply as acceptable, is not *certain* in any deep philosophical sense; it is not inconceivable that it should be falsified. It is true that any falsification of our premise would have serious effects on the entire structure of our physical knowledge; but in an important sense, that *could* happen. In another sense, a practical sense, it *couldn't* happen that one sample of a compound should melt at $T°$C and another sample should melt at another temperature. The other source of doubt of the conclusion, and the one which must be taken most seriously, enters through doubt of the particular statement. It seems, particularly to some philosophers, to be a very simple thing to *observe* one sample of a compound melt at $T°$C; to anyone who has used melting points as an aid to chemical analysis, the situation will seem quite different. Even more than other measurements, the measurement of a temperature is fraught with peril. We can have no more than *good grounds* (not certainty) for believing that the sample melted at *about* (not exactly) $T°$C. This suffices, of course. We can have perfectly adequate grounds for accepting the statement that the sample tested (and thus all samples) melted at $T \pm dT°$C. Indeed it is customary in reporting scientific results to report them in this form, where dT is the standard deviation of the measurement, and so can be used to construct statements of the form 'X melts at $T + k\,dT°$C' with any desired degree of probability. The details of this kind of argument must be postponed until we discuss statistical inference; meanwhile it is merely interesting to observe that statistical concepts and probability are involved even in those schemata of inductive inference that seem the most purely demonstrative.

EXERCISES

1. Prove that if F is a necessary condition of G, so is $F \vee F'$.
2. Prove that if F is a sufficient condition of G, so is $F \& F'$.
3. Sometimes the leaves of our houseplants become wilted. We may suppose that the possible sufficient and necessary conditions of this phenomenon are: A (lack of water), B (lack of light), C (excess heat), and D (lack of heat). What would eliminate D as a possible sufficient condition of wilting? What would eliminate A as a necessary condition of wilting?
4. What is the total list of possible necessary conditions in problem 3? If all but one of the necessary conditions is eliminated, what is the one that remains?
5. What is the total list of possible sufficient conditions in problem 3? If all but one of them is eliminated, what is the one that remains?
6. List ten members of the set of possible necessary and sufficient conditions of problem 3 which are such that they provide both for more than one necessary condition and for more than one sufficient condition.

7. Prove that in the general case, the elimination of all the possible necessary conditions but one leaves the disjunction of all the possible necessary conditions.

8. Prove that in the general case the elimination of all the sufficient conditions but one leaves the conjunction of all the candidates as the sole sufficient condition.

9. What kind of exception might arise to the general case of problem 8? (Hint: see problem 3.)

10. Scout is a horse who sometimes performs very well, and sometimes acts very balky. Various factors we might want to take into consideration are: *A* (he has been fed recently); *B* (his cinch is tight); *C* (he is being ridden by an expert rider); *D* (he is being ridden by an amateur); *E* (he is hungry). What are the first generalizations one might want to test? How would one perform the tests? Suppose none of these generalizations stands up to the tests: then what?

11. Alloys have characteristic thermal and electrical conductivities, heat capacities, tensile strengths, and the like. A new alloy is made, and tests indicate that the tensile strength of a few samples are 1.35, 1.41, and 1.38. What general form of conclusion may we draw, and what is the form of argument that leads to that conclusion?

12. Find examples of eliminative induction in your work in science courses in school, or in ordinary life.

13. Find examples of arguments from natural kinds in ordinary life.

BIBLIOGRAPHICAL NOTES FOR CHAPTER 9

W. I. Matson's unpersuasive diatribe "Against Induction and Empiricism" is to be found in the *Proceedings of the Aristotelian Society* **23**, 1961, pp. 143–58. The two articles by John O. Nelson, much more ingenious, but no more persuasive, are "The Confirmation of Hypotheses," *Philosophical Review* **67**, 1958, pp. 95–100, and "Are Inductive Generalizations Quantifiable?" *Analysis* **22**, 1961–62, pp. 59–65. Sober comments on Nelson's views are offered by Lawrence Resnick, "Confirmation and Hypothesis," *Philosophy of Science* **26**, 1959, pp. 25–30; and by J. E. Llewelyn, "Quantified Inductive Generalizations," *Analysis* **22**, 1961–62, pp. 134–37.

Kenale's views on this topic will be found in *Probability and Induction*, Oxford University Press, 1949, and "Some Aspects of Probability and Induction: A Reply to Mr. Bennett," *British Journal for the Philosophy of Science* **8**, 1957–58, pp. 57–63. See also John P. Day, *Inductive Probability*, Humanities Press, New York, 1961.

The first classical attempt to find a general approach to scientific inference in the logic of conditions is J. S. Mill's *A System of Logic*, Longmans Green, London, 1949; this was first published in 1843.

G. H. von Wright's very thorough and careful book on this subject is *A Treatise on Induction and Probability*, Harcourt, Brace and World, New York, 1951. I doubt that it is possible to do more with the logic of conditions than he has done here.

The clarity of style and thought make this an excellent textbook for its rather limited subject matter.

On the subject of the "something more" that is embodied in causal conditionals, see Nelson Goodman, *Fact, Fiction, and Forecast*, 2nd ed., Bobbs Merrill, New York, 1965; Arthur Burks, "The Logic of Causal Propositions," *Mind* **60**, 1951, pp. 363–82; H. A. Simon, "On the Definition of the Causal Relation," *Journal of Philosophy* **49**, 1952, pp. 517–28; and Hans Reichenback *Nomological Statements and Admissible Operations*, North-Holland, Amsterdam, 1954.

A general discussion linking induction and natural kinds is to be found in Wilfrid Sellars' "Counterfactuals, Dispositions, and the Causal Modalities," *Minnesota Studies in Philosophy of Science*, *II*, University of Minnesota Press, Minneapolis, 1957, pp. 225–303. This article also contains interesting material on causal necessity.

The only source I know of in which there is an explicit discussion of demonstrative inductive arguments concerning natural kinds is my "Demonstrative Induction," *Philosophy and Phenomenological Research* **21**, 1960–61, pp. 80–92. A general discussion of demonstrative arguments, including this one as a special case, will be found in my *Probability and the Logic of Rational Belief*, Wesleyan University Press, Middletown, Connecticut, 1961.

The work of Stefan Nowak referred to is "Some Problems of Causal Interpretation of Statistical Relationships," *Philosophy of Science* **27**, 1960, pp. 23–38.

10

Probabilities and Presuppositions

Presuppositions have been called upon to play a double role in discussions of induction, corresponding to the two questions about induction that philosophers have traditionally been concerned with: the justification of induction in general, and the elucidation of particular inductive arguments. The two questions are not unrelated. If we can find a general justification for induction, or for extrapolating our past experience into the future, we may reasonably expect to be able to elucidate specific inductive arguments in such a way that the general justification of induction may be employed to justify those arguments. On the other hand, if we can find general principles which will justify specific inductive arguments, we will in effect have found a general justification of induction. Nevertheless, the two questions may be distinguished conceptually; and in fact we shall find that the presuppositions that have been offered to justify induction in general do not, contrary to our expectation, throw much light on logical character of specific inductive arguments.

Most writers take inductive conclusions to be probable. If they understand probability to be an empirical concept, this requires that they make some assumptions about the world which will serve as grand premises for induction, if the results of induction are to have reasonably high probabilities. If they take probability to be a logical relation between premise and conclusion, it is not clear that any grand premises are required; but in point of fact many such writers have felt themselves forced to depend on factual presuppositions in order to establish the purely logical probability of inductive conclusions. In either event, there are various ways in which the details of a defense of induction by means of presuppositions can be worked out, and various defenses can be offered for the grand factual premises.

Those who interpret probability empirically often take the factual presuppositions of induction to be probabilistic in character. Bertrand Russell provides one example. In *Human Knowledge* Russell adopts an empirical (finite-frequency) interpretation of probability. To say that inductive conclusions are probably true is to say that for the most part they hold. In order for the conclusions of science to be given this kind of probability, postulates are necessary. Russell offers a set of empirical postulates, phrased in terms of frequencies, which he alleges to be sufficient to establish (with the help of empirical evidence) the cogency of inductive conclusions. The postulates are not to be certified on metaphysical grounds, but neither are they to be regarded as ordinary well-established material hypotheses like lists of possible conditioning properties or general conditional statements about natural kinds. Russell takes his postulates to be premises that must be believed if we are to be justified in believing in scientific conclusions; they constitute an answer to the question: Assuming that science, by and large, is correct, what must we suppose that we know about the world in order that our belief in science be rational? Whether that is an adequate ground for believing the premises, and why it is, if it is, remains obscure.

John O. Wisdom presents four postulates for induction that are much like those offered by Russell. They are: (1) the limitation of natural variety. This postulate dates back to Keynes' *Treatise on Probability*; even though Keynes' interpretation of probability was logical rather than empirical, he felt that some such postulate was required for the justification of induction. The import of the postulate is the contradictory of Hamlet's assertion to Horatio: for induction to work there must be less things under the sun than one might dream up in one's philosophy. Postulate (2) is the postulate of spatio–temporal proximity. This postulate assures us that things don't change magically and for no reason, but only in response to events that are nearby in space and time. Third is the uniform generation of properties—i.e., the same causes produce always the same effects. Postulate (4) is the principle of small and great changes. This last principle asserts the possibility that small changes (e.g., the addition of a neutron to one nucleus) can have profound effects. For

Wisdom, "... the four inductive principles constitute no more than a description of the universe where scientific conclusions have in fact held good ..." (p. 162). They thus are intended to provide no reason for believing that the universe is such that scientific conclusions will continue to hold good.

J. G. Kemeny, too, professes to find factual assumptions underlying science. "In short, induction cannot be justified. We can only base it on a more or less plausible sounding assumption ... [viz., that it works]. We may not be able to justify the assumption; but we must have faith in some such assumption if life is to be possible" (p. 121). Kemeny has made many contributions to the logical interpretation of probability, but in this context it is clear that he must have some empirical frequentist concept in mind when he speaks of our inability to justify induction.

One of the best known and most clear-cut and intelligible attempts to found both inductive logic and inductive justification on broad factual assumptions is that of Arthur W. Burks. In "The Presupposition Theory of Induction," Burks argues that we must simply accept the fact that induction depends on presuppositions; one argument for this is the existence of three conflicting inductive methods, each of which is a straightforward probabilistic method satisfying the axioms of the probability calculus. The three methods, informally, are these: the more often you see p, the more often it will recur (standard method); the more often you see p, the less often it will recur (inverse method); and, past and future occurrences of p are stochastically independent (random method). Burks argues that we can have no *inductive* ground for choosing among these three methods; to choose one is clearly to adopt a presupposition, an assumption.

In another article, "On the Presuppositions of Induction," Burks goes on to show that the natural presupposition (the normal method) does not suffice for the justification of induction. There he adds two new presuppositions: (1) a presupposition concerning limited variety—that there are a finite number of irreducible, first-order, extensional, monadic properties; and (2) a presupposition concerning uniformity—i.e., a causal principle. This latter principle has two parts: (a) if one substitution instance of a causal universal is true, then the causal universal is true; and (b) there is a region in which some causal connections hold. It is not hard to see that the generality of these presuppositions precludes their use in the justification of any particular inductive inferences; and for the general justification of induction for which they are designed, they are, as Burks recognizes; too weak. "If we could justify the claim that, relative to the presuppositions, each causal universal under consideration is as likely to be in the group of true ones as any other causal universal, we would have the result we are looking for. It is clear that our three presuppositions do not suffice to justify this claim, or any similar claim that leads to the result we are looking for, and we must confess that we have not yet found a presuppositional statement which will do this" (p. 597). There is no point, in Burks' view, in pretending that these presuppositions, if and when they are properly formulated, are anything but presuppositions, that is to say, bare-faced assumptions. To say that they are probable (as Keynes said of his Principle of the Limitation of Natural Variety) is just as synthetic an assertion (in virtue of Burks' empirical interpretation of probability) as to say that they are true.

All of these efforts to found inductive logic and the justification of induction on factual premises suffer from two fatal flaws. The first is that they offer us no ground, and can in the nature of things offer us no ground, for accepting the factual premises. None of the recent writers mentioned above attempts to justify his assumptions. Such a justification would be a direct justification of induction, and that, as Hume showed, is not to be hoped for. For none of them is the truth of their postulates more than a pious wish. This sort of postulation, as Russell has remarked, has the same advantages as theft. Other writers have attempted to show that it is possible, without circularity, to provide an inductive justification for the postulates required to justify induction. One attempt along these lines has been made by R. B. Braithwaite. The most concentrated efforts to provide an inductive justification of the principle of induction have been made by Max Black in a number of publications. Since the justification of induction, except insofar as it has a bearing on the contents of an inductive logic, is beside the main point of this volume, I shall not discuss either Black's arguments or the counterarguments that have been offered. A fairly complete bibliography of this discussion will be found at the end of the chapter, however; for our purposes here it suffices to observe that few inductive logicians have been persuaded by Professor Black's arguments.

The second fatal flaw of the approach to induction under discussion here is that there is not the slightest evidence that these postulates would suffice, combined with any amount of observational evidence, to yield any interesting scientific conclusion. The arguments offered by the authors of detailed postulates about the character of the universe are invariably highly abstract, and the more plausible a postulate is made to seem, the farther it appears to be removed from actual scientific argument. As Nelson Goodman says, the "course of accepting an unsubstantiated and even dubious assumption much more sweeping than any actual predictions we make seems an odd and expensive way of justifying inductions" (p. 65).

The attempts of writers who accept an interpretation of probability which is in some degree empirical to provide a general probabilistic justification of induction have thus been seen to come to naught. The attempt yields one of the most clear-cut failures in philosophy. Most of those philosophers who adopt an empirical interpretation of probability have given up the attempt to provide a probabilistic justification of induction. (Reichenbach, in a whimsical piece in which he pictures the shade of Hume scolding Russell for the postulates of *Human Knowledge*, has Hume say that at least he—Reichenbach—allows no form of rational belief.) Richard von Mises writes, "According to the basic viewpoint of this book [*Probability, Statistics, and Truth*] the theory of probability in its application to reality is itself an inductive science; its results and formulas cannot serve to found the inductive process as such, much less to provide numerical values for the plausibility of any other branch of inductive science . . ." (p. *ix*). Reichenbach himself, the writer who attributed the widest scope to the frequency conception of probability, did not propose to find any probabilistic justification for induction, but nevertheless felt that probability was so fundamental as to be able to throw light on all scientific argument. While most statisticians seem to side with von Mises in this matter (and we shall recur to their views in the chapter on statistical inference), there are philosophers—the most active is Wesley Salmon—who find Reichenbach's approach to induction still the most fruitful.

The focus of this approach is not the general problem of induction so much as it is the problem of finding principles which apply in a clear-cut way in specific cases, and which, if possible, can provide a general framework within which the analysis of any particular inductive argument can take place. Since the simplest and most direct form of induction, on this view, is the simple extrapolation of observed frequencies, it is this problem that has been taken to be central. Nevertheless, it should be born in mind that the treatment of this special kind of induction is intended to throw light, at least indirectly, on all forms of inductive inference.

In 1950 Herbert Feigl published an article "De Principiis non Disputandum . . . ?" which has become one of the most mentioned pieces on the inductive problem; in it he distinguished between *justification* and *vindication*. To ask for a general justification of inductive procedures is to ask the impossible, he argues. We can justify particular inductions by reference to general principles of induction, but we cannot justify the principles in the same way. What we can do, however, is to ask for a pragmatic vindication of the adoption of the rule of induction. The crucial problem is to show that we can vindicate the principle that allows us to suppose that what has worked in the past will continue to work in the future. What we need is the vindication of a principle of estimation, a principle for estimating relative frequencies. Such a vindication consists precisely in showing that *if* the goal of predicting the future can be achieved, such and such a definite rule of inductive estimation is a way to achieve it. We need not show that it is necessarily the only way, nor even that it is the best way.

This was precisely the kind of 'justification' Reichenbach tried to provide for his 'straight rule' of induction, which says that if you have observed that m out of n B's have been A's, you should estimate the limit of the relative frequency of A's among B's to be m/n. Reichenbach's argument was the following: If the limit of the relative frequency of A's among B's does not exist (recall the earlier definition of limit), then no rule can give you the correct limit, and the straight rule is no worse than any other. On the other hand, if the limit does exist, there may be any number or rules that will yield this limit. Even pure guessing *may* lead you to the correct limit. But (Reichenbach claimed) the straight rule is the only rule which is *guaranteed* to lead you to the correct limit. That is, it is a *deductive* consequence of the existence of a limit of the relative frequency of A's among B's that for any δ, however small, and for any ϵ, however small, there will come a point in the sequence of B's (say, starting with the Nth B) such that from that point on, the frequency probability of there being a difference as great as δ between the straight-rule estimate and the true limiting frequency is less than ϵ. The straight rule thus has the advantage that it guarantees the eventual attainment of approximate, probabilistic success, if success is attainable at all, even though it gives you no means of calculating N.

This kind of justification has been sought by many other writers—most notably in recent years by Wesley Salmon. It should also be observed that the particular rule of estimation that can be vindicated will lead to a certain sort of inductive logic: the straight rule leads to one sort of logic, the inverse rule mentioned by Burks, if it could be vindicated, would lead to a different sort of logic.

D. Kading argues that no pragmatic vindication of induction can succeed, since, given the aim of predicting the future correctly, "... we have no proof that inductive procedure would be the best method of fulfilling this aim." This argument misses the point: Feigl never claimed that induction was the *best* method. But both Max Black ("Can Induction be Vindicated?") and Edward Madden ("The Riddle of Induction") observe that in any *finite* run, we can't be sure that if anything will work induction will. This is the problem of the *short run*. Reichenbach felt that it could not be solved directly. John Lenz, in "Problems for the Practicalist's Justification of Induction," also mentions the short-run problem of the pragmatic vindication of induction, and he also points to the fact that *any* asymptotic rule of the form "Estimate the relative frequency of B's among A's to be $(m/n) + f(n)$, when of n observed A's, m have been B's", where $f(n)$ approaches 0 as n increases, allows the same justification as the straight rule. Finally, he argues that even the straight rule gives us "no assurance that any of the predictions that science actually makes are correct or even probably correct."

Starting in 1956, Salmon has launched a heroic one-man attack on the opponents of the pragmatic vindication. Black argued, in "The Justification of Induction," that the pragmatic justification could apply as well to the inverse inductive policy (if m of n A's have been B's, predict a limiting frequency of $(n - m)/n$ as to the conventional policy embodied in the straight rule. The inverse policy is self-corrective (that is, it reflects changes in our background knowledge), it may lead to success, and so on. Salmon shows (in "Regular Rules of Induction") that these claims are not warranted. Indeed, predictions made in accordance with the inverse rule are contradictory: if $\frac{1}{8}$ of the A's have been B_1, $\frac{5}{8}$ of them B_2, and $\frac{2}{8}$ of them B_3, where B_1, B_2, and B_3 are mutually exclusive properties, then Black's rule would lead to the prediction that $\frac{7}{8}$ of the A's are B_1, $\frac{3}{8}$ of them are B_2, and $\frac{6}{8}$ of them are B_3— which is to say that $\frac{16}{8}$ of the A's have one or another of the properties B_1, B_2, and B_3. Salmon formulates the following two conditions, which preclude such nonsensical results; the rules still allowed by them he calls *regular* rules, since their formal properties are those possessed by Carnap's regular confirmation functions.

Condition I: Give (1) a sequence S_i of events defined by the attribute A, (2) a set of properties $B_1 \cdots B_k$ which are mutually exclusive and exhaustive within S_i, and (3) a sample of n members of S_i, m_j of which have the property B_j ($1 \leq j \leq k$); then any rule R for making estimates E_j of the probability $P(A, B_j)$ or of the relative frequency $F(A, B_j)$ of B_j within the total sequence S_i must be such that

$$\sum_{j=1}^{k} E_j = 1$$

Condition II: Under the circumstances detailed in Condition I, E_j must never be negative ("Regular Rules of Induction," pp. 386–387).

Such irregular rules of induction as Black and Burks have considered as live possibilities are therefore ruled out as leading to contradiction.

There remain the problem of the short run and the problem of choosing the best rule of those that satisfy the two conditions quoted above. In "Vindication of Induction" Salmon suggested two criteria—the criterion of convergence and the criterion of linguistic invariance—which were offered in the hope that they would lead to plausible solutions both for the "short-run" problem and for the problem of selecting a *unique* member of the family of regular and asymptotic rules. The criterion of linguistic invariance states that "no inductive rule is acceptable if the results it yields are functions of the arbitrary choice of language" (p. 246). On this ground he rejects, for example, Carnap's theory of induction construed as a theory of estimation, since Carnap's degrees of confirmation reflect the richness of the language for which they are defined. In fact Salmon succeeds in showing that every methodological rule of estimation with the possible exception of the straight rule will ultimately violate these two criteria. This is a large step toward a vindication of induction; it is much more than one would have believed it possible to prove. In the same paper Salmon offers a solution to the short-run problem—the natural one of making the short-run estimate as close as possible to the estimate of the limiting frequency. Only this short-run rule, of all possible asymptotic short-run rules, appears not to violate the criterion of linguistic invariance.

Stephen Barker's comments, at the same conference, put this conclusion in rather depressing light; he showed that the straight rule also violates the criterion of linguistic invariance. Consider Nelson Goodman's curious predicate 'grue', meaning green before the year 2000 and blue thereafter. Clearly the straight rule, as applied to a sequence of emeralds will lead us to make the estimate that the proportion of emeralds that are green is 1; and also that the proportion of emeralds that are grue is 1; but nothing can be both grue and green, so that we are again led to inconsistency.

Salmon attempts to answer Barker by stipulating that the straight rule of estimation be applied only to purely ostensive predicates. He argues that predicates like 'grue' are not "purely ostensive" because they must be defined. Grue things don't look alike, while green ones do. A purely ostensive predicate is one which has these characteristics: "(1) it *can* be defined ostensively, (2) its positive and negative instances for ostensive definition *can* be indicated nonverbally, (3) the respect in which the positive instances resemble each other and differ from the negative instances is open to direct inspection" ("Vindicating Induction," p. 38).

This solution is not altogether satisfactory. As the discussion following Salmon's paper showed, not all philosophers find the criterion of linguistic invariance as natural as Salmon does. Furthermore, even if we accept Salmon's solution, it involves abandoning a large part of the program of inductive vindication. There remains, e.g., the problem of the short run. Finally, as Barker says, "It remains to show how other types of inductive rules can be vindicated. It seems to me especially important to vindicate a rule for inferring from the limit of a relative frequency to short-run relative frequencies and to introduce more complex rules of inference to deal with the relation between scientific hypotheses and their evidence" (p. 54). Here, for the moment, this approach to inductive logic, from the philosophical side, rests.

Something more may be said about it from the statisticians' point of view. One of the main things that statistics is concerned with is the estimation of statistical parameters, such as, among other things, the parameter p of a binomial distribution (in philosophical terms, the hypothetical limit of a relative frequency), the parameters representing the mean and variance of a normally distributed quantity, etc.

The major school of statistical theory—the British–American school, as it is often called—adopts an empirical (abstract-counterpart-of-relative-frequency) interpretation of probability. What corresponds in statistical theory to the inductive rules of the philosophers are estimation functions, or *estimators*. In the typical problem of estimating the statistical measure of B's among A's or (the same thing, scientifically) estimating the value of the parameter p that describes the (presumed, presupposed) binomial distribution of B's among A's, we may take our data to be a sequence of 0's and 1's: $(x_1, x_2, \ldots x_n)$, where x_1 has the value 1 if the first A is a B, the value 0 otherwise; ... and in general where x_i has the value 1 if the ith A is not a B. For the statistician, an estimator is any function of these n numbers $(x_1, \ldots x_n)$ whose value always lies between the limits 0 and 1. For example, the constant function $E_c(x_1, \ldots x_n) = \frac{1}{2}$ is a perfectly valid estimator, though no one would want to use it because it is totally insensitive to evidence. It is possible to study estimators in general and to consider various desirable properties that one would like an estimator to have. One would like to have it converge to the true value of what it is an estimator of, as the size of the sample is increased without limits; one would like to have its expected value be equal to the true value; one would like it to be as efficient as possible in the sense that the estimate will generally be close to what is being estimated. An estimator with the first property is called 'consistent'; Salmon's convergence criterion restricts consideration to consistent estimators. An estimator with the second property is called 'unbiased'. There are a few problems, such as the estimation of a binomial parameter from a random sample, in which all the desiderata of an estimator can be satisfied simultaneously; the best of all possible estimators in this case is none other than Salmon's straight rule. But in the general case we must weigh the advantages and disadvantages of an estimator in several respects, and statisticians have come up with no neat general formula for doing so. Statisticians of the school we are considering here do not consider that a part of their job; their job is merely to explore the various mathematical properties of various estimators. They therefore obviously do not see themselves as inductive logicians, even when they are doing estimation theory. Nevertheless, the considerations that they bring to bear on the problems of estimation are clearly of the most direct relevance for any philosopher who wishes to do inductive logic from the point of view of Reichenbach and Salmon. Philosophers have tended to restrict their studies to the problem of the estimation of a binomial parameter, and it is clear that this is in many ways not a typical estimation problem. On the other hand, statisticians do not consider the kind of problems raised by Goodmanesque predicates, so that there seem to be issues within statistics that might benefit from philosophical study.

EXERCISES

1. How might Wisdom's principles be employed in the search for the cause of the common cold? Suppose that the common cold has been found to be caused by a certain virus. What sort of evidence would be brought forward as justification for this claim? How would Wisdom's principles be useful, if at all, in reconstructing the argument from the evidence to the conclusion?

2. One of the postulates often employed in attempts at a general justification of induction is a postulate of universal causality. One possible formulation is: "For any kind of event E, there is another kind of event E' such that an event of kind E' is invariably followed by an event of kind E, and an event of kind E is invariably preceded by an event of kind E'." Defend this principle against the alleged counterexample: E is the breaking of a leg; but sometimes it is caused by falling down stairs, sometimes by automobile accidents, sometimes by skiing, etc.

3. Suppose we wish to investigate a certain kind of event A. How can such a principle as that expressed in problem 2 help us to plan our investigation?

4. Suppose we wish to investigate a certain kind of event A, and that we have a body of information (say, the results of experiments or observations)

pertaining to occurrences of A. How can such a principle as that expressed in problem 2 help us in the analysis of this information—i.e., in drawing inferences from the body of information concerning the cause of A?

5. Suppose we wish to investigate a certain kind of event A, and that we have a body of information pertaining to occurrences of A, and that this information is sufficient for us to conclude that events of kind B cause events of kind A. What kind of argument might we use to proceed from the body of information to the conclusion? What role might the principle of problem 2 play in validating that argument?

The bibliographical notes to this chapter contain references to a number of the works relevant to problems 6, 7, and 8. Very recent material must be dug up by the student on his own.

6. Write a brief essay setting forth Braithwaite's inductive argument for induction, and some of the counterarguments that have been brought against it; provide a reasoned appraisal of the situation.

7. Write a brief essay setting forth some of the claims and counterclaims concerning Max Black's view of the noncircularity of the inductive justification of induction; conclude with a reasoned appraisal of the situation.

8. Write a brief essay on Salmon's attempts to provide a vindication of induction, and some of the arguments that have been brought against these attempts.

BIBLIOGRAPHICAL NOTES FOR CHAPTER 10

Bertrand Russell's *Human Knowledge, Its Scope and Limits*, Simon and Schuster, New York, 1948, is eminently readable and contains a clear exposition of some rather unclear postulates. Somewhat simpler postulates of the same general nature are offered by John Oulton Wisdom, in *Foundations of Inference in Natural Science*, Methuen, London, 1952. The first statement of the principle of the limitation of natural variety is in John Maynard Keynes' *Treatise on Probability*, Macmillan, London, 1921. The quotation from John G. Kemeny comes from his slightly oversimple *A Philosopher Looks at Science*, D. van Nostrand, Princeton, New Jersey, 1959.

The two articles by Arthur W. Burks referred to in the text are "The Presupposition Theory of Induction," *Philosophy of Science* **20**, 1953, pp. 177–97, and "On the Presuppositions of Induction," *Review of Metaphysics* **8**, 1954–55, pp. 574–611.

R. B. Braithwaite attempted to provide an inductive justification of induction in his excellent book *Scientific Explanation*, Cambridge University Press, 1953. Comments on his efforts in this direction may be found in Abner Shimony, "Braithwaite on Scientific Method," *Review of Metaphysics* **7**, 1953–54, pp. 644–60, and my article "R. B. Braithwaite on Probability and Induction," *British Journal for the Philosophy of Science* **9**, 1958–59, pp. 203–20. Max Black's efforts at an inductive justification of induction are still continuing, but some of his papers on this topic are "The Justification of Induction," in *Language and*

Philosophy, Cornell University Press, Ithaca, New York, 1949, pp. 59–88; "Inductive Support of Inductive Rules," in *Problems of Analysis*, Cornell University Press, Ithaca, New York, 1950, pp. 191–208; "Self-Supporting Inductive Arguments," *Journal of Philosophy* **55**, 1958, pp. 718–25 (reprinted in Black's *Models and Metaphors*, Cornell University Press, Ithaca, New York, 1962). Professor Black's arguments have been attacked by Peter Achinstein, leading to the following exchange: Peter Achinstein, "The Circularity of a Self-Supporting Inductive Argument," *Analysis* **22**, 1961–62, pp. 138–41; Max Black, "Self-Support and Circularity: A Reply to Mr. Achinstein," *Analysis* **23**, 1962–63, pp. 43–44; Peter Achinstein, "Circularity and Induction," *Analysis* **23**, 1962–63, pp. 123–27.

The reference to Goodman is from *Fact, Fiction, and Forecast*, Harvard University Press, Cambridge, Massachusetts, 1955. Hans Reichenbach's amusing article is "A Conversation Between Bertrand Russell and David Hume," *Journal of Philosophy* **46**, 1949, pp. 545–49. Richard von Mises' viewpoint is expressed in his *Probability, Statistics, and Truth*, Macmillan, New York, 1957. Reichenbach's detailed treatment of induction, from his limiting-frequency point of view, is his monumental *Theory of Probability*, University of California Press, Berkeley and Los Angeles, 1949.

The Herbert Feigl epoch of vindication began with his "De Principiis non Disputandum...?" in *Philosophical Analysis* (Max Black, ed.), Prentice-Hall, Englewood Cliffs, New Jersey, 1963, pp. 113–47. Objections to the approach are to be found in Max Black, "Can Induction be Vindicated?" *Philosophical Studies* **10**, 1959, pp. 5–16 (reprinted in *Models and Metaphors*) and "'Pragmatic' Justifications of Induction," in *Problems of Analysis*, pp. 157–90; in D. Kading, "Concerning Mr. Feigl's 'Vindication' of Induction," *Philosophy of Science* **27**, 1960, pp. 405–407; and in Edward Madden, "The Riddle of Induction," *Journal of Philosophy* **55**, 1958, pp. 705–18.

The exchanges centering about Salmon's work are, by Wesley Salmon, "Regular Rules of Induction," *The Philosophical Review* **65**, 1956, pp. 385–88; "Vindication of Induction," in *Current Issues in the Philosophy of Science* (Feigl and Maxwell, eds.), Holt, Rinehart, and Winston, New York, 1961, pp. 245–56; "Rejoinder to Barker," in the same volume, pp. 260–62; and "On Vindicating Induction," in *Induction: Some Current Issues* (Kyburg and Nagel, eds.), Wesleyan University Press, Middletown, Connecticut, 1963, pp. 27–41. Controversy is provided by Stephen Barker, "Comments on Salmon's 'Vindication of Induction'" and "Rejoinder to Salmon," in *Current Issues in the Philosophy of Science*, pp. 257–60 and pp. 276–78; and Max Black, "Comments on Salmon's Paper," in *Induction: Some Current Issues*, pp. 42–44. This volume also contains a number of comments on Salmon's notion of linguistic invariance scattered through the discussion of his paper.

A fascinating, if somewhat difficult, paper on the relations of vindication, induction, and probability is Wilfred Sellars' "Induction as Vindication," *Philosophy of Science* **31**, 1964, pp. 197–231.

The statistician's point of view regarding estimation may be called from almost any up-to-date statistics text—for example, S. S. Wilks' *Elementary Statistical Analysis*, Princeton University Press, Princeton, 1951. In a small minority of such books, 'estimator' and 'estimation' may not be found in the index; such books include the same subject matter under 'tests of hypotheses'.

11

Statistical Inference

In the last chapter it was suggested that statisticians have much to say that is relevant to the concerns of inductive logic. Like logicians, statisticians can be divided according to the concept of probability they work with. Here our concern is primarily with those who adopt some sort of frequency or empirical interpretation of probability. Thus we lump together those for whom probability is a limiting frequency, those for whom it is simply an abstract counterpart of relative frequencies that exist in the world, observed or not, and those who really don't want to worry about the interpretation of probability with which they work, so long as it "has something to do with" empirical relative frequencies. This includes, however, the vast majority of statisticians today.

The literature of statistics is enormous, and highly technical. It would be absurd to attempt to summarize it or, for that matter, to attempt to read it. What I propose to do instead is to illustrate two of the major trends in the field of statistics—trends which have been picked up by a few philosophers, and which should certainly become familiar to more philosophers. These two trends are the testing of statistical hypotheses and, what has now for most statisticians come to supersede this approach, the general technique of viewing all statistical problems as problems of decision under circumstances of uncertainty. The latter technique goes under the banner "Decision Theory." There is no conflict between the two approaches; indeed it will be seen in what follows that there is a sense in which the former is merely a special case of the latter. Finally, we shall look at the connection between decision theory and game theory.

The same problem will serve to introduce the important concepts of the theory of testing statistical hypotheses and decision theory. Suppose that we are engaged in the manufacture of machines of a certain sort, and that there is a component we buy in lots of a thousand. A supplier offers us a lot either containing $\frac{1}{3}$ defective items (the usual proportion) or containing $\frac{3}{4}$ defective items. The price is good if the proportion is $\frac{1}{3}$, too high if the proportion is $\frac{3}{4}$. We must decide whether to buy the components from this supplier and run the risk of paying too much for a lot of which $\frac{3}{4}$ are defective, or to refuse to buy this lot, alienating our supplier, and bringing on ourselves the necessity of digging up a new supplier. The problem may be looked at as a problem in testing the statistical hypothesis that $\frac{1}{3}$ of the items in the lot are defective against the alternative hypothesis that $\frac{3}{4}$ of the items in the lot are defective. If this terminology seems strange here, we may consider another problem in which the numbers are the same but the terminology seems more suitable— e.g., suppose that we are testing a certain drug alleged to alter the genetic structure of a certain plant. In the ordinary course of nature, only $\frac{1}{3}$ of the offspring of the parent stock are fertile; according to the theory, if the drug works, $\frac{3}{4}$ of the offspring will be fertile. Thus we require to test the hypothesis that $\frac{1}{3}$ of the offspring are fertile against the hypothesis that $\frac{3}{4}$ of the offspring are fertile.

In the latter problem there is a clear ground for referring to one of the hypotheses as the *null hypothesis*, namely, the hypothesis that the proportion in question is $\frac{1}{3}$. This is the proportion we would observe in the long run if "nothing happened" or if our special hypothesis happens to be false. From the point of view of testing hypotheses, it is generally easier to calculate probabilities on the null hypothesis than on its alternative (in testing a medicine, for example, one might test the standard recovery rate $r = 0.90$ against an "improvement", $r > 0.90$). In problems like that of trying to decide what proportion of a certain batch of items are defective, the question of which hypothesis to call "null" is somewhat moot. But in any event, we take it to be part of the formalization of the problem that a certain hypothesis, to be called the null hypothesis, be chosen for test against an alternative hypothesis. Either of these hypotheses may be complex—e.g., in a given problem we could be testing the null hypothesis that $0.4 \leq p \leq 0.9$ against the alternative that $p < 0.4$ or $0.9 > p$.

Strictly speaking, from the classical point of view, the statistician as such does no more than exhibit certain characteristics of a test preselected by the scientist or other user of statistics. In point of fact, of course, the characteristics of various tests have much to do with the selection of a particular test, but from this classical point of view, that is merely accidental.

What is a test? A test consists of a decision to reject the null hypothesis under certain experimental conditions if certain specified outcomes are observed. The experimental conditions are these: We draw a sample from the population. This is a *random sample* in the frequentist sense that it is drawn by a method which in the long run will draw each element in the population equally often. In the simple testing of a hypothesis against an alternative, the number of elements in the sample—the sample size—is fixed in advance by the tester. (In a refinement of this theory one considers three alternatives: to reject the null hypothesis, to fail to reject it, or to continue testing.) In our particular example we shall take n, the sample size, to be 4. It is an unreasonably small sample size—ordinary intuition tells us—but we thus keep the calculations simple, and the principles would be the same for any value of n.

A test is then a decision to reject the null hypothesis if the sample has some specified character. Now let us consider a particular test, say R: reject H_0, the null hypothesis that $p = \frac{1}{3}$, if 3 or 4 defective items are found in the sample of 4. Otherwise we "fail to reject the null hypothesis." As statisticians often point out, to fail to reject the null hypothesis is not the same as to accept it; nevertheless, it is tantamount to accepting the null hypothesis for the time being. In the case of the mutation-producing drug, it suggests looking for another drug; in the case of the manufacturer, it means buying that particular lot of components. But what someone does is not the business of the statistician on this classical view; his business is merely to characterize the proposed test.

What characteristics of a test are of interest? According to the view under consideration, we are primarily interested in the possibilities of making (or avoiding) errors. On the interpretation of probability that is accepted as a framework for this chapter, we cannot give a probability for making an error. In the first place a single test is, like any other single event, not a fit subject of probabilities. It makes no sense to assign a probability except when we are talking about a whole reference class. In the second place even if there were some reasonable way of putting together an overall probability (interpreted, say, as the long-run frequency of error in applications of test R), there would be no plausible way of calculating its value. What we do instead is consider separately two kinds of error, traditionally called 'error of the first kind' or 'type I error', and (appropriately) 'error of the second kind' or 'type II error'.

These two kinds of errors represent the two possible ways in which a rule such as R may be wrong: For one thing, it may lead us to reject the null hypothesis, even though it is true; for another, it may lead us to fail to reject it even though it is false. Error of the first sort is called type I error; error of the second sort is called type II error. One of the requirements of reasonable tests is that the hypothesis tested, the null hypothesis, be such as to allow us to calculate the probability of making a type I error. Thus one would test the null hypothesis $p = \frac{1}{2}$ against the complex alternative $p > \frac{1}{2}$. On the alternative $p > \frac{1}{2}$, one could not ordinarily compute the probability that a rule such as R should lead to the mistaken rejection of that hypothesis, although one could compute a maximum value for that probability. Under the circumstances with which we are concerned, it happens—since we are concerned only with the choice between two *simple* hypotheses $p = \frac{1}{3}$ and $p = \frac{3}{4}$—that we can calculate the probabilities of type II errors as well as the probability of a type I error. The probability of committing a type I error, under a given rule for rejecting the null hypothesis, is known as the *significance level* or *size* of the test having that rule. In typical applications of testing theory one often finds a specification of the null hypothesis, together with the assertion that it is "rejected at the 0.05 level" (or at the 0.01 level, or at the 0.005 level). What this means is that *if* the null hypothesis is true, if the drug has no effect, if there is no difference in learning rate, if p is actually 0.25, ... *then* the probability of falsely rejecting the null hypothesis under the application of the rule we are using is 0.05 (or 0.01, or 0.005, etc.). It is worth reminding ourselves once more that this probability is a long-run prediction; it is an empirical assertion about the set of all such tests, and has only such bearing as we choose on subjective grounds to give it on the particular test we have performed.

Error of the second kind, or type II error, is related to the power of a test to reveal the falsity of the null hypothesis. We could reduce error of the first kind to 0 by simply agreeing *never* to reject the null hypothesis (for then we would never reject it falsely), but that rule would hardly yield a useful test of a statistical hypothesis. Such a test would have a power of 0, i.e., a probability of 1 of making an error of the second kind, i.e., of failing to reject the null hypothesis when it is in fact wrong. The power of a test is defined as 1 minus the probability of type II error. Often, as when we test a hypothesis $p = \frac{1}{2}$ against a complex alternative $p > \frac{1}{2}$, we do not know what the type II error is; but we can still often distinguish some tests as more powerful than others, in the sense that a test T_1 may be more powerful than a test T_2 regardless of what value $p > \frac{1}{2}$ actually obtains.

So far we have:

H_0: The null hypothesis; the hypothesis being tested.
H_1: The alternative hypothesis.
Type I error: The erroneous rejection of H_0.
Type II error: The erroneous acceptance of H_0, or the erroneous failure
   to reject H_0.

Size of a test: } The (maximum) probability of rejecting H_0 when it
Significance level: } is true.
Power of a test: The (maximum) probability of rejecting H_0 when it is
false.

Let us now return to the concrete example and see what these ideas come to in actual practice. We are testing the hypothesis that $\frac{1}{3}$ of a thousand items are defective against the hypothesis that $\frac{3}{4}$ of them are defective. The former is the null hypothesis. The test consists of drawing four items from the lot (in a statistically random manner) and applying rule R, i.e., rejecting the null hypothesis if 3 or 4 defective items are found in the sample.

Type I error. In the long run, when the null hypothesis is true, we will be led to reject the null hypothesis a predictable proportion of the time. The probability of getting a sample with four defective items is

$$\binom{4}{4}\left(\frac{1}{3}\right)^4\left(\frac{2}{3}\right)^0 = \frac{1}{81}$$

(by Bernoulli's Theorem), and similarly, the probability (would-be, long-run frequency) of getting three defective items in our sample of four is

$$\binom{4}{3}\left(\frac{1}{3}\right)^3\left(\frac{2}{3}\right)^1 = \frac{8}{81}.$$

The probability of rejecting the null hypothesis, when it is true, by acting on rule R, is thus $\frac{8}{81} + \frac{1}{81} = \frac{1}{9} = 0.11$. 0.11 is thus the probability of a type I error, or, most familiarly, the *level* of the test proposed. There is one chance in nine that it will wrongly lead to the rejection of the null hypothesis.

Type II error. Since in this particular case we have a simple hypothesis as the alternative to the null hypothesis, we can calculate actual probabilities for the error of the second kind. That is, we can calculate the probability, given that the null hypothesis is *false*, that rule R will *fail* to lead us to reject it. This is just the probability (long-run frequency, would-be) that when the proportion of defectives in the lot is $\frac{3}{4}$, our sample will contain 0, 1, or 2 defective items. This probability is

$$\binom{4}{0}\left(\frac{3}{4}\right)^0\left(\frac{1}{4}\right)^4 + \binom{4}{1}\left(\frac{3}{4}\right)^1\left(\frac{1}{4}\right)^3 + \binom{4}{2}\left(\frac{3}{4}\right)^2\left(\frac{1}{4}\right)^2 = \frac{67}{256}.$$

0.26 is therefore the probability of error of the second kind, or the probability of type II error. The power of the test proposed is $1 - 0.26 = 0.74$.

Here is where the work of the classical statistician comes to an end. He can characterize proposed tests, but he cannot, as a statistician, judge the relative importance of type I and of type II errors, and thus cannot propose a "best" test. Sometimes, given a null hypothesis, a sample size, and a required level (probability of type I error) he can find a test which is more powerful than any other test of that level against the given alternative, or against any alternative of a given class. But essentially, when the errors of the two kinds have been specified, the matter is in the hands of the user of statistics.

The next stage in the development of statistical theory is the attempt to take account of the relative importance of the different kinds of errors. This is the stage that leads to decision theory. To apply decision theory, we must specify the problem in somewhat more detail; we must stipulate the losses that arise in the case of various situations that may arise. Let us take the fair price of the lot as a datum; if $\frac{1}{3}$ of the items are defective, and we buy the lot, the loss will thus be taken as 0. If we buy the lot and it turns out that three quarters of the items are defective, then this is the worst error we can make; let us estimate the cost of this error to be 10. If in fact the null hypothesis is true— i.e., $\frac{1}{3}$ are defective—and we fail to buy that lot, we must go out and find another supplier, and at the same time we will pointlessly offend our present supplier. Let us call the loss involved in this situation 8. And finally, if the proportion of defectives is $\frac{3}{4}$, and we decline to buy the lot, we will have done the correct thing, but we will still have to go out to find a new supplier; this, let us say costs us 5. We can tabulate all this as follows:

Action	Proportion of Defectives	Cost
Buy	$\frac{1}{3}$	0
Don't buy	$\frac{1}{3}$	8
Buy	$\frac{3}{4}$	10
Don't buy	$\frac{3}{4}$	5

Again the sample on which we are to base our decision consists of four items selected from the lot by a method which will in the long run select each item equally often. A *strategy* is a rule for deciding on a course of action according to the character of the sample of four items. Strategies may be either *pure* or mixed. A pure strategy is a rule which stipulates, for every possible composition of the sample, which of the actions is to be performed. A mixed strategy is one which stipulates, for every possible composition of the sample, an auxiliary experiment whose outcomes have specified probabilities, and according to the outcome of that auxiliary experiment, which of the actions is to be performed. It is easy to see that pure strategies are a special kind of mixed strategy—one in which the outcomes of the auxiliary experiment have probabilities 0 and 1. In view of the fact that the outcomes of the auxiliary experiment have probabilities of 0 and 1 in this special case, the auxiliary experiment can be disposed with. In our example, a mixed strategy might be to accept the lot (with probability 1) if there are fewer than 3 defective items in the sample of 4; to reject the lot (with probability 1) if there are 4 defective items in the sample; and if there are 3 defective items in the sample to accept the lot with probability $\frac{1}{2}$ by flipping a coin and accepting the lot if and only if the coin lands heads.

We shall restrict our attention, at the moment, to pure strategies. One possible strategy would be to buy the lot if there are 0 or 4 defective items in the sample and to reject it otherwise. Another (also peculiar) would be to buy the lot if the first item in the sample is defective, or if the last two items in the sample are not defective, and to reject it otherwise. A more natural strategy would be to follow the test proposed above, buying the lot if and only if the rule R, applied to the sample, fails to cause us to reject the null hypothesis. Decision theory goes further, however. It gives us a way of looking at *all* the possible strategies according to the costs involved of the various possible outcomes.

In a given state of nature—i.e., under the assumption that a given simple hypothesis is true—it is possible to calculate the probabilities of the various outcomes of the random sampling. According to a given pure strategy, each outcome will lead to a specific decision. Given a decision and a state of nature, the above table gives the cost. Since this can be done for each possible outcome, we can calculate, for each strategy and each state of nature, the *value* of that strategy in that state of nature. The value of any course of action which may have any one of n results is its *mathematical expectation*, where 'mathematical expectation' is defined as the sum of the possible values of the outcomes, each multiplied by its probability. Thus if one undertakes a gamble on the toss of a coin in which one gets $1.00 if the coin lands heads and pays $2.00 if the coin lands tails, one's mathematical expectation is

$$\tfrac{1}{2}(1.00) + \tfrac{1}{2}(-2.00) = -\$0.50.$$

Before illustrating this calculation for some of the strategies, let us consider how many strategies there are. There are $2^4 = 16$ different possible samples (the first item may be defective or nondefective; the second item may be defective or nondefective;...); a strategy corresponds to a selection of a *subset* of these 16 samples, the observation of any member of which will lead to the decision to buy the lot. There are a total of 2^{16} subsets of a set of 16 entities, including the empty subset (never buy the lot) and the universal set (buy the lot whatever sample you observe). There are thus 2^{16} strategies to consider—an impressive number, for such a simple problem. But, as we shall see, we need to consider only the following six (pure, unmixed) strategies:

S_0 Buy the lot if there are fewer than 0 defective items in the sample, i.e., never buy.
S_1 Buy the lot if there are fewer than 1 ...
S_2 Buy the lot if there are fewer than 2 ...
S_3 Buy the lot if there are fewer than 3 ...
S_4 Buy the lot if there are fewer than 4 defective items in the sample.
S_5 Buy the lot if there are fewer than 5 defective items in the sample.

We can now calculate the expectation of each strategy under each of the two hypotheses. The expectation of S_4 under the hypothesis that $\frac{1}{3}$ of the items are defective is the probability[1] that there will be exactly 4 defective items in the sample,

$$\binom{4}{4}\left(\frac{1}{3}\right)^4\left(\frac{2}{3}\right)^0 = \frac{1}{81},$$

multiplied by the cost of failing to buy the lot when the proportion is $\frac{1}{3}$ (8, from the table above) plus the probability that there will be fewer than 4 defective items ($\frac{80}{81}$) multiplied by the cost of buying the lot when the proportion is $\frac{1}{3}$ (0 from the table above).

Expectation of loss of S_4 under hypothesis $p = \frac{1}{3}$:

$$\left(\tfrac{1}{81} \times 8\right) + \left(\tfrac{80}{81} \times 0\right) = \tfrac{8}{81}.$$

Similarly, we may calculate the expectation of loss of S_4 under the hypothesis that the proportion of defectives is $\frac{3}{4}$. It will be the probability that exactly 4 items in our sample, under this hypothesis, are defective, multiplied by the cost of declining to buy the lot when the proportion is $\frac{3}{4}$; plus the probability of finding fewer than 4 defective items in our sample, times the cost of buying the lot when $\frac{3}{4}$ of the items are defective.

Expectation of loss of S_4 under hypothesis $p = \frac{3}{4}$:

$$\binom{4}{4}\left(\frac{3}{4}\right)^4\left(\frac{1}{4}\right)^0 \times 5 + \left[1 - \binom{4}{4}\left(\frac{3}{4}\right)^4\left(\frac{1}{4}\right)^0\right] \times 10$$

$$= \frac{81}{256} \times 5 + \frac{175}{256} \times 10 = \frac{2155}{256} = 8.5.$$

The expected losses of the other strategies under the two hypotheses may be computed similarly. The results are tabulated in Table I.

TABLE I

Strategy	Expected Loss If $\frac{3}{4}$ Are Defective	Expected Loss If $\frac{1}{3}$ Are Defective
S_0	5.0	8.0
S_1	5.05	6.4
S_2	5.25	3.25
S_3	6.3	0.78
S_4	8.5	0.1
S_5	10.0	0.0

[1] Calculated as though we were drawing with replacement, since the error thus introduced is small.

It has been claimed that these are the only six strategies we need to consider. The detailed proof of this claim is beyond the scope of this book, but an example or two will serve to illustrate the ideas involved. We shall say that one strategy S *dominates* another strategy T, if under (at least) one hypothesis the expectation of S is greater than that of T, and under no hypothesis is the expectation of T greater than that of S. When S dominates T, we clearly should prefer to follow strategy S, and we may disregard T. In the case at hand every one of the possible strategies other than the six we have listed is either dominated by one of those strategies or by a mixture of two of them.

For example, consider the strategy S' according to which we buy the lot unless there are exactly three defective items in our sample. If the proportion of defectives in the lot is $\frac{3}{4}$, the probability that we will buy the lot under strategy S' is 148/256, and our expectation is 7.84. If the proportion of defectives is $\frac{1}{3}$, the probability that we will buy the lot is 73/81, and our expectation is 0.79. These losses compare with 6.3 and 0.78 under strategy S_3; so whatever the state of nature—i.e., whatever the true proportion of defectives—strategy S_3 is preferable to strategy S'.

For another example, consider the strategy S^* under which we buy the lot if there are 0 or 1 defective items in the sample, or if just the first two items of the sample are defective. The probability that we will buy the lot under this strategy if $\frac{3}{4}$ of the items are defective is 22/256; the expected loss under this hypothesis is 5.43. Under the hypothesis that a third of the items are defective, the probability of buying the lot is 52/81, and the expected loss is 2.86. There is no strategy among our six which dominates S^*; but we can compute a mixture of two strategies which will dominate it. Suppose we follow a mixed strategy which leads us to use S_2 a proportion α of the time, and S_3 a proportion $(1 - \alpha)$ of the time. Under the hypothesis that $\frac{1}{3}$ of the items are defective, the expectation of this strategy is $3.25\alpha + (1 - \alpha)0.78$. Let us set this equal to 2.86 and calculate the corresponding value of α: $\alpha = 0.754$. Thus if our mixed strategy is to use S_2 75.4% of the time, and S_3 24.6% of the time, we will do just as well under the mixed strategy as under S^*, when the proportion of defective items is $\frac{1}{3}$. How will we do when the proportion is $\frac{3}{4}$? Our expectation under this hypothesis, using our mixed strategy, is $0.754(5.25) + 0.246(6.3) = 5.40$, which is less than 5.43. Thus S^* is dominated by our mixed strategy.

Table I is as far as the decision theorist can take us. It is, at any rate, farther than the classical statistician took us, for we have not merely probabilities of errors under the two hypotheses, but expectations of loss under the two hypotheses. Furthermore, instead of being presented with the characteristics of some particular strategy chosen by us, we are in a sense presented with the results of a survey of all the possible $2^{16} = 65,536$ strategies. Any choice other than the six listed here or some mixture of them is poorer than one of these six (or some mixture of two of them), but the final choice of one to follow is still ours.

In order to make this choice on a rational basis, we need some sort of rational policy to follow. If the circumstances are such that we can accept a statistical hypothesis about the frequency with which the two states of affairs ($\frac{1}{3}$ defectives and $\frac{3}{4}$ defectives) occur, then a straightforward application of mathematical expectation yields the rational choice of strategy. If a lot with $\frac{3}{4}$ defective occurs only $\frac{2}{5}$ of the time, we can compute the weighted expected loss under S_0 as $(5 \times \frac{2}{5}) + (8 \times \frac{3}{5}) = 6\frac{4}{5}$. We can compute the expected loss under the other live strategies in the same way, and get Table II:

TABLE II

Strategy	Weighted Expected Loss
S_0	6.8
S_1	5.9
S_2	4.0
S_3	2.6
S_4	3.5
S_5	5.0

A glance at this table shows that the strategy which minimizes the expected loss is S_3—to buy the lot if there are less than three defective items in the sample.

In general, of course, these prior probabilities of the alternative hypotheses will not be available. We may be just starting out in the manufacture of machines, or we may not have kept records in the past on the basis of which to estimate these prior probabilities. In the interesting scientific cases, where we are testing consequences of a general theory (in the alternative formulation, e.g., in which we are looking for changes in genetic structure) such prior probabilities are out of the question. When we cannot use prior probabilities, we must turn to a policy of a different sort. One such policy has been elaborated by game theorists. This is minimax policy, and its rationale is as follows: As manufacturers of machines, one of our healthy concerns is to protect ourselves as much as possible against unpleasant surprises. Look at Table I. If we follow strategy S_4, we may, if the proportion of defectives is $\frac{1}{3}$, be undergoing an expected loss of only 0.1. But on the other hand, if a competitor of ours can choose which the proportion of defectives will be, and if he knows that we are following strategy S_4, he might choose the proportion of defectives to be $\frac{3}{4}$, and we will be subject to an expected loss of 8.5. If we were to follow strategy S_0, on the other hand, we could be assured of an expected loss of 5, if $\frac{3}{4}$ of the items were defective; but our competitor would then perhaps arrange for $\frac{1}{3}$ of the items to be defective, so that our expected loss would turn out to be 8.

What can we do in this sort of competitive (or possibly competitive) situation? We can protect ourselves as much as possible by choosing a strategy according to the following minimax policy: Choose the strategy which minimizes the maximum risk. Table III lists the strategies with their associated maximum expected losses:

TABLE III

Strategy	Maximum Expected Loss
S_0	8.0
S_1	6.4
S_2	5.25
S_3	6.3
S_4	8.5

Minimax policy therefore directs us, in the absence of knowledge of the prior probabilities of the two hypotheses, to follow strategy S_2.

A somewhat different analysis results if, instead of attempting to minimize the maximum loss, we attempt to minimize the *maximum regret*, where *regret* is the increment of expected loss we suffer from coming to the wrong decision in a given state of nature. Thus one might plausibly argue that if $\frac{3}{4}$ of the items in the lot are defective, we lose 5 under any circumstances; and so the part of the expected loss under that hypothesis which is under our control is merely the difference between the minimum value, 5, and the tabulated value in Table I, for each of the pure strategies listed there. Since in column two of Table I the minimum entry is 0, the expected loss and expected regret are the same. The table of expected regrets is Table IV.

TABLE IV

Strategy	Expected Regret If $\frac{3}{4}$ Are Defective	Expected Regret If $\frac{1}{3}$ Are Defective	Maximum Expected Regret
S_0	0.0	8.0	8.0
S_1	0.05	6.4	6.4
S_2	0.25	3.25	3.25
S_3	1.3	0.78	1.3
S_4	3.5	0.1	3.5
S_5	5.0	0.0	5.0

Applying the minimax principle to this table leads to the choice of a different strategy: S_3 instead of S_2. This is not surprising, since different criteria are being applied in the choice of a strategy.

There are still other criteria one might employ in choosing a strategy; for example, in the absence of information concerning the relative frequency with which lots of the two sorts turn up, one might choose the strategy which minimizes the *average* expected loss under the two hypotheses.

So much for an indication of the major trend of statistical inference. A critique of this illustrative fragment would be out of place as well as grossly unfair, but before passing on we should mention some matters that are deserving of further thought. First, the game-theoretic (minimax) approach with which we ended up is rather questionable even when it comes to choosing a strategy for deciding whether or not to accept a lot of items. Even in a competitive society, it is not plausible to suppose that the supplier is trying to do in the buyer—and yet it was considerations of that sort that were cited in the rationale for the minimax policy. It is even more implausible to picture the scientist and nature as antagonists in an epistemological game. There is no plausible way of construing scientific inference as a statistical game played by man against nature.

Second, while one could reasonably suppose that the losses were known (at least to an approximation) in the circumstances of deciding whether or not to buy a lot of 1,000 items, one cannot assign values in a similarly straight-forward way to the losses involved in deciding to accept a scientific hypothesis which is wrong or to reject one that is right. Various attempts have been made to formulate a concept of epistemic or scientific utility which would allow the application of the same statistical techniques currently used in deciding whether or not to accept a box of bolts to be used in deciding whether or not to accept a scientific hypothesis. But since these attempts have been developed only within the framework of a degree-of-entailment or logical measure interpretation of probability, they will be discussed in the chapter devoted to confirmation theories of induction.

Third, the general approach to testing statistical hypotheses initiated by Neyman and Pearson requires that we conceive of a test, not in relation to a particular observed result of an experiment, but as a general procedural rule. It is thus appropriate, on this approach, that we seek a rule which will rarely reject a null hypothesis when it is true and which will as often as possible reject an alternative hypothesis when it is false. But when we are concerned with choosing between two statistical hypotheses in a given actual situation, on a given body of data, these criteria may be irrelevant, as Ian Hacking has shown.

Hacking ("Guessing by Frequency", p. 96) offers the following clearcut and simple example, in which we have two rules for choosing between two statistical hypotheses, one of which is superior to the other on the classical criteria, and yet the other, in a concrete situation, is demonstrably preferable. There are two hypotheses, h and i. The test we perform has four possible outcomes, E_1, E_2, E_3, and E_4. The (frequency) probabilities of these outcomes are given by Table V.

TABLE V

	$P(E_1)$	$P(E_2)$	$P(E_3)$	$P(E_4)$
h	0.00	0.01	0.01	0.98
i	0.01	0.01	0.97	0.01

The two rules are these: R_1 is to reject h if and only if E_3 occurs. R_2 is to reject h if and only if either E_1 or E_2 occurs. Table VI gives the characteristics of the rules.

TABLE VI

	Probability of Type I Error (False Rejection of h)	Probability of Type II Error (False Acceptance of h)	Power
R_1	0.01	0.03	0.97
R_2	0.01	0.98	0.02

By the classical criteria, R_1 is definitely to be preferred. The long-run frequency of falsely rejecting h is 0.01, and the long-run frequency of correctly accepting h is 0.97. Using rule R_2 we will falsely reject h no more often, but we will rarely (2% of the time) be right in deciding not to accept h.

But, Hacking says, suppose we have already observed E_1. Then which is the preferable rule? Obviously R_2. For if we have observed E_1, R_2 will never lead us astray, while R_1 always will. Of course there is a rule which is better by the classical criteria than either R_1 or R_2, and which does not have the shortcoming Hacking is pointing out—namely, R_3: Reject h if and only if either E_1 or E_3 is observed. This test will lead to the false rejection of h only 1% of the time, like R_1 and R_2, but has power of 0.98. Nevertheless, Hacking's point is valid: there are many statistical situations in which criteria for applying the classical criteria are required.

Two writers have attempted to develop theories of statistical inference which embody solutions to these three problems, and which are still based on an empirical concept of probability. One is the statistician R. A. Fisher, to whom many important results in the abstract theory of statistical inference are due. Unfortunately his writings are very difficult, and their interpretation is more than a little controversial. This is particularly true of his most philosophical work, *Statistical Methods and Scientific Inference*. Ian Hacking's book *Logic of Statistical Inference* is quite clear, and contains a number of very telling arguments against the classical Neyman–Pearson approach. However, it, too, is rather too technical for summary here, and any criticism would have to be correspondingly technical. Nevertheless, both these books are required reading for anyone who wishes to wax philosophical about statistical inference.

In recent years a new movement based on the subjectivistic interpretation of probability has gained considerable force in statistics. This approach to statistical inference will be discussed in the chapter on confirmation theories of induction, since it bears more logical affinities to the work of Carnap and other philosophers than to traditional statistics.

EXERCISES

1. Suppose we have two hypotheses, H_1 and H_2, to consider. The only way we have of deciding between them is to perform a certain experiment (which we can only perform once) and to decide on the basis of the outcome of the experiment. The experiment has three possible outcomes, and the probabilities of these outcomes on each of the two hypotheses is given by the table:

	$P(E_1)$	$P(E_2)$	$P(E_3)$
H_1	0.01	0.05	0.94
H_2	0.92	0.06	0.02

We regard H_1 as the null hypothesis. Consider test I: reject H_1 if and only if E_1 is observed. Consider test II: reject H_1 if and only if either E_1 or E_2 is observed. What are the characteristics of these tests?

2. In a botanical study of an extremely rare plant, we become interested in whether a certain characteristic C (which we have reason to regard as genetically independent of other characteristics) is dominant or recessive. We have only four seeds, from only hybrid cross available. If C is dominant, then, on the average, three out of four of the offspring will have C; if C is recessive, the long-run frequency with which it would appear in the offspring of a hybrid cross is $\frac{1}{4}$. Let the null hypothesis H_1 be the hypothesis of dominance, and H_2 be the hypothesis that C is recessive. Devise three tests of H_1, based on the results of planting the four seeds and observing whether or not the resultant plants have the characteristic C. Compute the size and power of each of these tests.

3. Suppose we are testing the null hypothesis H_1 that $\frac{1}{10}$ of the A's are also B's against the hypothesis H_2 that $\frac{2}{3}$ of the A's are B's. We may only take a sample of two A's. Devise a test of size 0.01. What is the power of this test? Suppose the alternative is not H_2, but the hypothesis H_3 that $\frac{1}{2}$ of the A's are B's. What is the power of the test against this hypothesis? Suppose the alternative is the complex hypothesis that more than $\frac{1}{10}$ of the A's are B's. What can we say about the power of the test in this case?

4. Suppose we are testing the hypothesis that a certain coin lands heads with a probability of $\frac{1}{2}$ against the alternative that it lands heads with the probability of $\frac{1}{4}$. Devise a test (it will require a mixed strategy) of size exactly equal to 0.10. What is the power of this test?

5. In the decision-theory example of the text, show that the following strategy is not admissible (i.e., that it is dominated by one of the strategies $S_0 \ldots S_5$, or by a mixture of two of them). The strategy is 'buy the lot if exactly one item is defective; otherwise do not buy it'.

6. In the decision-theory example show that the strategy 'buy the lot if and only if the first item is not defective' is not admissible.

7. In the decision-theory example, show that the strategy 'buy the lot if and only if either there are no defective items, or only the first item is defective, or only the second item is defective' is not admissible.

8. In the same example, show that to choose the strategy which will minimize the average expected regret is to choose the strategy which will minimize the average expected loss Show that this is true in general.

9. In the same example, given that the prior probability that $\frac{3}{4}$ of the items in the lot are defective is p, show that the strategy which minimizes the overall expected loss is the same as that which will minimize the overall expected regret. Show that this is true in general.

10. In the same example, for each admissible strategy, suggest *general* criteria which would lead to the choice of that strategy.

BIBLIOGRAPHICAL NOTES FOR CHAPTER 11

The beginnings of the modern theory of testing statistical hypotheses can be found in a number of papers by Jerzy Neyman and by Egon Pearson. Neyman's more recent views, in which he rejects altogether the term "inference" as applied to what statisticians do, and speaks instead of "inductive behavior," will be found in elementary form in his book *First Course in Probability and Statistics*, Henry Holt and Company, New York, 1950. A quite complete and up-to-date presentation of this theory is to be found in E. L. Lehman, *Testing Statistical Hypotheses*, John Wiley and Sons, New York, 1959.

An elementary introduction to decision theory that is highly readable and requires very little mathematics is *Elementary Decision Theory*, by Herman Chernoff and Lincoln Moses, John Wiley and Sons, New York, 1959. A more advanced book is David Blackwell and M. A. Girshick's *Theory of Games and Statistical Decisions*, John Wiley and Sons, New York, 1950. This latter book also contains a relatively technical and formal presentation of the principles of game theory. For a delightful and elementary exposition of game theory, see J. D. Williams, *The Compleat Strategyst*, McGraw-Hill, New York, 1953.

The classical work on statistical decision theory is Abraham Wald's *Statistical Decision Functions*, John Wiley and Sons, New York, 1950. The corresponding classic for game theory is the book by John von Neumann and Oskar Morgenstern, *Theory of Games and Economic Behavior*, Princeton University Press, Princeton, New Jersey, 1947.

One of Fisher's early works which sets forth his approach to statistical inference in a way which is not very contrary to the approach of Neyman and Pearson is his *The Design of Experiments*, (6th ed.), Oliver and Boyd, Edinburgh, 1951. A more recent and much more controversial, penetrating, and philosophical work is R. A. Fisher, *Statistical Methods and Scientific Inference*, London, 1956. In my paper

"Logical and Fiducial Probabilities," *Bulletin de l'Institute Internationale de Statistique* **40**, 1963, pp. 884–901, I attempt to show that, contrary to his explicit avowal, Fisher really entertained a logical conception of probability similar to my own. Finally, Ian Hacking's book *Logic of Statistical Inference*, Cambridge University Press, 1965, contains by a large margin the most sophisticated and competent attempt by a philosopher to found the theory of statistical inference on an empirical conception of "chances." Both it and Hacking's paper "Guessing by Frequency," *Proceedings of the Aristotelian Society*, n.s. LXIV, 1063–64, pp. 55–70 contain examples in which the classical approach has patent shortcomings.

12

Simplicity and the
Hypothetico-Deductive Method

The general scheme of the hypothetico-deductive method has been around for so long that it is hard, and probably inappropriate, to assign credit for it. John Dewey was one of its earliest defenders; indeed he defended it in a very general form, almost as a way of life. Morris R. Cohen and Ernest Nagel assigned to the hypothetico-deductive method, in their general logic text, a role that was less than universal; but it was still central to their discussion of scientific inference.

In recent years this approach to scientific inference has been followed, with variations, by Karl Popper, Stephen Barker, John O. Wisdom, and others. It consists, first of all, in the denial that "induction" is fundamental to scientific inference. It is to be suspected that these writers have something quite specific in mind when they anathematize induction; for example, the naïve view that science merely generalizes from concrete experience—what has been happening before will continue to happen. But no one, I think—at any rate no contemporary writer—seriously proposes that there is no more to science than this sort of feeble generalization, although there are many who, like Reichenbach, regard this form of inference as basic or fundamental. In its extreme form, this repudiation of induction is strengthened into a denial that there is any form of inference from experimental results to general scientific hypotheses, and that the contrary assertion is to be regarded as a regression into authoritarianism. On this view of scientific method what is fundamental is the free, unhindered construction of imaginative scientific hypotheses, on the one hand, and on the other, the subjection of these free creations to the most conscientious, rigorous, and severe tests we can devise.

One of the most attractive features of this view is its simplicity. There is no need to worry about the relation between a scientific hypothesis and the data that suggested it, because the source of a hypothesis is utterly irrelevant. Whether I arrive at H by observing nature, by observing a crystal ball, or by a combination of deep breathing and free association doesn't matter once the hypothesis is there. What matters is how well it stands up to tests. But the *logical* relationship between a hypothesis and the tests devised to put the hypothesis on trial is straightforwardly *deductive*: from H and boundary conditions and perhaps auxiliary hypotheses, a statement is deduced which can be directly tested. The relationship between a hypothesis and the tests we apply to it is *more* than logical, of course; the tests, to be significant, must represent our sincere attempts to refute the hypothesis. But this is a psychological matter, and offers nothing to the logician.

There are still problems for the logician to consider, however. For one thing, it is obvious that there will be in any stage of knowledge an infinite number of hypotheses that have not been refuted by experience. It is true that we may not have thought of them explicitly, but this seems to be accidental, and at any rate there is no doubt but that there are occasions when we explicitly consider a large number of hypotheses. We could say that in considering functional generalizations—when we seek the function that will relate pressure to temperature of a gas kept under constant volume, for example—there are an infinite number of possible laws we are considering, of which an infinite number will never be refuted whatever (finite) amount of evidence we have. Two kinds of criteria have been suggested for making a choice among not-yet-refuted hypotheses: simplicity and content.

According to some writers we should choose the *simplest* hypothesis that is in accord with the evidence (perhaps on the grounds that it is the most probable); while according to others we should choose the hypothesis that *says the most* (perhaps on the ground that it is the most falsifiable, i.e., the least probable!).

The most common view is that when we have to make a choice among unfalsified laws, we properly just choose the simplest. For the inductive logician, however, this merely raises the question as to what simplicity is and how it should be measured and compared. A number of proposals have been made in recent years concerning the definition and measurement of simplicity, ranging from the elegant proposal made by Svenonius to the rather simple-minded suggestion made by me. There are two sorts of proposals; some concern the logical simplicity of primitive extralogical vocabularies, and this seems to have relatively little to do directly with the problems of inductive logic. This is particularly so since the demonstration by Quine that in a language comfortably rich enough for science, the extralogical predicates can be reduced to a single two-place predicate. Other suggestions are directed at elucidating the relative simplicity of alternative hypotheses or theories within the same language. Harold Jeffreys, for example, offers a definition of simplicity for functional laws which depends on the number and type of parameters in the algebraic form of the law. Stephen Barker proposes a measure of simplicity which uses Kemeny's logical measure function, and which applies to theories: theory S is simpler than theory T if its logical measure is less than that of T, i.e., if for large enough n, T can be true of n things in more ways than S can. Note the connection to probability; measure corresponds to prior probability (on the logical interpretation), so that to say that S is simpler than T, on Barker's proposal, is just to say that its prior logical probability is less than that of T. At the same time, however, Barker, like Jeffreys, argues that we choose the simpler law or theory not just because it is simpler, but also because it is "most probably true." This is not as inconsistent as it sounds; Barker is not concerned with prior probability, but with posterior probability, when he says that the simpler hypothesis is the most probable, and he is anyway not employing a logical interpretation of probability at all when he says that the simplest hypothesis is the most *probably* true. However, observe that on any standard logical interpretation of probability, the posterior probability of a hypothesis S, relative to evidence E entailed by it, will be greater than the posterior probability of an alternative hypothesis T, relative to evidence E entailed by it, if and only if the prior probability of S is greater than the prior probability of T. That is,

$$c(S, E) > c(T, E) \quad \text{if and only if} \quad \frac{m(S \,\&\, E)}{m(E)} > \frac{m(T \,\&\, E)}{m(E)},$$

$$\text{and thus} \quad \text{if and only if} \quad m(S \,\&\, E) > m(T \,\&\, E).$$

Since E is entailed by S and by T,

$$m(S \,\&\, E) = m(S) \quad \text{and} \quad m(T \,\&\, E) = m(T).$$

Therefore,

$$c(S, E) > c(T, E) \quad \text{if and only if} \quad m(S) > m(T).$$

This result is perfectly general for all standard logical interpretations of probability. On the hypothetico-deductive reconstruction, the surviving hypothesis (i.e., the hypothesis that has not been refuted) which has the highest probability, relative to the evidence, is just that one of the surviving hypotheses whose *prior* probability was highest. Collecting evidence may refute some hypotheses altogether, but it cannot alter the probability ranking of the surviving alternative hypotheses.

The whole discussion of simplicity has been curiously inconclusive. Not only has there been no growing body of agreement concerning the measurement of simplicity, but there has been no agreement concerning the concept of simplicity for which we should seek a measure, or concerning the precise role that simplicity should play in the acceptance of scientific hypotheses. R. Harré has introduced a distinction which might help to explain some of the conflicts about simplicity: the distinction, reflected above, between *formal* and *conceptual* simplicity. Svenonius, Goodman, Kemeny, and Suppes have mainly been concerned with conceptual simplicity—the simplicity of the extralogical basis of the language of science. Jeffreys, Barker, and others have been concerned with the simplicity of various laws written within a given language. But even this useful distinction has not served to render the discussion more constructive and enlightening. For one thing, as Harré observes, formal and conceptual simplicity are not independent.

Karl Popper prefers to base the selection of a hypothesis from among those that have been proposed but not yet refuted on a principle of falsifiability rather than on a principle of simplicity. We should accept that hypothesis which will be most quickly eliminated by tests if it is false; i.e., the most falsifiable hypothesis, the hypothesis with the greatest content. But Popper also shows (Chapter 7) that falsifiability in this sense corresponds closely to our intuitive notion of simplicity. This correspondence leads to one of those curiously paradoxical-sounding conflicts that seem more prone to rise in inductive logic than in any other field. The conflict in this: Baker and Jeffreys claim that, given a choice, we should select the *most* probable hypothesis— 'most probable' corresponding to 'simplest'. Popper, on the other hand, claims that, given a choice, we should select the *least* probable hypothesis, on the grounds that it is the one easiest to test, and easiest to refute if it is in error (Jeffreys, *Scientific Inference*, p. 36). This conflict has been discussed by J. C. Harsanyi, who tends to side with Jeffreys by saying that while the most daring hypothesis may have a low prior probability, we should, after the evidence is in, prefer that hypothesis with the highest posterior probability. This resolution misses the point for three reasons: First, Popper does not regard the notion of posterior probability (Carnap's degree of confirmation) a useful one; second, as established above, within the hypothetico-deductive framework, the unrefuted hypothesis most probable *a posteriori* is just the unrefuted hypothesis most probable *a priori*; and third, the hypothesis with the highest posterior probability is simply that which describes what *has happened* (i.e., just describes the evidence E) and leaves the whole future course of events undetermined. But this hypothesis would be selected by no one.

Indeed the most interesting thing about this entire conflict is that neither Barker, Popper, Jeffreys, nor any other inductive logician or analyst of scientific procedure would have any difficulty at all in deciding what hypothesis to accept in an ordinary experimental situation. This suggests that the very hypothesis 'most probable' for Jeffreys is precisely that which is 'least probable' for Popper. There are a number of factors that may be involved here. Jeffreys is supposing that we have a list of possible general laws which might possibly govern occurrences of a certain sort. Thus he does not even consider the laws Popper regards as trivially 'most probable'—i.e., laws going only slightly or not at all beyond our observations. Furthermore, Jeffreys is using Bayes' Theorem, according to which the probability of the hypothesis on the given evidence is equal to the probability of the evidence on the hypothesis (1, on the hypothetico-deductive model), multiplied by the ratio of the *a priori* probability of the hypothesis to the *a priori* probability of the evidence. Disregarding the *a priori* probability of the hypothesis, we obtain a partial reconciliation of the two views by observing that to say that the hypothesis is highly falsifiable is to say that the *a priori* probability of the evidence is very small. But this is just (part of) what Jeffreys says: the posterior probability, and hence desirability, of a hypothesis is proportional to the reciprocal of the probability of the evidence. Even the ranking of laws in order of simplicity is roughly the same on the two views: a straight-line relationship is highly falsifiable (and highly improbable) on Popper's view, and in general a theory involving a small number of parameters will be less probable than one involving a great number of parameters (pp. 380–381). For Jeffreys, the theory with the fewer adjustable parameters is both more probable and simpler. Other things being equal, then, the simplest law on both views is the one with the lowest number of parameters.

The major, and the only serious, conflict between the two views is that expressed by Popper's refusal to identify corroboration with posterior probability. This refusal is based on his denial that we choose the most probable hypothesis, and his assertion that we accept the hypothesis that has the greatest content and that has stood up to the most severe tests and the most sincere attempts to refute it. Of course, this conception of scientific acceptability raises certain problems, as Popper's critics have been quick to point out. D. C. Stove argues that these psychological characterizations of what constitutes a test of a hypothesis (it must be "sincere", an "attempt to falsify", etc.) are quite irrelevant to the matter of evidential import: "To suppose otherwise would be to let differences of intention between two persons who subjected the same theory to the same test affect the question of the support, if any, which passing the test gives to the theory." Then there is the question of whether 'test' is to be understood in a generic sense: if so, then we may ask, as G. J. Warnock does, why passing one application of a test should convince us that a theory will pass subsequent applications of the same test; and if not, why we should believe that it will pass different tests. P. C. Gibbons rejects the notion that there can be any useful ordering of tests into more and less severe. Popper himself admits that the requirement of sincerity cannot be formalized. This will become clear in the discussion of the paradoxes of confirmation; even J. W. N. Watkins admits that there are circumstances in which the observation of a white shoe constitutes a "test" of the hypothesis that all ravens are black. And R. H. Vincent has shown that Popper's criteria, like everyone else's, founder on Goodman's reef.

All of this psychologism is distasteful to the logician who is looking for the timeless quality of evidential power. Furthermore, everyone does in fact recognize differences in the degree to which hypotheses have been tested and stood up to the tests. Not all advocates of the hypothetico-deductive method agree that the problem of distinguishing between well-supported hypotheses and highly speculative ones is a serious one, but Popper, for example, has taken it seriously enough to offer a definition of 'degree of corroboration' to explicate the distinction. In fact, he offers two definitions, and a number of other writers have also offered definitions of analogous concepts—degree of factual support, degree of plausible implications, and so on. All of these definitions make use of a probabilistic measure function defined over the sentences of a language. It is additive, it has a maximum value 1, and so on.

Popper's formulas are presented in a series of three notes in the *British Journal for the Philosophy of Science*. In the first of these articles he defines the degree of explanatory of x, with respect to a body of evidence y, $E(x, y)$, as

$$E(x, y) = \frac{P(y, x) - P(y)}{P(y, x) + P(y)},$$

where $P(x)$ is the logical measure of x, and $P(y, x)$ is the conditional measure of y, given x, i.e., $P(y, x) = P(x \ \& \ y)/P(x)$. This definition is very nearly the same as that used by Kemeny and Oppenheim for degree of factual support. For Popper it is only a starting point; he goes on to define the degree of corroboration of x given by y, $C(x, y)$, as

$$C(x, y) = E(x, y) \ [1 + P(x) P(x, y)]$$

and shows that this function satisfies all the conditions of adequacy he has laid down for degree of corroboration.

Both the concept of explanatory power and the concept of degree of corroboration may be relativized to a statement z (a statement of background knowledge, for example). The explanatory power of the hypothesis x, with respect to the evidence y, in the presence of z, $E(x, y, z)$, is defined as

$$E(x, y, z) = \frac{P(y, x \ \& \ z) - P(y, z)}{P(y, x \ \& \ z) + P(y, z)},$$

and $C(x, y, z)$, the degree of corroboration of hypothesis x, by evidence y, in the presence of background knowledge z, is defined as

$$C(x, y, z) = E(x, y, z)[1 + P(x, z) P(x, y \,\&\, z)].$$

Popper later discovered that his desiderata could be satisfied by a simpler formula:

$$C(x, y) = \frac{P(y, x) - P(y)}{P(y, x) - P(x \,\&\, y) + P(y)}.$$

Isaac Levi argues that considerations of epistemic utility (about which more in the last chapter), in particular the principle that the utilities involved in accepting or not accepting scientific hypotheses be independent of the evidence for the hypothesis, are violated by Popper's notion of degree of confirmation, if that is taken as a guide to acceptance of scientific hypotheses. Instead, Levi offers the very simple utility assignments $P(\sim x)$ for the utility of accepting x when it is true; and $-P(x)$ for the utility of accepting x when it is false. Using these as utilities, we calculate the expectation of accepting hypothesis x on the basis of evidence y to be

$$U(x, y) = P(x, y) P(\sim x) - P(\sim x, y) P(x).$$

Another proposal along the same lines has been made by Kemeny and Oppenheim. Again a logical measure function m, giving each state description in a definite language a weight, is presumed to be on hand. Kemeny and Oppenheim lay down ten conditions which an adequate theory of factual support should, on their view, satisfy. The fourth condition, for example, concerns logically equivalent hypotheses and logically equivalent evidences: If $\vdash H \equiv H'$ and $\vdash E \equiv E'$, then $F(H, E) = F(H', E')$, i.e., the degree of factual support given H by E will be the same as that given H' by E'. The sixth condition stipulates that F is to be a function of the following measures only: $m(H, E)$, $(H, \bar{E})$, $m(\bar{H}, E)$, and $m(\bar{H}, \bar{E})$. Having laid down conditions of adequacy, they look for the simplest function of the measures mentioned in the sixth condition that will satisfy the other nine conditions as well. The result is surprising and interesting. The function p which assigns to each state description the same measure (the "Wittgensteinian" measure function) is introduced as an auxiliary function; it is related to the general measure function m by a certain number q. In the final formula, if the m-functions are expressed in terms of q and the p-functions, all the q's cancel out, and we are left with

$$F(H, E) = \frac{p(E, H) - p(E, \bar{H})}{p(E, H) + p(E, \bar{H})}$$

for the degree of factual support lent H by the evidence E.

Nicholas Rescher also provides us with a formal concept of degree of evidential support. He defines the degree of evidential support that the evidence q gives to the hypothesis p, $des(p, q)$, by reference to a logical measure function L, as follows:

$$des(p, q) = \frac{L(p, q) - L(p)}{1 - L(p)} L(q).$$

Henry A. Finch has also dealt with the problem of the relation between the confirming power of observations among hypotheses. He works from the point of view of modern decision theory and from the point of view of information theory, and comes to the conclusion that the crucial quantity in confirming power is

$$\frac{Pr(o|h)}{Pr(o)} - 1,$$

where o is an observation statement, h a hypothesis, and Pr a logical measure function related to information content. The displayed quantity is the measure of the power of o to confirm or disconfirm h.

Just to make the picture complete, Carnap's measure of *increase of confirmation* of a hypothesis h by evidence e, over the *a priori* probability of h, should also be mentioned; expressed in terms of a confirmation function c, this is

$$c(h, e) - c(h).$$

Although it seems as if we have an enormous variety of concepts being offered here, Table VII shows that this impression is largely erroneous. In compiling the table, I have rendered the notation uniform, representing by 'P' the logical measure function presupposed by all the measures of corroboration. I have also performed some algebraic manipulations (supposing that $P(x)$ is never 0), and arranged the resulting factors in columns.

The function recommended by each author is the product of the entries in the corresponding row of the table. The factors in column 1 reflect the differences between the probability of the evidence, given the hypothesis, and either the *a priori* probability of the evidence (in six instances) or the probability of the evidence given the negation of the hypothesis (in two instances). Three of the authors include $P(h)$ as a factor; Popper 1b includes $(1 + P(h) \times P(h, e))$—which is monotonically increasing in $P(h)$—as a factor. Two authors (one of whom also includes $P(h)$ as a factor) include the reciprocal of $P(\bar{h})$ as a factor; the reciprocal of $P(\bar{h})$ is also a monotonically increasing function of $P(h)$. Column 4, finally, contains terms reflecting the improbability of the evidence. In three cases, the factor is simply the reciprocal of the *a priori* probability of the evidence; for Popper's three formulas it is the reciprocal of

TABLE VII

Author	1	2	3	4
Carnap	$P(e, h) - P(e)$	$P(h)$	1	$\dfrac{1}{P(e)}$
Rescher	$P(e, h) - P(e)$	$P(h)$	$\dfrac{1}{P(\bar{h})}$	1
Popper 1a	$P(e, h) - P(e)$	1	1	$\dfrac{1}{P(e, h) + P(e)}$
Popper 1b	$P(e, h) - P(e)$	$1 + P(h)P(h, e)$		$\dfrac{1}{P(e, h) + P(e)}$
Popper 2	$P(e, h) - P(e)$	1	$\dfrac{1}{P(\bar{h})}$	$\dfrac{1}{P(e, h) + P(e)}$
Finch	$P(e, h) - P(e)$	1	1	$\dfrac{1}{P(e)}$
Kemeny–Oppenheim	$P(e, h) - P(e, \bar{h})$	1	1	$\dfrac{1}{P(e, h) + P(e, \bar{h})}$
Levi	$P(e, h) - P(e, \bar{h})$	$P(h)$	$P(\bar{h})$	$\dfrac{1}{P(e)}$

an expression, $(P(e, h) + P(e))$, which is plainly an increasing function of $P(e)$; and the same may be seen to be true of the factor used by Kemeny and Oppenheim, if we notice that

$$P(e, h) + P(e, \bar{h}) = P(e)\left(\frac{P(h, e)}{P(h)} + \frac{P(\bar{h}, e)}{P(\bar{h})}\right)$$

or that $P(e) = P(h)\, P(e, h) + P(\bar{h})\, P(e, h)$, so that $P(e, h) + P(e, \bar{h})$ is just the unweighted average of the quantity of which $P(e)$ is the weighted average.

A novel definition of information is discussed by Håkan Tornebohm, in "Two Measures of Evidential Strength." One of these measures is the ordinary Bayesian conditional probability; the other is a novel information-theoretic measure. The novel measure is the following (p. 83):

$$\frac{\log P(H|E) - \log P(H)}{-\log P(H)}.$$

As a basis for choice among hypotheses, this is obviously similar to those discussed in the table. By simple transformations, we can convert it to

$$\frac{\log P(E|H) - \log P(E)}{-\log P(H)}.$$

Since $\log P(A)$ is monotonically increasing in $P(A)$, the numerator corresponds to the kind of factor listed in column 1 of the table: it increases as $P(E, H)$

increases, and it increases as $P(E)$ decreases. (Observe, however, that $\log P(E|H) - \log P(E)$ is not generally monotonically increasing in $P(E|H) - P(E)$.) The denominator is decreasing in $P(H)$; since $P(\overline{H}) = 1 - P(H)$, the denominator is monotonically increasing in $P(\overline{H})$ and thus represents the kind of factor listed in column 3 of the table.

In any event, it is easy to see that most of these authors, despite the occasional polemics they exchange, have just about the same criteria in mind for the acceptance (or serious consideration) of a scientific hypothesis. It is all the more significant, then, that no one, not even the authors themselves, seem to take these measures very seriously. They point to interesting factors involved in the judicious evaluation of hypotheses, but they are more like an empirical reflection of what we do do than like a logical explanation of why we do it or why we should do it.

EXERCISES

1. In what respects is the Ptolemaic theory, according to which the sun, the stars, and the planets, revolve about the earth, simpler than the Copernican theory, according to which the sun and the stars remain fixed? And in what respects might the Ptolemaic theory be regarded as simpler than the Copernican?

2. Given experimentally a number of pairs of value (time, distance; pressure, volume; etc.), the scientist wishes to choose a function $y = f(x)$ which will be satisfied by those pairs of values he has experimentally determined, but which will also, in addition to representing the pairs of values he already has, serve to enable him to predict new pairs of values. Given any finite number of pairs of values, however, there are an infinite number of functions which are satisfied by them. On what grounds does the scientist pick one function out of this infinite supply? Explain.

3. Is the function chosen under the circumstances of problem 2 chosen because it is more probable than any other? Because it is simpler? Because it is the simplest of all those which are most probable? Because it is the most probable of all those which are most simple? Discuss.

4. When a scientist has a number of pairs of values (say of pressure and volume of a fixed quantity of gas) and claims that they support a particular law (say, Boyle's law that the product of pressure and volume is constant at given temperature for a given quantity of gas), it is almost never the case that any of these pairs of values satisfies his chosen function exactly. Furthermore, there always do exist functions (perhaps complicated functions) which are *exactly* satisfied by his values. Why does he choose the particular function he does?

5. The murderer of Lord Burncastle was clearly one of those gathered in the parlor: the spoiled son and heir; the irascible great aunt; or the butler Williams. At a certain stage in the investigation, Scotland Yard assessed the probabilities that each of these three had committed the crime at (in

order) 0.6, 0.3, and 0.1. An excited under-inspector burst into the room with the startling news that clutched in Lord Burncastle's dead hand were Williams' false teeth. The probability that if the murderer were other than Williams, Williams' false teeth would be found under such circumstances is extremely small—say 0.05. On the other hand, even if Williams did commit the crime, the probability that he would leave his teeth under such circumstances is small—say, 0.4. What is the degree of corroboration or factual support of each of the hypotheses as to the identity of the murderer, relative to this new piece of evidence, on each of the views described in the text? What is the new probability of each of these hypotheses?

6. Suppose we consider four hypotheses, with prior probabilities as tabulated below, and we wish to evaluate these hypotheses by reference to some evidence e whose prior probability is $\frac{1}{4}$; the conditional probabilities of e, given each hypothesis, are also tabulated below. Compute the degree to which e supports each hypothesis according to the formulas discussed in the text. Also compute the posterior probability of each hypothesis.

$$P(H_1) = \tfrac{1}{2} \quad P(e|H_1) = \tfrac{1}{3}$$
$$P(H_2) = \tfrac{2}{3} \quad P(e|H_2) = \tfrac{1}{2}$$
$$P(H_3) = \tfrac{3}{4} \quad P(e|H_3) = \tfrac{1}{6}$$
$$P(H_4) = \tfrac{1}{4} \quad P(e|H_4) = \tfrac{3}{4}$$

(Note that these hypotheses are not logically exclusive; but that is the typical scientific situation.)

BIBLIOGRAPHICAL NOTES FOR CHAPTER 12

John Dewey's writings are often difficult, largely because of his style, for the modern reader. His most unified treatment of scientific inference will be found in *Logic: the Theory of Inquiry*, Henry Holt and Co., New York, 1938. See also his *Essays in Experimental Logic*, Dover Publications, New York, 1953. Morris R. Cohen's and Ernest Nagel's fine logic book, embodying the best of Dewey's ideas in a coherent and relatively formal framework, is *An Introduction to Logic and Scientific Method*, Harcourt, Brace and World, New York, 1934. There is a reprint of the deductive logic part of that book, but the reprint contains none of the "scientific method" sections.

Karl Popper's views are largely to be found in his *The Logic of Scientific Discovery*, Hutchinson, London, 1959. This book is an English translation of his *Logik der Forschung* (1934), but it contains much added material, notably the articles on corroboration mentioned above. For other expressions of Popper's views on science and scientific inference, see his collection of papers *Conjectures and Refutations*, Routledge and Kegan Paul, London, 1963. Stephen Barker's views on this subject are expressed in greatest detail in his *Induction and Hypothesis*, Cornell University Press, Ithaca, New York, 1957. The work of John O. Wisdom referred to is *Foundations of Inference in Natural Science*, Methuen, London, 1952.

J. Agassi's polemics in support of Popper's view are to be found in

"Corroboration versus Induction," *British Journal for the Philosophy of Science* **9**, 1958–59.

On simplicity, besides the work of Barker already cited, we have Nelson Goodman, "New Notes on Simplicity," *Journal of Symbolic Logic* **17**, 1952, pp. 189–91; "Axiomatic Measurement of Simplicity," *Journal of Philosophy* **52**, 1955, pp. 709–22; and "Recent Developments in the Theory of Simplicity," *Philosophy and Phenomenological Research* **19**, 1958–59, pp. 429–46; John G. Kemeny, "Two Measures of Complexity," *Journal of Philosophy* **52**, 1955, pp. 722–33, and *A Philosopher Looks at Science*, D. van Nostrand, Princeton, New Jersey, 1959; Patrick Suppes, "Nelson Goodman on the Concept of Logical Simplicity," *Philosophy of Science* **23**, 1956, pp. 153–59; Lars Svenonius, "Definability and Simplicity," *Journal of Symbolic Logic* **20**, 1955, pp. 235–50; Kyburg, "A Modest Proposal Concerning Simplicity," *Philosophical Review* **70**, 1961, pp. 390–95; R. Ackermann, "Some Remarks on Kyburg's Modest Proposal," *Philosophical Review* **71**, 1962, pp. 236–40; and Harold Jeffreys, *Scientific Inference*, Cambridge University Press, 1937, 1957.

John C. Harsanyi's attempt to make peace between probabilists and improbabilists is "Popper's Improbability Criterion for the Choice of Scientific Hypothesis," *Philosophy* **35**, 1960, pp. 332–40. Other comments on Popper's views are: D. C. Stove, review of Popper's, *Logic of Scientific Discovery*, *Australasian Journal of Philosophy* **38**, 1960, pp. 173–87; G. J. Warnock, review of Popper's, *Logic of Scientific Discovery*, *Mind* **69**, 1960, pp. 99–101; P. C. Gibbons, "On the Severity of Tests," *Australasian Journal of Philosophy* **40**, 1962, pp. 79–82. J. W. N. Watkins' comment on black ravens and white shoes comes from a long exchange of articles that will be referred to in the next chapter, as they are concerned mainly with the paradoxes of Carnapian confirmation theory; and R. H. Vincent's comment comes from "Popper on Qualitative Confirmation and Disconfirmation," *Australasian Journal of Philosophy* **40**, 1962, pp. 159–66.

Isaac Levi's compelling demonstration that Popper's corroboration concept lies in the face of ordinary conventions about utility (though it does presuppose what Popper would no doubt deny, that it makes sense at all to talk of epistemic utilities) is "Corroboration and Rules of Acceptance," *British Journal for the Philosophy of Science* **13**, 1962–63, pp. 307–13. The paper by John Kemeny and Paul Oppenheim referred to is "Degree of Factual Support," *Philosophy of Science* **19**, 1952, pp. 307–24. Rescher's formalization of the concept under discussion here is to be found in "Theory of Evidence," *Philosophy of Science* **25**, 1958, pp. 83–94; a shorter and later piece that is also relevant is his "Plausible Implication," *Analysis* **21**, 1960–61, pp. 128–35. Henry A. Finch's detailed discussion of the matter is "Confirming Power of Observations Metricized for Decisions Among Hypotheses," *Philosophy of Science* **27**, 1960, pp. 293–307, 391–404. Rudolf Carnap's corresponding formula for increase of confirmation is taken from the preface to the second edition of his *The Logical Foundations of Probability*, 2nd edition, University of Chicago Press, Chicago, 1962 (1st edition 1950). Håkan Tornebohm's article "Two Measures of Evidential Strength" appears in *Aspects of Inductive Logic* (Hintikka and Suppes, eds.), North-Holland, Amsterdam, 1966, pp. 81–95. In the same volume Jaakko Hintikka and Juhani Pietarinen ("Semantic Information and Inductive Logic" pp. 96–112) also discuss various measures of information content, and conclude that the only appropriate one is $P(H|E) - P(E)$, which is just Carnap's proposal.

13

Confirmation Theories

The inductive logic that is associated with either the logical or the sub-jectivistic interpretation of probability is gratifyingly simple: everything hinges on the use of Bayes' Theorem; the degree of confirmation, the probability, of a hypothesis H, relative to the total body of evidence we have at our disposal, E, is just

$$\frac{P(H \ \& \ E)}{P(E)}.$$

For the subjectivist the problem remains of evaluating these prior probabilities $P(H \ \& \ E)$ and $P(E)$; it is possible to evaluate someone's degree of belief in terms of his preferences, but as Isaac Levi has pointed out, preferences

165

can often be just as vague and confused as degrees of belief. This is just to say that the difficulties of an inductive logic based on the subjectivistic interpretation of probability are just the difficulties of that interpretation itself. There remain, of course, a large number of practical problems—soluble ones —in the actual application of the theory; but these are primarily statistical problems rather than theoretical or philosophical problems.

The logical interpretation of the probability calculus has always been developed with the idea in mind of removing—by stipulations and conventions, if need be—the vaguenesses and confusions that surround inductive inference. But possibly as a consequence of this very clarity and precision, the logicist program for inductive logic is open to counterexamples and paradoxes.

The oddities that are referred to as the "paradoxes of confirmation" were first noted by Janina Hosiasson-Lindenbaum in 1940; they were christened by Carl Hempel in 1945. Consider the statement 'all ravens are black'. Anyone who believes in a logic of confirmation at all would regard the observation of a black raven to be a (possibly slight) confirmation of this statement. One of the most natural properties of confirmation is that if a sentence S confirms a sentence T, and T is logically equivalent to T', then S confirms T' as well, and indeed to the same degree. Now 'all ravens are black' is logically equivalent to 'all non-black things are non-ravens', so the observation of a white shoe, which confirms the latter generalization in the same way that the observation of a black raven confirms the former, will also confirm 'all ravens are black'. Finally, the original hypothesis can be expressed: 'Everything is either a raven, or else it is not black'; and it is not hard to show that this hypothesis is confirmed by any observation of an object that is black (whether it is a raven or a cat or any other thing) as well as by any observation of an object that is not a raven (regardless of its color). Thus as confirming instances for the law that all ravens are black, we have one sensible sort of instance, a black raven, and two paradoxical sorts of instances, e.g., a white shoe, and a black cat.

J. W. N. Watkins recently offered this paradox as an argument against an inductivist view of the distinction between analytic and empirical statements ("Between Analytic and Empirical"). In answer, Hempel admitted ("Empirical Statements and Falsifiability") that these consequences of confirmation theory are "intuitively paradoxical," but insisted that they are "systematically unobjectionable." This is the tack taken by Hosiasson-Lindenbaum in her early article, and the tack Hempel himself took in his "On Studies in the Logic of Confirmation" in 1945. In his answer to Watkins, Hempel also pointed out that perfectly analogous consequences arise on the Popper–Watkins theory of falsification. A white shoe can perfectly well be regarded as the outcome of an attempt to falsify the theory that all ravens are black: when I first looked, I thought it was a raven, even though it was white, but then when I examined it, I saw that it was a shoe. The argument was carried on by Israel Scheffler, who attacked Watkins' arguments and finally pointed out that the disagreement may have stemmed from the fact that Hempel is not offering methodological prescriptions, while Popper is. Another exchange was instigated by D. C. Stove (mentioned earlier) who tried to throw some light on the argument by distinguishing between the pragmatic notion of a *test* and the logical (better, "semantical") notion of *evidence*. The "attempt" to falsify the hypothesis that all ravens are black by examining white shoes is obviously futile on anybody's theory, but "the *attempts* that might be made to falsify or instantially confirm a hypothesis are quite irrelevant to the weight of the evidence, if any, resulting from such attempts" ("Popperian Confirmation and the Paradox of the Ravens"). H. Gavin Alexander also observed that the Watkins–Popper theory of falsification was subject to the same paradoxes as the theory of confirmation, but he pointed out that if we take account of our background knowledge we can save confirmation theory by looking at the matter quantitatively; following Hosiasson-Lindenbaum, he pointed out that since we know that most things in the world aren't ravens, the observation of a white shoe is not going to confirm 'all ravens are black' as much as the observation of a black raven will.

The recent discussion was admirably summed up by J. L. Mackie, who traced the whole argument and came to much the sort of conclusion one would expect. Given a complete lack of background knowledge, Hempel is perfectly correct, and a white shoe, a black cat, and a black raven will all confirm the generalization 'all ravens are black'. Given merely some knowledge about the relative numbers of black objects and ravens and non-black objects and non-ravens, the bite may be taken out of the paradox by quantitative considerations as Hosiasson-Lindenbaum, Alexander, I. J. Good, and Patrick Suppes (the latter two from a subjectivistic point of view) all show. And if we allow unlimited background knowledge to give meaning to the notion of a *test*, the observations of black ravens and non-black non-ravens confirm the generalization to a worthwhile degree only if they are made in a genuine test.

A recent article by G. H. von Wright has done much to clarify the relation between the confirmation of instances of universally quantified generalizations and the equivalence condition which stipulates that if two formulas are logically equivalent they should be confirmed by the same instances. Von Wright introduces the concept of a *range of relevance* of a generalization; it is the set of entities which the generalization is being construed as being *about*. Thus the classical generalization about ravens may be construed as a generalization simply *about* ravens, or as a generalization *about* birds or as a generalization about all things whatever. "The generalization that all ravens are black is a different generalization, when it is about ravens and ravens only, and when it is about birds and birds only, and when it is—if it ever is—about all things in the world unrestrictedly" (p. 216). On the basis of very simple axioms for confirmation (or inductive probability) von Wright shows that since the probability that something from outside the range of the generalization will not refute the generalization is maximal (1), it will lead to no increase in degree of confirmation of the generalization. On the other hand, anything within the range of relevance of the generalization, even if it is not a raven, will contribute to its confirmation. The *natural* range of relevance of a generalization is just the set of things to which the antecedent term applies—in the case of 'all ravens are black', it is the set of ravens; in the case of 'all non-black things are non-ravens', it is the completely distinct set of non-black things. Within the natural range of relevance of 'all ravens are black', the only kinds of instances that confirm the generalization are ravens that are black.

Another way of achieving the same result is to construe all generalizations as essentially statistical generalizations—though of a limiting form—about a subject matter corresponding to von Wright's range of relevance. In the case of statistical generalizations, there is no contraposition: from 'nearly all A's and B's' one cannot infer (even probabilistically) 'nearly all non-B's are non-A's'. If we construe 'all ravens are black' as the limiting form of a generalization like 'nearly all ravens are black', then clearly only ravens are relevant to the generalization. If, on the other hand, we construe the same generalization as being implicitly about birds in general, then it is the limiting form of quite a different statistical generalization, namely 'nearly all birds are such that they are not nonblack ravens'. To confirm this generalization, we not only may but should examine birds of various other feathers, as well as ravens.

In all of this there is an element which does not meet the eye when one encounters a generalization running around loose in a philosopher's garden. When we consider a generalization apart from the body of knowledge of which it is a part, it is difficult to know that the *intended* range or relevance is, or what statistical hypothesis the generalization is a generalization and purification of. On the other hand, it is possible, within a specific area of inquiry, to be quite clear what the background statistical assertion concerned. In all of this there is a vast improvement over the oversimplification and artificiality that Max Black has complained of in the classical discussions of the paradoxes of confirmation.

Another paradox engendered by the logicist interpretation of probability, which also arises for the subjectivist interpretation, is the paradox of ideal evidence. This has been discussed both by Karl Popper and by R. H. Vincent ("The Paradox of Ideal Evidence"). Let a be the assertion that a particular toss of a given coin yields heads. It is clear that in the absence of any knowledge at all the *a priori* probability of a may plausibly be supposed to be $\frac{1}{2}$. Now let us subject the coin to extensive tests, and suppose that (say on the basis of a million tosses) we become very sure that the relative frequency of heads is $\frac{1}{2} \pm \epsilon$. Let the body of evidence for this assertion be E. Then the probability of a given E is also $\frac{1}{2}$. Therefore the examination of a million tosses of the coin is utterly irrelevant to a. This is clearly paradoxical. The problem here is that of finding a way to take account of the weight of the evidence, but according to Popper this cannot be done in view of the fact that "the fundamental postulate of the subjective theory [confirmation theory] is the postulate that degrees of the rationality of beliefs in the light of evidence exhibit a linear order" (p. 408).

Although this is a serious difficulty for most theories of degrees of confirmation, it is not as decisive as Popper makes it sound. These theories always contain, as an extraformal requirement, a principle of total evidence which demands that if we have information about the behavior (or structure) of the coin, we use it; this may be taken as a principle demanding that we maximize the weight of evidence; this is intended in the sense that we should use all the information we have, not in the sense that we should go on collecting information indefinitely. The question of when to stop gathering information is a pragmatic one, and one that has been considered by relatively few statisticians and almost no philosophers. It could also be maintained that there is no behavioristic way of distinguishing between the two situations Popper describes: one would, in either case, be willing to wager on the truth of a at even money. If there is no way of distinguishing them behavioristically, then there is no point in distinguishing them epistemologically.

Another reply to Popper is that although the logical (or subjectivistic) theory will lead to the same behavior with respect to a bet on a *single* toss of an untested coin as on a *single* toss of a thoroughly tested coin, the two situations are easily distinguished in the logical or subjectivistic theory when it comes to a bet on a sequence of tosses. If the coin is well tested, the probability of heads on a given toss will be relatively insensitive to what has happened on previous tosses, and the probability, say, of ten heads in a row will be very close to $(\frac{1}{2})^{10} = \frac{1}{1024}$. On the other hand, if the coin is untested, the probability of heads on a given toss may depend a lot on what has happened on earlier tosses. Given that a coin has yielded heads on each of its first nine tosses, and that that's all we know about the coin, we may be tempted (properly!) to take the probability of heads on the tenth toss to be close to 1, rather than close to $\frac{1}{2}$. Thus the probability of ten heads in a row, for the untested coin, will be much greater than $\frac{1}{1024}$. Thus we can, after all, given a body of beliefs about the behavior of a coin, distinguish between the body of beliefs based upon lack of knowledge and the body of beliefs based on ideal evidence.

This answer, however, leads directly to another difficulty already alluded to in Chapter 6 in connection with the subjectivistic interpretation of probability. Our purely *a priori* probabilities may lead us to assign very high probabilities to very powerful empirical statements; e.g., the *a priori* probability that less than 10% of the balls drawn from an urn in an infinitely long sequence of trials will be purple might be over 0.99. More specifically, this result follows from the assumption that the draws are regarded as *exchangeable* (the probability of drawing a particular sequence of purple and nonpurple balls depends only on the number of purple balls in the sequence); that the prior probability that a ball will be purple is 0.01; and that the conditional probability that the second ball will be purple, given that the first ball is purple, is 0.02. Again the logicist will point to the principle of total evidence and remind us that as soon as we collect empirical evidence, the *a priori* probability statement becomes academic and irrelevant. But one may well wonder why, in the face of such high prior probabilities, one should bother to find evidence. Particularly if one takes an epistemological view, according to which probability should serve as a guide to rational belief, something seems to have gone awry. The discussion still goes on. Further references will be found in the bibliographical notes to this chapter.

The next paradox arises, like the classical one of the white shoes and the black ravens, from a conflict between our intuitive assessments of probability and our lightning calculations of degrees of confirmation. R. H. Vincent uses it to attempt to show that no plausible theory of confirmation can accept the multiplication axiom ("A Note on Some Quantitative Theories of Confirmation"). Let q consist of a hypothesis (such as Newton's laws) together with boundary conditions sufficient to entail p, where p is the statement, 'A freely falling body near the earth will fall 144 feet in 3 seconds'. Since q entails p, the conjunction of q and p is equivalent to p, and (writing $c(x, y)$ for the degree of confirmation of x given y)

$$c(p \ \& \ q, r) = c(q, r)$$

According to the multiplication axiom,

$$c(p \ \& \ q, r) = c(p, r) \times c(q, p \ \& \ r)$$

or

$$c(p, r) = \frac{c(q, r)}{c(q, p \ \& \ r)}$$

Since p cannot alone contribute much to the confirmation of q, $c(q, p \ \& \ r) \approx c(q, r)$ and $c(p, r) \approx 1$. In other words, under the circumstances outlined, it is practically certain, in the absence of Newton's laws, that a freely falling body near the earth will fall 144 feet in 3 seconds!

A numerical example shows that the conclusion is not valid, and that its paradoxical air results from thinking loosely about numbers. I borrow the example from Vincent, making it only slightly more specific. He says that if q is 'all balls in urn U are red' and p is 'the first three balls drawn are red', then by the above argument p will be practically certain relative to our background knowledge. But assuming the equiprobability of structure descriptions (because the cards would be stacked in our favor if we used the hypothesis of equiprobable state descriptions), and assuming that we have five balls in the urn, we have

$$c(p, r) = \tfrac{3}{10} \quad \text{(drawing with replacement)}$$
$$c(p, q \ \& \ r) = 1$$
$$c(q, p \ \& \ r) = \tfrac{5}{9}$$
$$c(q, r) = \tfrac{1}{6}$$

so that

$$c(p, r) = \tfrac{3}{10} = \frac{c(q, r)}{c(q, p \,\&\, r)} = \frac{\tfrac{1}{6}}{\tfrac{5}{9}}.$$

To say that if the number of balls were larger so that $c(q, p \,\&\, r)$ were closer to $c(q, r)$ we would find more of a paradox is false: $c(q, r)$ and $c(q \,\&\, r)$ will both decrease, but their ratio need not at all approach unity; indeed on the supposition of equiprobable structure descriptions it will *decrease*.

Here is a last paradox that is regarded by Popper as an out-and-out contradiction in Carnap's system. The paradox is that

> "There are cases in which x is strongly supported by z and y is strongly undermined by z, while at the same time x is confirmed by z to a lesser degree than is y" (p. 390).

For example, if x is the statement that a six will turn up on the next throw of a die, and y is the statement that some number other than six will turn up, and z is the statement that an even number has turned up, then z increases the probability of x and decreases that of y, while at the same time confirming x less than it confirms y:

$$\begin{aligned} c(x) &= \tfrac{1}{6} & c(x, z) &= \tfrac{1}{3} \\ c(y) &= \tfrac{5}{6} & c(y, z) &= \tfrac{2}{3} \end{aligned}$$

while

$$c(x, z) < c(y, z)$$

Popper claims that this is a self-contradictory state of affairs, for he claims that it is always self-contradictory to say that "x has the property P ... and y has not the property P and y has the property P in a higher degree than x" (p. 391).

This is a valid objection to Carnap's way of talking, for Carnap himself claimed that the statement 'a is warm and b is not warm and b is warmer than a' was self-contradictory, and the statement about confirmation sounds the same. In fact, however, it is not the same, and the similarity stems from a confusion in the *informal* characterization of the classificatory concept of confirmation. This confusion is cleared up in the preface to the new edition of the *Logical Foundation of Probability*, where Carnap distinguishes two distinct triples of concepts, neither of which allows Popper's paradox.

Firmness	Increase in Firmness
1 h is firm on e.	h is made firmer by i.
2 h on e is firmer than h' on e'.	h is made firmer by i than h' is by i'.
3 The degree of firmness of h on e is u.	The increase in firmness of h by i is u.

Each of these concepts admits of a simple and obvious explication in terms of confirmation functions. The paradox observed by Popper only arose through Carnap's mistaken selection of (1) under *increase in firmness* and (2) and (3) under *firmness* as a triple of concepts analogous to 'warm' 'warmer', and 'of such and such a temperature'. It is not the case, of course, that x can be firm on z, and y not firm on z, and y firmer on z than is x on z. One of the most serious-sounding objections to the basic idea of confirmation theory thus turns out to be (as Bar-Hillel has observed) a matter of terminological confusion.

We have already encountered Nelson Goodman's famous predicate 'grue' in Chapter 10 on estimation. Such predicates imply the existence of a serious difficulty with confirmation theory as it is ordinarily approached. I have not included this difficulty among the "paradoxes" of confirmation theory, both because it seems to be more in the nature of a straightforward problem to be overcome by straightforward methods, than something as cute as a paradox, and because it is a problem which affects all inductive theories equally, as well as theories of scientific inference which call themselves noninductive. Something is grue, recall, if it is green up until the year 2000, and blue thereafter. Goodman's original paradox amounted simply to the observation that whatever evidence we have which justifies our belief that all emeralds are green, or which gives to that generalization a high degree of confirmation, is equally a justification for believing that all emeralds are grue, or gives an equally high degree of confirmation to the generalization 'all emeralds are grue'. As observed in Chapter 10, speaking of estimation won't help us. The universality of the generalization is irrelevant: we face the same problem if we consider only the statistical assertions 'almost all emeralds are green' and 'almost all emeralds are grue'. Since they are contraries, and since whatever is evidence for one is also evidence for another, neither can have a probability of more than a half. And since we can multiply predicates *ad libitum* (gred = green now and red later; grellow, grentian griolet, etc), we can reduce the degree of confirmation of the generalization 'all emeralds are green' to as low a level as we choose.

The same kind of thing happens to probability statements made on the basis of statistical hypotheses. Everyone who would agree to assigning a probability to heads on the next toss of this coin at all would, if they knew it was a coin which yielded heads half the time, assign the value $\frac{1}{2}$ to that probability. But the next toss is also a member of the set of all tosses that either yield heads or belong to the intersection of the unit class of the next toss, and the set of tosses yielding tails:

$$\vee \cup (\{\text{next toss}\} \cap T),$$

and the proportion of heads in this class is arbitrarily close to 1; why not say the probability of heads is 1, even though the coin is well tested? As noted earlier, the problems we are led to in defining randomness seem insuperable if we take any definable class to be a legitimate reference class. It seems that one cannot consider all definable classes on an equally legitimate footing in inductive logic.

Furthermore we can raise an analogous problem in terms of such purely statistical predicates as 'exhibits a relative frequency of A's lying between the limits 0.3 and 0.4'. Consider, for example:

Practically all samples of 1000 B's exhibit a proportion of A's lying outside the limits $r - \epsilon$ and $r + \epsilon$, where r is the measure of A's among B's.

Practically all samples of 1000 B's exhibit a proportion of A's lying between $r - \delta_1$ and $r + \delta_2$.

Practically all samples of 1000 B's exhibit a proportion of A's lying between $r - \gamma_1$ and $r + \gamma_2$.

We may choose $\epsilon, \delta_1, \delta_2, \gamma_1, \gamma_2$ in such a way that all three of these statements are true, and can be used in conjunction with a statement reflecting the observation of a particular sample of 1000 B's, to arrive at high probabilities or acceptance of the three statements:

The measure of A's among B's does not lie between $k - \epsilon$ and $k + \epsilon$.

The measure of A's among B's lies between $k - \delta_1$ and $k + \delta_2$.

The measure of A's among B's lies between $k - \gamma_1$ and $k + \gamma_2$.

where these statements cannot be jointly true.

For example, if we are drawing balls from an urn (with replacement) and find that 600 of them have been black, it is more probable than not that between 0.00 and 0.61 of the balls drawn from the urn will turn out to be black, and it is more probable than not that between 0.59 and 1.00 of the balls drawn from the urn will turn out to be black, and more probable than not that it will *not* be the case that between 0.59 and 0.61 of the balls will turn out to be black.

Nearly all of the more or less formal theories of scientific inference that I have discussed so far have at one point or another run into the 'grue' problem or some variant of it. The problem has many ramifications that haven't been explored yet. So far, the peculiar predicates have resisted any general characterization; no solution even to the simplest cases has gained anything like universal acceptance. Goodman offered a relative solution in terms of "entrenchment"—the degree to which a predicate is entrenched in our language. But might it not be that we could be speaking a different language? For example a language in which 'grue' and 'bleen' (understood as referring to objects blue before 2000 and green thereafter) are primitive color words. Barker and Achinstein attempt to show that we could not;

Goodman, in "Positionality and Pictures," rejects their attempt to establish a logical asymmetry between 'grue' and 'green', and so does Ullian, in another article. Salmon's solution is that we should project only ostensively definable predicates, and that a predicate can only be ostensively definable if it applies to things that *look alike*. Salmon's solution is like Goodman's in presupposing a principle of induction of the very sort it is supposed to elucidate. Salmon presupposes that things that look alike will continue to look alike, while Goodman admits that entrenchment in the past must be assumed a good guide to usefulness in the future. Even granted all this, we must accept the conventional meaning of 'looks alike'; I find it easy to imagine creatures (grue-blees) to whom all grue things look alike and who would be horribly surprised if in the year 2000 all grue things suddenly turned bleen! Salmon's solution, like Goodman's, applies only to ostensive predicates, and thus not to predicates like 'has a mass of 5 until the year 2000 and a mass of $\frac{1}{5}$ thereafter' or like the statistical predicates mentioned above.

Both Hugues Leblanc and Carl Hempel ("Inductive Inconsistencies") have dealt recently with the problem created by Goodman's peculiar predicates. Leblanc carefully discusses the alleged inconsistencies into which one is led by the usual rules of inductive extrapolation when one allows Goodman's peculiar predicates, and shows that we are led to no *formal* inconsistencies. Hempel points out that the problem is not one of being able to determine which statements are lawlike and which are not (as Goodman claimed), because the same problem arises in connection with the extrapolation of numerical relations as quantitative laws: there are an infinite number of laws of the form $y = f_1(x)$, $y = f_2(x)$, ... which are mutually inconsistent, which are equally supported by the evidence, and which are equally lawlike. He also has no solution to offer, though both he and Leblanc point out that in formal theories of confirmation no *inconsistencies* are generated by the peculiar predicates. They nevertheless have unwelcome consequences.

It has been suggested—e.g., by Stephen Barker—that this is a problem peculiar to the view that enumerative induction is basic to scientific inference. But it is clearly just as much a matter of concern to those who claim that scientific inference is a matter of selecting the simplest from a class of acceptable hypotheses, for, if we spoke in a grue-bleen language, the hypothesis that all emeralds are grue would be much simpler (it would involve no reference to time, for example) than the hypothesis that they are green—i.e., grue until the year 2000, and bleen thereafter. The problem of finding some way of distinguishing between sensible predicates like 'blue' and 'green' and the outlandish ones suggested by Goodman, Barker, and others is thus surely one of the most important problems to come out of recent discussions of inductive logic. It is also one of the most pressing, since there are now only some thirty years left in which to solve it.

Furthermore the existence of these problems has not discouraged people from following the path of confirmation theory. For a thoroughgoing subjectivist like Richard Jeffrey, the Goodmanesque predicates present no more than an idle academic amusement; no one ever assigned a positive probability to the hypothesis that all emeralds are grue, so that no matter how many we observe to be grue, we will still not be compelled to find the queer hypothesis probable. From this point of view, admirably adumbrated in Jeffrey's *Logic of Preference*, the whole point of inductive logic is to explicate the notion of *rational behavior*. The data are people's beliefs (probabilities) and people's values (utilities), and the upshot is an explication of the rationale which underlies or ought to underlie the choice of a course of action under circumstances of uncertainty. There is no question by itself of believing or disbelieving hypotheses, much less any questions of *accepting* hypotheses. Indeed, on Jeffrey's refinement of the subjectivistic position, one no longer has even to suppose that *evidence* statements come to be accepted; it suffices to consider new subjectivistic probability functions appropriate to changed circumstances.

Carnap's new system of inductive logic circumvents the difficulties introduced by peculiar predicates by the simple expedient of not being designed for a language rich enough to allow the definition of these predicates. But even in a more powerful language, the way of avoiding those difficulties would be clear: one would assign exceedingly small (or zero) *a priori* probabilities to state descriptions which exhibited radical discontinuities—i.e., in which every object up to a_n had a certain property P_i, and every subsequent object had a different property P_j.

Even in Carnap's new system, however, we are faced with the problem that universal generalizations (in a language referring to an infinite number of individuals) always have the *a priori* probability 0, and hence also the *a posteriori* probability 0. Carnap conceives of inductive logic in the manner of Jeffrey, as a guide to decision under uncertainty, and therefore can get along with instance confirmation—i.e., the probability that the next instance will satisfy the generalization. Instead of demanding that the generalization 'all ravens are black' be itself highly probable, on this view it is sufficient that the instantial statement 'the next raven will be black' is highly probable.

This brings us to a very live issue that affects both the subjectivistic theories of induction, such as Jeffrey's, and certain of the logicist theories, like Carnap's. The issue is the problem of whether or not inductive conclusions are ever accepted. Jeffrey and Carnap say "no"; other subjectivists and logicists say "yes". Those who regard inductive logic as essentially the hypothetico-deductive method tend to answer "yes". The more carefully one attends to the arguments between proponents of the hypothetico-deductive method and inductivists (falsification theorists and confirmation theorists), the more important does this problem appear. Popper regards Carnap as going beyond the pale of true Humean skepticism in saying that hypotheses can ever be "probable"; Popper will *accept* a hypothesis (tentatively, of course; until further notice), but will never make the assertion that it is probable. Ironically, Carnap frowns upon Popper for nearly the same reason: it would on his view be altogether unwarranted, and flying in the face of sound Humean skeptical arguments, ever to *accept* a hypothesis, tentatively or in any other way. All we can hope for is to be able to assign some degree of probability to the hypothesis.

What is at issue here is precisely the question of whether we should speak of accepting hypotheses; it is the question of whether inductive logic is to have a rule of acceptance. Carnap is one of the few philosophers to take a very definite stand on this issue and to recognize it as a fundamentally important one. He says that the great majority of contemporary writers make "one basic mistake": they regard the result of inductive reasoning as the acceptance of a new proposition ("The Aim of Inductive Logic"). On Carnap's view, the result of an induction is the assignment of a degree of confirmation to a new proposition. Now this is all, he would argue, that we need or can possibly want in the way of inductive conclusions. On the basis of these degrees of confirmation, we can define mathematical expectations and make decisions among courses of action.

Aside from general philosophical considerations, the most serious argument against the rule of acceptance is the lottery paradox. Consider a fair, 1,000,000-ticket lottery, with one prize. On almost any view of probability, the probability that a given ticket (say ticket No. 1) will win is 0.000001, and the probability that it will not win is 0.999999. Surely if a sheer probability is ever sufficient to warrant the acceptance of a hypothesis, this is a case. It is hard to think of grounds on which to base a distinction between this case and the cases of thoroughly acceptable statistical hypotheses, The same argument, however, goes through for ticket No. 7, ticket No. 156, etc. In fact, for any *i* between 1 and 1,000,000 inclusive, the argument goes through and we should rationally be entitled—indeed, obligated—to accept the statement 'ticket *i* will not win'. A commonly accepted principle of acceptability is that if *S* and *T* are acceptable statements, then their conjunction is also acceptable. But this means that in the lottery case, since each statement of the form 'ticket *i* will not win' is acceptable, so is the conjunction of 1,000,000 of these statements, which is equivalent to the statement than *no* ticket will win the lottery, which contradicts the statement which we initially took to be acceptable that one ticket would win the lottery. A similar paradox can be formulated with statistical hypotheses in the place of lottery tickets. One response to this paradox has been to reject the possibility of a rule of acceptance for inductive logic.

Popper, Black, Day, and others, however, have argued that scientists do accept hypotheses, if only provisionally. Hempel has pointed out that there are difficulties involved in supposing that they do, and Levi has shown how even on Popper's own scheme the relation between corroboration and acceptance is complicated. The issue is still wide open. Some arguments in favor of a rule of detachment are these:

1. People do in fact accept statements that are probable enough; they regard them as practically certain. I know that it is only *probable* (in one sense) that I shall

find paper in my desk drawer, but in another sense I am *certain* that there is paper there, because I just now put it there. It is unrealistic, a violation of good sense, to demand that all such statements always be regarded as only probabilities.

2. Among the statements that are "practically certain" are those which report sense experience, and which writers like Carnap must regard as absolutely certain. He must regard such statements as certain in order to have statements relative to which he can compute the probabilities of other statements. By incorporating a rule of detachment in our inductive logic, we can avoid this necessity, and we can admit that observation statements are only overwhelmingly probable—probable enough to be included directly in our rational corpora, but not so probable as to be incorrigible.

3. As remarked earlier, most of the scientific inferences that one encounters in practice are deductive in form; one argues that since one sample of X melted at about $t°C$, all samples of X will melt at about $t°C$; one argues that potash is necessary for plant growth, because plants on those plots deficient in potash were stunted; etc. All such arguments can be reconstructed in a straightforward enough manner, *provided* that we can use as premises statements for which the evidence is partial and inconclusive, strictly speaking, though it should certainly be strong enough to yield practical certainty.

Whether or not these arguments are persuasive, they suggest that the search for a plausible rule of acceptance for inductive conclusions is not wholly misconceived. In the following chapter we shall consider three systems of inductive logic which do allow for a rule of acceptance.

EXERCISES

1. Devise a numerical example to support the claim that the paradox of confirmation created by the white shoe is a quantitative illusion.
2. If the observation of a bullfinch is taken to support the generalization that all ravens are black, what is the range of relevance of that generalization likely being taken to be?
3. In general how would you be able to tell what the range of relevance of a generalization was?
4. What other ways, besides eschewing a rule of inductive acceptance, might one use to avoid the lottery paradox?
5. Show that if the acceptance probability is taken to be $1/n$ no lottery with less than n tickets will lead to a paradox—not even a biased one.

6. Provide counterarguments to each of the three numbered arguments with which the chapter ends.
7. Give a detailed illustration of how the grue–bleen problem may affect a hypothetico-deductive view of induction.
8. Discuss various ways of handling the grue–bleen problem proposed in the relevant articles mentioned in the bibliography.

BIBLIOGRAPHICAL NOTES FOR CHAPTER 13

Isaac Levi's criticism of the subjectivistic interpretation of probability will be found in his book, *Gambling With Truth*, Alfred A. Knopf, New York, 1967, which will be discussed at length in the next chapter, and in his review article on Jeffrey's *Logic of Decision*, "Probability Kinematics," *British Journal for the Philosophy of Science* **18**, 1967, pp. 205–206.

Papers concerning the paradoxes of confirmation are: Janina Hosiasson-Lindenbaum, "On Confirmation," *Journal of Symbolic Logic* **5**, 1940, pp. 133–48, and Carl Hempel, "Studies in the Logic of Confirmation," *Mind* **54**, 1945, pp. 97–121; these are the two basic ones. There was a flurry (a blizzard?) of papers on this topic in the late 1950's: Hempel, "Empirical Statements and Falsifiability," *Philosophy* **33**, 1958, pp. 342–48; "Inductive Inconsistencies," *Synthese* **12**, 1960, pp. 439–69, and "Deductive-Nomological vs. Statistical Explanation," *Minnesota Studies in the Philosophy of Science*, Vol. III (Feigl, ed.), 1962, pp. 98–169; J. W. N. Watkins, "Between Analytic and Empirical," *Philosophy* **32**, 1957, pp. 112–31; "A Rejoinder to Professor Hempel's Reply," *Philosophy* **33**, 1958, pp. 349–55; "Mr. Stove's Blunders," *Australasian Journal of Philosophy* **37**, 1959, pp. 240–41; "A Reply to Mr. Stove's Reply," *Australasian Journal of Philosophy* **38**, 1960, pp. 54–58; "Confirmation without Background Knowledge," *British Journal for the Philosophy of Science* **10**, 1959–60, pp. 318–20, and "Professor Scheffler's Note," *Philosophical Studies* **12**, 1961, pp. 16–19; Israel Scheffler, "A Note on Confirmation," *Philosophical Studies* **11**, 1960, pp. 21–23, and "A Rejoinder on Confirmation," *Philosophical Studies* **12**, 1961, pp. 19–20; D. C. Stove, "Popperian Confirmation and the Paradox of the Ravens," *Australasian Journal of Philosophy* **37**, 1959, pp. 149–55; "A Reply to Mr. Watkins," *Australasian Journal of Philosophy* **38**, 1960, pp. 51–54; H. Gavin Alexander, "The Paradoxes of Confirmation," *British Journal for the Philosophy of Science* **9**, 1958–59, pp. 227–33, and "The Paradoxes of Confirmation—A Reply to Dr. Agassi," *British Journal for the Philosophy of Science* **10**, 1959–60, pp. 229–34; J. L. Mackie, "The Paradox of Confirmation," *British Journal for the Philosophy of Science* **13**, 1962–63, pp. 265–77; and I. J. Good, "The Paradox of Confirmation," *British Journal for the Philosophy of Science* **11**, 1960–61, pp. 145–49, "The Paradox of Confirmation (II)," *British Journal for the Philosophy of Science* **12**, 1961–62, and "The White Shoe is a Red Herring" *British Journal for the Philosophy of Science* **17**, 1966–67, p. 322.

Patrick Suppes "A Bayesian Approach to the Paradoxes of Confirmation" is to be found in *Aspects of Inductive Logic* (Suppes and Hintikka, eds.), North-Holland Publishing Co., Amsterdam, 1966, pp. 198–207. The same volume contains Max Black's careful review of the philosophical questions raised by the paradoxes, in "Notes on the Paradoxes of Confirmation," pp. 175–97 and G. H.

von Wright's very persuasive proposal involving the range of relevance of a generalization in "The Paradoxes of Confirmation," pp. 208–19.

The paradox of ideal evidence is discussed in Karl Popper, *The Logic of Scientific Discovery*, Hutchinson, London, 1959, and R. H. Vincent, "The Paradox of Ideal Evidence," *Philosophical Review* **71**, 1962, pp. 497–503. The other paradox discussed by Vincent is presented in "A Note on Some Quantitative Theories of Confirmation," *Philosophical Studies* **12**, 1961, pp. 91–92.

For Carnap's Response to Popper's alleged contradiction, see the new preface to his *Logical Foundations of Probability* (2nd edition), University of Chicago Press, Chicago, 1962; Bar-Hillel's remarks are to be found in "Comments on 'Degree of Confirmation' by Professor K. R. Popper," *British Journal for the Philosophy of Science* **6**, 1955–56, pp. 155–57.

Nelson Goodman's grue–bleen problem was introduced in *Fact, Fiction, and Forecast*, Harvard University Press, Cambridge, 1955. Discussion of the problem will be found (among other places) in Goodman, "Positionality and Pictures," *Philosophical Review* **69**, 1960, pp. 523–25; S. Barker and P. Achinstein, "On the New Riddle of Induction," *Philosophical Review* **69**, 1960, pp. 511–22; J. Ullian, "More on 'Grue' and Grue," *Philosophical Review* **70**, 1961, pp. 386–89; W. Salmon, "On Vindicating Induction," in *Induction* (Kyburg and Nagel, eds.), Wesleyan University Press, Middletown, Connecticut, 1963, pp. 27–41; Hugues Leblanc, "A Revised Version of Goodman's Paradox on Confirmation," *Philosophical Studies* **14**, 1963, pp. 49–51; Donald Davidson, "Emeroses by Other Names," *Journal of Philosophy* **63**, 1966, pp. 778–80; J. Vickers, "Characteristics of Projectible Predicates," *Journal of Philosophy* **64**, 1967, pp. 280–86; Howard Smokler, "Goodman's Paradox and the Problem of Rules of Acceptance," *American Philosophical Quarterly* **3**, 1966, pp. 1–6; Richard Jeffrey, "Goodman's Query," *Journal of Philosophy* **63**, 1966.

Richard Jeffrey's splendidly clear exposition of the subjectivistic view of induction and inductive behavior is *The Logic of Decision*, McGraw-Hill, New York, 1966. Carnap's most recent system, *Basic System of Inductive Logic*, will appear soon, it is hoped. The quotation in the text comes from his nontechnical article "The Aims of Inductive Logic," in Nagel, Suppes, and Tarski (eds.) *Logic, Methodology, and Philosophy of Science*, Stanford University Press, Stanford, California, 1962, pp. 303–18.

The lottery paradox was first presented in my *Probability and the Logic of Rational Belief*, Wesleyan University Press, Middletown, Connecticut, 1961, where, however, the moral I drew from it was that deductive closure among accepted statements should be abandoned, rather than that an acceptance rule was impossible. The problem was noticed at the same time by Carl Hempel, "Deductive-Nomological vs. Statistical Explanation," in *Minnesota Studies in the Philosophy of Science*, Vol. III (Feigl and Maxwell, eds.), University of Minnesota Press, Minneapolis, 1962, pp. 98–169. An improved version is stated in Levi, *Gambling with Truth*. The problem is also discussed in Fred Schick's "Consistency and Rationality," *Journal of Philosophy* **60**, 1963, pp. 5–19, and in my response, "A Further Note on Rationality and Consistency," *Journal of Philosophy* **60**, 1963, pp. 463–65, as well as, from a less formal point of view, by Robert C. Sleigh, "A Note on Some Epistemic Principles of Chisholm and Martin," *Journal of Philosophy* **61**, 1964, pp. 216–18, and Keith Lehrer, "Knowledge and Probability," *Journal of Philosophy* **61**, 1964, pp. 368–72.

14

Acceptance Theories

There are three confirmation theories which take the existence of an inductive rule of acceptance to be important. The theory we shall consider first, instigated by Jaakko Hintikka and developed by Hintikka and Hilpinen, is very close in spirit to the theory of Carnap. A number of new technical terms have made their appearance in Hintikka's writings; they will be explained here, but it must be re-emphasized here that this volume is a guide to, and not a substitute for, the original sources.

Consider a language L_k, containing k primitive one-place predicates, an arbitrary number (perhaps an unlimited number) of individual constants, and the usual array of sentential connectives and individual variables, but not the identity sign. By means of these k predicates it is possible to characterize 2^k

kinds of individuals. Thus if $k = 2$, each of the following matrices would be satisfied by a different *kind* of individual:

$$
\begin{array}{ll}
C_1(x) & P_1(x) \ \& \ P_2(x) \\
C_2(x) & P_1(x) \ \& \sim P_2(x) \\
C_3(x) & \sim P_1(x) \ \& \sim P_2(x) \\
C_4(x) & \sim P_1(x) \ \& \ P_2(x)
\end{array}
$$

These possible kinds of individuals are described by matrices that Hintikka calls *attributive constituents*, or *Ct-Predicates*. There are thus, in the general case in which we have k one-place predicates, 2^k attributive constituents; let us abbreviate them as follows:

$$Ct_1(x), \ Ct_2(x), \ Ct_3(x), \ldots \ Ct_i(x), \ldots \ Ct_{2^k}(x).$$

These attributive constituents, observe, are simply Carnap's Q-predicates, or *strongest* predicates.

When one has said of an individual that it satisfies a certain attributive constituent, there is simply nothing more to say about that individual in this language.

Distinct from attributive constituents, which are matrices, we have *constituents*, which are not matrices but statements. (This is perhaps not the happiest terminology, but there is nothing to be done about it.) An arbitrary constituent C_w has the form

$$(\exists x) \ Ct_{i_1}(x) \ \& \ (\exists x) \ Ct_{i_2}(x) \ \& \cdots \& \ (\exists x) \ Ct_{i_w}(x)$$
$$\times \ (x) \ (Ct_{i_1}(x) \ \lor \ Ct_{i_2}(x) \ \lor \cdots \lor \ Ct_{i_w}(x)).$$

In other words, a constituent is a statement saying that each of a certain set of attributive constituents is instantiated, is satisfied by some individual, and that furthermore only these particular attributive constituents are instantiated. In the case where $k = 2$, considered before, the attributive constituents were listed above, and the constituents are as follows:

1. $(\exists x) \ C_1(x) \ \& \ (x) \ (C_1(x))$
2. $(\exists x) \ C_2(x) \ \& \ (x) \ (C_2(x))$
3. $(\exists x) \ C_3(x) \ \& \ (x) \ (C_3(x))$
4. $(\exists x) \ C_4(x) \ \& \ (x) \ (C_4(x))$
5. $(\exists x) \ C_1(x) \ \& \ (\exists x) \ C_2(x) \ \& \ (x) \ (C_1(x) \ \lor \ C_2(x))$
6. $(\exists x) \ C_1(x) \ \& \ (\exists x) \ C_3(x) \ \& \ (x) \ (C_1(x) \ \lor \ C_3(x))$
7. $(\exists x) \ C_1(x) \ \& \ (\exists x) \ C_4(x) \ \& \ (x) \ (C_1(x) \ \lor \ C_4(x))$
8. $(\exists x) \ C_2(x) \ \& \ (\exists x) \ C_3(x) \ \& \ (x) \ (C_2(x) \ \lor \ C_3(x))$
9. $(\exists x) \ C_2(x) \ \& \ (\exists x) \ C_4(x) \ \& \ (x) \ (C_2(x) \ \lor \ C_4(x))$
10. $(\exists x) \ C_3(x) \ \& \ (\exists x) \ C_4(x) \ \& \ (x) \ (C_3(x) \ \lor \ C_4(x))$
11. $(\exists x) \ C_1(x) \ \& \ (\exists x) \ C_2(x) \ \& \ (\exists x) \ C_3(x)$
$$\& \ (x) \ (C_1(x) \ \lor \ C_2(x) \ \lor \ C_3(x))$$

12. $(\exists x)\ C_1(x)\ \&\ (\exists x)\ C_2(x)\ \&\ (\exists x)\ C_4(x)$
$$\&\ (x)\ (C_1(x)\ \vee\ C_2(x)\ \vee\ C_4(x))$$

13. $(\exists x)\ C_1(x)\ \&\ (\exists x)\ C_3(x)\ \&\ (\exists x)\ C_4(x)$
$$\&\ (x)\ (C_1(x)\ \vee\ C_3(x)\ \vee\ \bar{C}_4(x))$$

14. $(\exists x)\ C_2(x)\ \&\ (\exists x)\ C_3(x)\ \&\ (\exists x)\ C_4(x)$
$$\&\ (x)\ (C_2(x)\ \vee\ C_3(x)\ \vee\ C_4(x))$$

15. $(\exists x)\ C_1(x)\ \&\ (\exists x)\ C_2(x)\ \&\ (\exists x)\ C_3(x)\ \&\ (\exists x)\ C_4(x)$
$$\&\ (x)\ (C_1(x)\ \vee\ C_2(x)\ \vee\ C_3(x)\ \vee\ C_4(x))$$

We suppose that there is something in the universe, that is, that at least one of the attributive constituents is instantiated. There are therefore $(2)^{2^k} - 1$ *constituents*, in the general case. Each of these constituents describes a possible state of the world; the first, in our example, describes the state of the world which obtains when everything in the world satisfies the first attributive constituent; the thirteenth describes a state of the world in which the generalization '$(x)\ (P_1(x) \supset P_2(x))$' holds.

The first step in defining the measure function which is to characterize our inductive logic, is to distribute our prior measure over these possible states of the world, or constituents. Then the probability assigned to a given constituent is divided among the state descriptions corresponding to that constituent. In the simplest case, we assign the same probability to each of the constituents, and then we divide that probability equally among the state descriptions (defined as they are for Carnap) that compose that constituent. The number of constituents depends only on the number of predicates in our system, but the number of state descriptions depends also on the number of individual constants. In the simple example we have in any case fifteen constituents, each of which would be given an *a priori* probability of $\frac{1}{15}$. If there are five individual constants (note that if we have fewer than four individual constants, the fifteenth constituent cannot hold), then we have $(2^k)^5 = 4^5 = 1024$ state descriptions. In general if we have N individuals, we have $(2^k)^N = 2^{Nk}$ state descriptions. There is only one state description corresponding to the first constituent, so that single state description receives the whole *a priori* probability of that constituent, $\frac{1}{15}$. To the fifth constituent, however, there correspond 30 state descriptions, so to each of these state descriptions is assigned the measure $\frac{1}{450}$; to the eleventh constituent, there correspond 150 state descriptions, each of which gets therefore *a priori* probability of $\frac{1}{3600}$. It will be observed that what we would normally regard as the simpler kinds of universes (universes in which fewer attributive constituents are instantiated) have higher probabilities, *a priori*, than more complex universes.

Evidence serves to eliminate some of the constituents and the probability becomes piled up on the remaining constituents. The first individual observed, in our hypothetical example, serves to eliminate three of the four first constituents. The observation of individuals having the attributive constituents C_1, C_3, and C_4 would eliminate the first twelve constituents in our list, and the fourteenth, leaving only the thirteenth (representing the generalization '$(x)(P_1(x) \supset P_2(x))$') and the fifteenth. It is possible to show that in general the most probable constituent, relative to a body of evidence, is the one which says that in the whole universe there exist only such kinds of individuals as we have already observed.

Here is already one important difference between systems of genus Hintikkensis and those of genus Carnapiensis: universal generalizations, on Carnap's system, have generally small probabilities, and for languages in which they are an infinite number of individual constants, the probability of any universal generalization is 0. This is not the case for Hintikka's systems. There a universal generalization such as '$(x)(P_1(x) \supset P_2(x))$' can achieve a respectable probability even in a universe containing an infinite number of individuals. Furthermore, since every consistent generalization can put into a distributive normal form in which we have merely a disjunction of constituents, every generalization which is not refuted by the evidence will have a finite posterior probability.

Furthermore, as Hintikka and Hilpinen show, it is possible to construct an acceptance rule which does not lead to any of the usual problems. For example, the set of statements accepted, in accordance with this acceptance rule, on the basis of a given body of evidence, is demonstrably consistent; furthermore, any statement entailed by the conjunction of any set of the statements that are acceptable under the rule will itself turn out to be acceptable under the rule. The rule they offer for the acceptance of general statements h is this (p. 11):

○ **(D. AC.)**

$$Ac(h, e) = \text{Df.} \quad \begin{array}{ll} (i) & P(h, e) > 1 - \epsilon, \quad \text{where} \quad 0 < \epsilon \leq 0.5 \\ (ii) & n > n_0 \end{array}$$

The first part of the rule stipulates that relative to the evidence e, the probability of h must be greater than $1 - \epsilon$, where $1 - \epsilon$ represents the *level* of acceptance. This part of the rule is purely probabilistic. In the second part of the rule n represents the number of individuals included in the evidence e, and n_0 is a number such that if $n > n_0$, one and only one constituent C_w may be accepted on the basis of e. This constituent will be the constituent asserting that only those kinds of individuals already observed exist in the universe.

There is also a rule for the acceptance of singular statements (p. 18):

○ **(D. AC. SING.)**

A singular hypothesis $A(a_i)$ is acceptable if and only if the generalization $(x) A(x)$ is acceptable.

Hintikka and Hilpinen show that this rule avoids the lottery paradox, since when the corresponding universal generalization is probable enough (i.e., has probability greater than $1 - \epsilon$), then the probability of the conjunction of any number of singular hypotheses of the form $A(a_i)$ will also have a probability greater than $1 - \epsilon$. But they also show that we cannot achieve a general acceptance rule by construing the 'h' of (D. Ac) as ranging over singular hypotheses as well as general ones; for they show that if the general statement $(x) A(x)$ is *not* acceptable, then the lottery paradox will arise in connection with singular hypotheses of the form $A(a_i)$, even if these singular hypotheses happen to have probabilities greater than $1 - \epsilon$.

The probability values that one obtains in Hintikka's original system seemed too optimistic to him in the sense that they lead to the acceptance of generalizations on the basis of very slender evidence. He proposed subsequently that instead of assigning *a priori* probability evenly among all the attributive constituents, some preference be given to more complex constituents by taking the probability assigned to any constituent asserting that exactly w attributive constituents are instantiated in the universe to be proportional to $(w/K)^\alpha$, where K is the number of constituents and α an arbitrary constant characteristic (like Carnap's λ) of a particular inductive method.

In "A Two-Dimensional Continuum of Inductive Methods," Hintikka adds another parameter to the characterization of the inductive methods of his system. He takes the probability of a constituent C_w to depend on a parameter α which functions in a way similar to that in which the preceding parameter α functioned (the larger α is, the more evidence it takes to render a generalization probable; with $\alpha = 0$, we arrive at Carnap's classical λ-system, in which the probability of any nontautological generalization is, *a priori* and *a posteriori*, 0), and on a parameter λ, which functions like Carnap's λ as an index of caution concerning the predictive inference (the larger λ, the more are our singular predictions determined by *a priori* considerations, and the less by the observed frequencies).

Two generalizations of Hintikka's one-parameter systems have appeared; one, "Inductive Generalization in an Ordered Universe," extends Hintikka's original system in such a way as to apply to the special polyadic case of an ordered universe of individuals; the other, "On Inductive Generalization on Monadic First-Order Logic with Identity," extends Hintikka's system to logics that include identity. It is interesting to observe that though this task is successfully carried out, it is exceedingly difficult.

There are two very attractive aspects to Hintikka's approach. The first concerns the fact that, unlike Carnap's systems, it allows universal generalizations to attain respectable probabilities. One factor underlying this virtue is that it does not allow the construction of Goodmanesque predicates; as matters stand none of the languages to which Hintikka's methods have been applied (not even that with a dyadic ordering predicate) have been rich enough to allow the definition of predicates like 'grue'. Nevertheless, the approach by which these peculiar predicates would be avoided is clear: beginning with a set of relatively ostensive predicates, like 'blue' and 'green', the prior probability of a constituent which entailed that all emeralds were blue or one that entailed that all emeralds were green would be very much larger than the prior probability of a constituent that entailed that all emeralds were grue. Hintikka sensibly takes the task of inductive logic or confirmation theory to be that of providing a rationale for scientific inference within the framework provided by a *given* language.

The other attractive aspect of Hintikka's systems is that, as we have seen, they allow for a very simple and natural rule of acceptance. This rule of acceptance does not lead to any inconsistencies, and does have desirable consequence that the body of statements it leads to is logically closed; any logical consequence of any set of statements that are accepted on the basis of Hintikka's acceptance rules is also a statement that is acceptable on the basis of his acceptance rules.

There are also, however, serious shortcomings to Hintikka's approach. One is the extreme simplicity of the languages for which it has been developed. The complications pile up at a furious rate even when we begin to take account of first-order languages with dyadic predicates. No attempt has been made, as yet, to deal with first-order languages with general polyadic predicates (although this seems in principle perfectly possible), and the problem of a language containing predicates of various types as well as predicates of various degrees within each type seems overwhelming. Yet it is precisely a rich language of this sort which is required for any sort of scientific investigation, and if inductive logic is to remain more than an academic exercise, if it is to have any effect on the soundness of scientific inference, or even to be capable of characterizing scientific inference in a realistic way, it must be capable of handling inferences within rich languages.

Furthermore, the difficulty discussed in connection with the subjectivistic and logicalistic interpretations of probability applies here; we will be able to arrive at large *a priori* probabilities for approximate statistical generalizations. In virtue of the part of the acceptance rule which requires that n be greater than n_0, it is easy to see that we might never be obliged to *accept* these statistical statements, but nonetheless their existence is a little disturbing.

Finally, with any such approach as that pursued by Hintikka or Carnap, one is haunted by the arbitrariness of the initial probability assignments. If one assignment seems too optimistic, one multiples by a factor $(w/K)^\alpha$; if another assignment seems too negativistic, one tries a different initial distribution of probability. To be sure, nothing is being concealed. The inductive methods are characterized by parameters. But there appears to be no obvious and natural way of settling on any one particular set of values of the parameters.

The approach to scientific inference pursued by Isaac Levi takes as its fundamental task the elucidation of what he calls 'local justification'. Local justification is opposed to global justification. Global justification is primarily what we have been concerned with in the foregoing, in which we have discussed the relation between statements that may be supposed to be known directly or believed without argument and other statements that are evidentially supported by those statements. The evident statements, in the context of global justification, are taken to be statements like 'of one hundred balls drawn, 40 were red', 'this is a black raven', 'the fifth toss resulted in heads', and the like. In local justification, we are concerned with something like the actual conduct of scientific inquiry. We take as *evident* not only observation reports but theoretical assumptions and, in general, "those of the investigator's findings and beliefs that are relevant to the problem at hand and are not likely to be questioned by any participant in the inquiry or by anyone who is qualified to evaluate its results" (p. 4). Thus the evidence relative to which one is to evaluate the plausibility of a hypothesis includes both background knowledge b, not open to question in that inquiry, but not on that account immune from *all* further question, and also specific evidence e, comprising observation reports and the like.

The context of local justification is characterized, according to Levi, not only by specific background knowledge b and specific evidence e, but—and this is Levi's ingenious and original contribution to the analysis of scientific justification—by the question the investigator has in mind and by the set of *relevant answers* that the investigator regards as appropriate to the question: "... in defending a given conclusion as warranted by the evidence, it seems plausible to suppose that such defense should be made relative to a set of sentences that are taken to be relevant answers..." (p. 33). The set of relevant answers is supposed to have a certain structure. An *ultimate partition* U_e is a set of sentences of L such that $b \& e$ entails that exactly one element of U_e is true, such that no element of U_e is entailed by $b \& e$, and such that each relevant answer considered by the investigator using U_e is logically equivalent to an element of the set M_e generated by U_e in the following manner: M_e contains the (inconsistent, relative to $b \& e$) conjunction of all the elements of U_e, C_e; M_e contains S_e, the disjunction of all the elements of U_e; and M_e contains the disjunction of every nonempty subset of U_e (one of these disjunctions, S_e, is entailed by $b \& e$ and contains every element of U_e).

An example, borrowed from Levi, will help to make this terminology clear. Consider an election forecaster who is interested in ascertaining which of the three candidates X, Y, and Z, will win an election. His ultimate partition, U_e, will be the three statements

X will win.
Y will win.
Z will win.

and the set M_e generated by this ultimate partition will be

(i) Either X or Y or Z will win (S_e).
(ii) Either X or Y will win.
(iii) Either X or Z will win.

(iv) Either Y or Z will win.
(v) X will win.
(vi) Y will win.
(vii) Z will win.
(viii) X and Y and Z will win (C_e).

In the circumstances in which we seek to provide local justification, we are supposed to have two further items of information: a numerical probability assignment to the elements (hypotheses H_i) of the ultimate partition U_e, satisfying the usual axioms, and such that $p(H_i, e) > 0$, and $\sum p(H_i, e) = 1$, where the sum is taken over all the elements of U_e; and an epistemic utility function (the phrase is Hempel's) representing the value of accepting a hypothesis when it is true or of accepting it when it is false. We have already encountered the concept of epistemic utility in connection with the measures of corroboration discussed in Chapter 11. Levi's first step in constructing the utility function he requires is to define the *content* of a hypothesis. This is defined only relative to an ultimate partition, U_e. The content of a hypothesis H in M_e, given evidence e, $cont(H, e)$, is taken to be m/n, where n is the number of elements in the ultimate partition U_e, and m is the number of elements in the ultimate partition that are inconsistent with H—that are *ruled out* by H. Observe that this is quite novel, though analogous to previous proposals to take the content of a hypothesis as $1 - p(H)$, where $p(H)$ is the *a priori* probability of H. The novelty is that the content of a hypothesis is defined only relative to a *given* ultimate partition, and all the elements of that ultimate partition are given the same weight. Furthermore, the *conditional* content of H, given e and new evidence f, is defined in just the same way relative to the ultimate partition $U_{e\&f}$ which contains only elements consistent with e and f. The value of accepting H when it is true, given e, $U(H, e)$, and $u(H, e)$, the disvalue of accepting it when it is false, given e, are defined in terms of the content of H, given e, and an arbitrary constant q, $0 < q < 1$:

$$U(H, e) = 1 - q \; cont(\sim H, e),$$

$$u(H, e) = -q \; cont(\sim H, e).$$

Levi shows that every pair of utility functions that satisfies certain very general and plausible requirements (such as that correct answers are to be preferred to incorrect answers) are linear functions of $U(H, e)$ and $u(H, e)$ as he has defined them.

With the help of these utility functions and the already mentioned probability function, we can define the mathematical expectation of epistemic utility of accepting H under circumstances e, $E(H, e)$, as

$$E(H, e) = p(H, e) \; U(H, e) + p(\sim H, e) \; u(H, e).$$

Together with a rule for breaking ties in expected epistemic utility, Bayes'

Rule (maximize expected utility) leads to the following inductive acceptance rule (p. 86):

○ **RULE A**

1. Accept *b* & *e* and all its deductive consequences.
2. Reject all elements a_i of U_e such that $p(a_i, e) < q \, cont(\sim a_i, e)$—i.e., accept the disjunction of all unrejected elements of U_e as the strongest element in M_e accepted via induction from *b* & *e*.
3. Conjoin the sentence accepted as strongest via induction according to (2) with the total evidence *b* & *e* and accept all deductive consequences.
4. Do not accept (relative to *b*, *e*, U_e, the probability distribution, and *q*) any sentences other than those in your language.

This rule embodies the central point in Levi's work; two thirds of his book is devoted to exploring its consequences.

There are a number of parameters involved in the statement of this rule that call for comment. Consider *b*, the background knowledge. This is something that clearly requires mention in many instances of scientific inference, and not only those in which the form of the inference is deductive. Levi makes good use of *b* in dealing with both direct and indirect statistical inferences; it is difficult to see how disregard of background knowledge can have any but deleterious consequences. The specific evidence *e*—presumably observational evidence—is something that makes its appearance in all the theories we have been considering. It would perhaps be desirable to have criteria for admissibility of statements as background knowledge; Rule A itself provides such criteria, but of course at the cost of changing the context: whether a given member of some ultimate partition relevant to an item in *b* is acceptable or not is a different question from the one concerning which element of M_e is acceptable. The controversial and difficult parameters in Rule A are the ultimate partition U_e, the probability distribution, and the number *q*.

The number *q* represents a degree of caution: the closer *q* is to 0, the more cautious will the investigator be about accepting hypotheses; the closer *q* is to 1, the more eager will the investigator seem in replacing agnosticism by belief—i.e., the more eager will he be to accept a relatively strong member of M_e. The selection of a number *q* is a subjective matter. We might nevertheless suppose that a group of investigators could commit themselves to definite values for *q*, says Levi. "Perhaps these values of *q* will not reflect their true feelings in some sense. But the choice of a value of *q* will be a commitment on the part of an investigator to have his conclusions evaluated according to certain standards" (p. 89).

Both the ultimate partition U_e and the probability function $p(H, e)$ represent even graver difficulties. The probability function required by Rule A is an inductive probability function—it must assign probabilities to sentences. It may on occasion be based on known statistical probabilities (p. 191). In general, however, statistical information or no statistical information, it "indicates the risks that the agent is prepared to take in acting as if the hypotheses are true" (p. 190). Levi does not have much to say about these inductive probabilities assigned to sentences, except insofar as they can be related to statistical probabilities. "They may be subjective probabilities—i.e., the probabilities assigned by agents. Or they may be probabilities that ought to be assigned according to some standard method [as in the theory of confirmation]" (p. 191, n). A number of problems concerning such probabilities have already been raised. The standarized methods of assigning them have not been worked out for languages anywhere near rich enough to answer the purposes of reconstructing genuine scientific inferences, as Levi himself remarks, and as he also remarks, the derivation of subjective probabilities from subjective preferences is a slippery business. The standardized methods that are current also seem to involve the introduction of still more arbitrary constants: Carnap's λ and η, Hintikka's α and λ. And both subjectivistic and logical probabilities seem to give rise to unreasonably strong *a priori* degree of belief concerning long-run relative frequencies.

The question of what, in a given context, can be accepted as an ultimate partition is a particularly knotty one. Obviously, different ultimate partitions will lead to the acceptance via induction of different strongest hypotheses. "Whether for any given context there is a system of criteria for determining the ultimate partitions that ought to be used is a difficult question; it cannot be answered here" (p. 37). Indeed, an obvious technique for avoiding unwelcome conclusions suggests itself: Given that H is not entailed by the evidence, but that Rule A directs the acceptance of H, relative to b, e, U_e, a probability distribution (perhaps depending on η and λ), and q, we can avoid having to accept H by preferring to use as our ultimate partition U'_e, consisting of hypotheses of the form $a_i \& H^0$ and $a_i \& \sim H^0$, where a_i is a member of the original partition U_e, and Rule A leads to the rejection of some element of U'_e, $a_i \& H^0$ or $a_i \& \sim H^0$, where a_i is a disjunct in the element of M_e equivalent to H. This is easy to arrange, since a necessary and sufficient condition is merely that for some disjunct a_i in the element M_e originally equivalent to H,

$$p(a_i \& H^0, e) \neq \tfrac{1}{2}p(a_i, e).$$

This shows not merely that a high probability is sufficient for acceptance in virtue of the fact that there will always be some ultimate partition relative to which a statement with a high probability may be accepted, as Levi points out (p. 95), but that any statement whose probability is more than $\frac{1}{2}$ may be accepted, relative to some ultimate partition. One even has a sneaking feeling that by an ingenious construction of ultimate partitions, one might be able to arrange for any proposition whatsoever, with nonzero probability, to be accepted. Indeed, it is possible on Levi's reconstruction of inductive acceptance that a given individual, with given evidence, may at the same time (though not in relation to the same ultimate partition) accept both a proposition and its negation. One should not be too quick to condemn this out of hand, for our intuitions about the general and abstract notion of accepting inductive conclusions are far from clear to begin with; but it may yet give us pause, and then make us wish that somehow ultimate partitions could be characterized in such a way that they would not lead to these results. Other writers also have found the notion that beliefs can be defended only relative to some set of possible alternatives unpersuasive—e.g., Fred Schick (p. 477).

All of this leaves to one side two very strong attractions in Levi's approach. For one thing, he has seen to it that his rule of inductive acceptance preserves what he calls *deductive cogency*: (1) every statement entailed by statements whose acceptance is indicated by Rule A will also be accepted in accordance with Rule A, and (2) the set of statements whose acceptance is authorized by Rule A, relative to a *given* partition, is demonstrably consistent. This attractive feature of Levi's system is shared, it will be recalled, with the system provided by Hintikka. The other attractive feature of Levi's system is the realistic way it enables him to reconstruct important kinds of scientific inference. Furthermore, he is able, within the framework he sets out, to provide penetrating analyses of various other (Popperian, Carnapian) theories of scientific inference, which reveal both the element of truth and the limitations of that truth in these other theories. Nothing can provide more persuasive evidence of the usefulness of the concept of a body of knowledge, of being able to consider as evidence statements that are not self-evident, than the use Levi makes of '*b* & *e*' in these analyses.

The final approach we shall consider is my own approach, which attempts to combine the virtues of a global approach to justification with the flexibility appropriate to local justification. The original system was developed in *Probability and the Logic of Rational Belief.* The basic concept is that of a rational corpus or body of beliefs of a given level. This may be construed as a set of statements. A rational corpus of a given level is characterized by a set F of statements (perhaps observation statements) that are accepted as being practically certain in the highest degree, and by a number i ($1 \leq i \leq n$) reflecting the degree of practical certainty embodied in that rational corpus. The number i is called the *level* of the rational corpus, and the set of statements represented by 'F' is called the *basis* of the rational corpus. The rational corpus of the highest level, n, was to contain the statements of F, together with axioms for set theory and logic, together with all the deductive consequences of these statements. With each number $i \leq n$ there was to be associated a number r_i ($\frac{1}{2} < r_i \leq 1$) such that for all i and j, if $i > j$, then $r_i > r_j$. The set of statements comprising the rational corpus of level i ($i < n$) and basis F was to consist of all and only those statements whose probability, relative to the rational corpus of level $i + 1$, was (p, q) where $\ulcorner p > r_i \urcorner$ was a theorem of arithmetic.

This original system was shown to be defective by Fred Schick. He showed that given a certain rational corpus of level i, one could derive a contradiction corresponding to a version of the lottery paradox in the rational corpus of level $i - 2$. I had proved in my system that if the conditional $\ulcorner S \supset T \urcorner$ is a member of the rational corpus of level i, and S is a member of the rational corpus of level $i - 1$, then T will also be a member of the rational corpus of level $i - 1$. Now consider a fair lottery described in the rational corpus of level i, with so many tickets that for every ticket k the statement 'ticket k will not win' is a member of the rational corpus of level $i - 1$. Let each such statement be abbreviated by L_k. Also in the rational corpus of level i will appear each of the conditionals

$$\ulcorner L_1 \supset (L_2 \supset L_1 \, \& \, L_2) \urcorner,$$

$$\ulcorner L_3 \supset (L_1 \, \& \, L_2 \supset L_1 \, \& \, L_2 \, \& \, L_3) \urcorner,$$

$$\ulcorner L_4 \supset (L_1 \, \& \, L_2 \, \& \, L_3 \supset L_1 \, \& \, L_2 \, \& \, L_3 \, \& \, L_4) \urcorner.$$

By the first-mentioned fact about the system, the conditional $\ulcorner L_2 \supset L_1 \, \& \, L_2 \urcorner$ will also appear in the rational corpus of level $i - 1$, as well as

$$\ulcorner L_1 \, \& \, L_2 \supset L_1 \, \& \, L_2 \, \& \, L_3 \urcorner,$$

$$\ulcorner L_1 \, \& \, L_2 \, \& \, L_3 \supset L_1 \, \& \, L_2 \, \& \, L_3 \, \& \, L_4 \urcorner.$$

So far, so good. But what will appear in the rational corpus of level $i - 2$? Since L_2 is an element of the rational corpus of level $i - 1$, it will appear in the rational corpus of level $1 - 2$. Since the conditional $\ulcorner L_2 \supset L_1 \, \& \, L_2 \urcorner$ appears in the rational corpus of level $i - 1$, the conjunction $\ulcorner L_1 \, \& \, L_2 \urcorner$ will appear in the rational corpus of level $i - 2$. Since the conditional $\ulcorner L_1 \, \& \, L_2 \supset L_1 \, \& \, L_2 \, \& \, L_3 \urcorner$ appears in the rational corpus of level $i - 1$, and the conjunction $\ulcorner L_1 \, \& \, L_2 \urcorner$ appears in the rational corpus of level $i - 2$, the conjunction $\ulcorner L_1 \, \& \, L_2 \, \& \, L_3 \urcorner$ will appear in the rational corpus of level $i - 2$. Since the conditional $\ulcorner L_1 \, \& \, L_2 \, \& \, L_3 \supset L_1 \, \& \, L_2 \, \& \, L_3 \, \& \, L_4 \urcorner$ appears in the rational corpus of level $i - 1$, and the conjunction $\ulcorner L_1 \, \& \, L_2 \, \& \, L_3 \urcorner$ appears in the rational corpus of level $i - 2$, the conjunction $\ulcorner L_1 \, \& \, L_2 \, \& \, L_3 \, \& \, L_4 \urcorner$ will appear in the rational corpus of level $i - 2$. And so on. Thus the conjunction of all of the statements of the form L_k will appear in the rational corpus of level $i - 2$, in plain contradiction to the statement, also inherited in that rational corpus, that the lottery is fair.

This result can be avoided by considering no more than two levels of rational corpus at a time. Let us take F to be a set of statements of whatever sort we have decided to use as our basis for global justification. The rational corpus of highest level, denoted by $_1 RC_F$, contains the sentences of F, axioms for logic and mathematics, and everything that is entailed by this group of sentences. The rational corpus of the highest level thus satisfies Levi's requirement of deductive cogency; it is closed under deduction, and if any inconsistency were to arise in it, we would change our mathematical axioms or the contents of F, as required, though in either case we would properly speak of "changing the whole basis of our empirical knowledge."

The rational corpus of level r will consist of those statements whose probability, relative to the rational corpus of level 1, is greater than r. More precisely, if S is a sentence of our language, and the probability of S, relative to the rational corpus of level 1 and basis F, $_1RC_F$, is the pair of fractions (p, q), and $\ulcorner p > r \urcorner$, is a theorem, then $S \in {}_rRC_F$. The contents of the rational corpus of level r is only made precise, of course, when we have made precise the definition of probability in our language, and this, as remarked earlier, requires settling on a set of rational classes. This is not a trivial problem, but it is supposed that it will be done on *a priori* grounds—i.e., that it is built into the language as it stands that, for example, 'grue' is not an appropriate predicate. The monadic case has been discussed in the chapter on epistemological probability. Here I shall only add that it is conceivable, after all, that all emeralds are grue; but for us to have *reason* to *believe* that all emeralds are grue would be for us to have reason to accept a new theory about the world; one of the characteristics of a *theory* is that it enlarges or changes the set of classes or properties we regard as rational. In this new theory it might be that 'green' was no longer a rational and useful predicate.

We can prove that rational belief is hereditary from the higher-level rational corpus to the lower-level rational corpus—that is, any statement S which is a member of $_1RC_F$ will also be a member of $_rRC_F$. Thus in particular $_rRC_F$ will be deductively closed with respect to the elements of F and with respect to logical and mathematical truths, because $_1RC_F$ is deductively closed. We can also prove that is S is any statement in a rational corpus (of any level) and $\ulcorner S \supset T \urcorner$ is a logical truth, then T will also be a member of that rational corpus.

Nevertheless it is not the case that $_rRC_F$ is deductively closed. The condition that Levi regards as supremely important, the condition of deductive cogency, is not satisfied. My intuition is that no grounds can be offered for failing to accept the statement 'ticket 1 will not win' which cannot equally well be applied to many a scientific hypothesis. Levi shows merely that there are ultimate partitions which will not allow the acceptance of 'ticket i will not win'; the same is true of any statement S not entailed by the evidence. His intuition demands deductive cogency; my intuition demands a once-for-all (for a *given* body of evidence, and *given* choice of r) acceptance or non-acceptance of a statement. But as he says (p. 42), the only way to put such conflicting intuitions to the test is to develop the systems of inductive logic to which they lead.

What is the nature of the inductive logic based on the system of rational corpora and the epistemological interpretation of probability? Relative to the rational corpus of level 1, all our inductive inferences are strictly statistical. In the rational corpus of level 1, however, there are a number of (logically true) statistical statements—e.g., that the proportion of samples of 1000 objects from a population of A's that reflect within limits $\pm\epsilon$ the proportion of B's among A's, for example, lies between 0.91 and 1.0. This proportion depends on the value of the parameter p true of the population of A's. But at the very worst, if $p = \frac{1}{2}$, the proportion of ϵ-representative samples will be 0.91, while if $p = 0$ or $p = 1$, all the samples will be ϵ-representative. Suppose that our evidence is a description of a sample of 1000 A's containing 400 B's, which, relative to $_1RC_F$, is a random member of the set of all 1000 member samples of A's with respect to the property of being ϵ-representative. It is not at all implausible that these conditions might be met; remember that under the characterization of epistemological randomness offered earlier, the *onus probandi* is on the person who wishes to deny randomness; most of the time, to be successful in establishing that an entity is *not* a random member of one set with respect to a certain property is *ipso facto* to establish that it is a random member of another set with respect to that property.

We may plausibly have, then, the grounds for asserting that relative to the rational corpus of level 1 and basis F, the probability that our particular 1000-member sample, of which 400 members are B's, is ϵ-representative is (0.91, 1.0). In a rational corpus of level 0.9, then, we can simply accept the statement that this sample is ϵ-representative. But that this particular sample is ϵ-representative is logically equivalent to the statement that the measure of B's among A's differs from the ratio in the sample by less than ϵ. In turn this justifies our acceptance, in the rational corpus of level 0.9, of the measure-theoretic statement '$\%(A, B, 0.4 - \epsilon, 0.4 + \epsilon)$'.

Let us pause to consider the probability statements we can make about A's, relative to these rational corpora. Let a be a member of A. If a happens to be a member of our sample, and we happen to know that it is a B (i.e., if '$a \in B$' belongs to F), then of course a will not be a random member of A, with respect to B, relative to our rational corpus of any level. There may be information in our rational corpus of level 0.90, for example, which prevents 'the next A to be observed' from being a random member of A with respect to belonging to B, relative to that rational corpus. Such will be the case if, for example, we happen to have found some periodicities in our original 1000-member sample. But let us suppose that a is a random member of A, with respect to B, relative to our rational corpus of level 0.9. Then we will be able to say that the probability that it is a B is $(0.4 - \epsilon, 0.4 + \epsilon)$.

In a similar vein we may consider a rational corpus of level 0.8. In general we shall be able to include a stronger statistical statement concerning the measure of B in A in the rational corpus of that level than in the rational corpus of the higher level. Suppose that in the rational corpus of that level, and the same basis, we find that we can include the statistical statement '$\%(A, B, 0.4 - \delta, 0.4 + \delta)$', where $\delta < \epsilon$. If a is a random member of A with respect to B, relative to the rational corpus of level 0.8, then the probability that a is a B, relative to the rational corpus of this level and basis, will be $(0.4 - \delta, 0.4 + \delta)$. Observe that the truth values of the two logical statements 'a is a random member of A with respect to B relative to the rational corpus of level 0.8 and basis F' and 'a is a random member of A with respect to B, relative to the rational corpus of level 0.9 and basis F' are independent, and both are independent of 'a is a random member of A with respect to B, relative to the rational corpus $_1RC_F$'. In general, if the first is true, the second and third will be true; but whether or not this is the case in a particular instance depends on the actual contents F of the rational corpora in question.

Relative to the rational corpus of level 1 and basis F there is a perfectly sound, but not very interesting, probability statement that can be made. If A and B are empirically defined classes, all we will be able to say a priori is that the measure in the A's of things that are B's falls in the interval $(0, 1)$, endpoints included. So that if a is a random member of A, with respect to B relative to the rational corpus of level 1 and basis F (which it won't be, if we happen to have observed that particular a), then the probability that a will belong to B, relative to this rational corpus will be $(0, 1)$.

A more general treatment of statistical inference would consider not merely simple measures of the sort contemplated here, but general probability distributions. Most of the detachable conclusions such a theory will be concerned with that are of interest from an applied point of view will be detached from the rational corpus in which general (well-supported) empirical statements appear. But any detailed consideration of these questions would take us too far afield.

One particular case that concerns us is that which leads, through the agency of a supplementary principle, to universal generalizations. Let us suppose that we have examined 1000 C's, and found that they were all D's. By an argument similar to the above, under appropriate conditions of randomness, we will be able to detach and accept into the rational corpus of level 0.9 the statistical statement '$\%(C, D, 0 - \epsilon, 1)$'.

Assuming randomness, the corresponding probability statements we have concerning an individual a are as follows. Relative to the rational corpus of level 0.9 and basis F, the probability that a is a D is $(1 - \epsilon, 1)$, where $1 - \epsilon$, let us suppose, is greater than 0.9. Relative to the rational corpus of level 1 and basis F, the probability that a belongs to D is $(0, 1)$. But if a is a random member of C with respect to D, relative to the rational corpus of level 0.9 and basis F, then the statement '$a \in D$' is as probable (though relative to a rational corpus not of the highest level) as any of those statements included among the statements of the rational corpus of level 0.9.

All of the foregoing holds, even when it is known that there are C's that are not D's. Of course any individual a that is known to be a C and *not* a D will fail to be a random member of C with respect to D, relative to the rational corpus of level 0.9, and so, of course, in those circumstances the probability of '$a \in D$' will be $(0, 0)$ rather than $(1 - \epsilon, 1)$. When it is *not* known that there are any C's that are not D's, a special situation arises. Suppose that '$(\exists x)(x \in C \& \sim x \in D)$' does not appear in any of the rational corpora we are considering. This precludes not only our having observed any C's that are not D's, but also our having any theoretical grounds for supposing that there is a C which is not a D. Consider any individual a who is known to belong to

C. Two possibilities exist: either a is a random member of C, with respect to D, relative to the rational corpus of level 0.9; or else it is a member of some class K, about which we have conflicting or more precise information. In the first case, we will be able to regard '$a \in D$' as overwhelmingly probable relative to the rational corpus of level 0.9. In the second case, if all we are worrying about is more precise information, we will again have grounds for asserting that '$a \in D$' is overwhelmingly probable relative to the rational corpus of level 0.9. It is doubtful that the case of conflict can arise without yielding grounds for accepting '$(\exists x)(x \in C$ & $\sim x \in D)$' in the rational corpus of level 0.9.

Thus if the statement '$(\exists x)(x \in C$ & $\sim x \in D)$' does not occur in any rational corpus, then every time '$a \in C$' occurs in the rational corpus of level 0.9, '$a \in D$' will be overwhelmingly probable relative to that rational corpus. This is tantamount to accepting the generalization '$(x)(x \in C$ & $\sim x \in D)$' in the rational corpus of level 0.9. So let us include the generalization in this rational corpus, provided we have no grounds for including the contradictory existential statement in any rational corpus. We preserve precisely the degree of deductive cogency we had before—no contradiction can arise, for the general statement leads us to accept no particular statements that we would not already have been almost authorized to accept by the statistical statement. The general statement is not authorized by our purely probabilistic rule of acceptance, but its acceptance leads to the acceptance of no new statements that are in conflict with those authorized by purely probabilistic rule. Thus we may add:

> If no statement of the form $\ulcorner(\exists x)(x \in \phi$ & $\sim x \in \psi)\urcorner$ appears in either of the rational corpora $_1RC_F$ or $_rRC_F$, and the statistical statement $\ulcorner\%(\phi, \psi, r, 1)\urcorner$ belongs to the rational corpus $_rRC_F$ then the universal generalization $\ulcorner(x)(x \in \phi \supset x \in \psi)\urcorner$ may be accepted in the rational corpus of level $_rRC_F$.

This supplementary rule, of course, contains a reference to F; any alteration in F may of course alter the situation with respect to the acceptability of the generalization. Not only may we observe an entity b which is ϕ but not ψ—i.e., which requires us to accept $\ulcorner b \in \phi$ & $\sim b \in \psi\urcorner$ and therefore $\ulcorner(\exists x)$ $(x \in \phi$ & $\sim x \in \psi)\urcorner$ in all our rational corpora, but we may simply expand our knowledge in such a way that on very indirect grounds we come to include $\ulcorner(\exists x)(x \in \phi$ & $\sim x \in \psi)\urcorner$ in the rational corpus of level r.

Given the presence of universal generalizations in the rational corpus of level r, it is easy to see how inductive evidence may lead us to regard other universal generalizations as overwhelmingly probable relative to the rational corpus of level 0.9 by means of essentially deductive arguments of the kind considered in detail in an earlier chapter. Such arguments require universal empirical premises; but we have now seen how these premises can sometimes be provided.

Theories are often regarded as complex universal generalizations. As such, they could perhaps be handled by the foregoing techniques. Another way of looking at theories, however, would be to regard them as conceptual frameworks. In the latter case, we might find it advantageous to restrict our concerns to the truth of the consequences of a theory, in effect including a theory in the rational corpus of level r and basis F, provided that there is no counterinstance in that rational corpus. (The claim that theories are accepted when it is known that some of their consequences are false is unwarranted; a far more plausible way of looking at the matter is to say that a different theory, more restricted in scope than the old theory, has replaced the old theory.) Certain elements of a theory are embedded in the language, and thus in the rational corpus of the highest level. Other elements will be included in the rational corpus of level r on quite ordinary grounds. What is at issue here is merely whether there are elements of general theories which require, for their acceptance, rules differing from the rule proposed above for simple generalizations. This is an extremely knotty problem in the philosophy of science. There are many writers who regard the role of theories as essentially that of providing conceptual frameworks in which the inductive part of science is carried on. Pierre Duhem, F. P. Ramsey and, most recently, T. Kuhn are among the best-known of such writers. Since their primary claim is that the criteria for adopting theories are quite completely distinct from criteria for accepting empirical hypotheses, we shall not attempt to review their conclusions and arguments.

It is inappropriate for me to presume to assess the defects of my own system. However, three features that are regarded as defects by some people deserve to be mentioned. First, there is the interpretation of probability which is the basis of the system. This interpretation has a number of awkward features, already commented upon. There is the lack of a probability calculus which provides for easy calculation; there is the complexity of the definition of randomness. Second, there is the failure of deductive cogency for the rational corpora of level r. By some writers (Levi, for example) this is regarded as fatal. Finally, there is a problem which affects my system no less because it also arises in other systems, and that is the problem of choosing a set of predicates to be regarded as rational. In the case of a first-order logic containing monadic predicates, the proposal outlined earlier seems reasonable enough; but the system briefly described here can't get off the ground on the basis of that slender a language. A great deal more must be done by way of distinguishing, no doubt on the basis of a given primitive vocabulary, both ostensive and theoretical, the expressions which are going to be taken as standing for possible reference classes and for plausibly projectible properties, and those that are not. This is a necessity for nearly all the approaches to induction considered here.

Much work has been done in recent years, both on the interpretation of the probability concept and on the analysis of inductive logic. The greatest strides have been made in the analysis of statistical inference, and yet statisticians are largely divided into two or three quite widely separated schools. Various systems of inductive logic and various approaches to inductive logic have been proposed. Many of the prejudices of earlier years have been shaken off. But as is clear from the foregoing, the job is far from complete; there is a large field, nubile, if not virgin, calling for the future efforts of devoted scholars.

EXERCISES

1. In a language containing three one-place logically independent predicates, $P_1 \cdots P_3$, and eight individual constants, how many constituents are there? List them. How many state descriptions are there? How many state descriptions are there in each of the constituents? (Hint: the number of ways of putting n distinct individuals into r distinct containers, in such a way that no container is empty, is given by the formula

$$A(n, r) = \sum_{i=0}^{r} (-1)^i \binom{r}{i} (r - i)^n.$$

2. Suppose that a scientist believes that there is just one organism necessary to the occurrence of the common cold, and that it is either virus A, virus B, or virus C. What is the question he is concerned with? What is his ultimate partition? What is the total set of relevant answers? Suppose an experimental program results in the evidence e. Suppose that the conditional probability of finding that evidence, if virus A is responsible for colds, $P(e|H_A)$, is 0.1; that $P(e|H_B) = 0.4$; and that $P(e|H_C) = 0.1$; and suppose the antecedent probabilities of the three hypotheses are $P(H_A) = 0.5$; $P(H_B) = 0.3$; $P(H_C) = 0.2$. If the scientist takes $q = 1$, what does he accept? If the scientist takes $q = \frac{1}{2}$, what does he accept?

3. Show that $_rRC_F$ is deductively closed with respect to the members of F. Show that if S is any statements in a rational corpus, and $\ulcorner S \supset T \urcorner$ is a logical truth, then T will also belong to that rational corpus. Show that if S is a member of $_1RC_F$ and T is a member of $_rRC_F$ then $\ulcorner S \& T \urcorner$ is a member of $_rRC_F$.

4. In the framework provided by the theory of rational corpora, analyze the common-sense claim that because 51% of recorded births have been births of males (a) approximately 51% of all births are births of males, and (b) the probability that Mr. Jones' first child will be a boy is about 0.51, and (c) the probability that my daughter is a boy is zero.

5. In the framework provided by the theory of rational corpora, analyze the common-sense claim that because all the crows that anybody has seen have been black, (a) probably practically all crows are black; (b) probably all crows are black; (c) it is practically certain that the next crow you will see will be black.

BIBLIOGRAPHICAL NOTES FOR CHAPTER 14

Jaakko Hintikka's approach to inductive logic is to be found in "Towards a Theory of Inductive Generalization," *Proceedings of the 1964 International Congress for Logic, Methodology, and Philosophy of Science* (Bar-Hillel; ed.), North-Holland, Amsterdam, 1965, pp. 274–88; "Distributive Normal Forms in First-order Logic," in *Formal Systems and Recursive Functions, Proceedings of the Eighth Logic Colloquium*, Oxford, 1963 (Crossley and Dummet, eds.), North-Holland, Amsterdam, 1965, pp. 48–91; "On a Combined System of Inductive Logic," *Studia Logico-Mathematica et Philosophica in Honorem Rolf Nevalinna, Acta Philosophica Fennica* **18**, 1965, pp. 21–30; and "A Two-Dimensional Continuum of Inductive Methods," in *Aspects of Inductive Logic* (Hintikka and Suppes, eds.), North-Holland, Amsterdam, 1956, pp. 113–32. In the same volume there is "Knowledge, Acceptance, and Inductive Logic," pp. 1–20, by Hintikka and Risto Hilpinen; "Inductive Generalization in an Ordered Universe," pp. 155–74, by Raimo Tuomela; and "On Inductive Generalization in Monadic First-Order Logic with Identity," pp. 133–54, by Risto Hilpinen. All quotations are taken from *Aspects of Inductive Logic*.

Levi's work is to be found mainly in his book *Gambling with the Truth*, Alfred A. Knopf, New York, 1967, from which all quotations have been taken. Other relevant articles of his are "Belief and Action," *The Monist* **48**, 1964, pp. 306–16; "Corroboration and Rules of Acceptance," *British Journal for the Philosophy of Science* **13**, 1963; "On the Seriousness of Mistakes," *Philosophy of Science* **29**, 1962, pp. 307–13; "Decision Theory and Confirmation," *Journal of Philosophy* **58**, 1961, pp. 614–25, and "Must the Scientist make Value Judgements?" *Journal of Philosophy* **57**, 1960, pp. 345–57. Of relevance to the problem of deciding what are relevant answers to a question, which is of fundamental importance in Levi's system, are two works by David Harrah: "A Logic of Questions and Answers," *Philosophy of Science* **28**, 1961; and *Communication: A Logical Model*, MIT Press, Cambridge, Massachusetts, 1963.

My own views are developed most completely in *Probability and the Logic of Rational Belief*, Wesleyan University Press, Middletown, Connecticut, 1961. The system presented there was demolished by Fred Schick, in "Consistency and Rationality," *Journal of Philosophy* **60**, 1963, pp. 5–19. A repair, similar to the one embodied here, was made in "Probability, Rationality and a Rule of Detachment," *Proceedings of the 1964 Congress for Logic, Methodology, and Philosophy of Science* (Bar-Hillel, ed.), North-Holland, Amsterdam, 1965, pp. 301–10. Other relevant publications of mine are "A Further Note on Rationality and Consistency," *Journal of Philosophy* **60**, 1963, pp. 463–65; "The Rule of Detachment in Inductive Logic?" *Proceedings of an International Colloquium on Inductive Logic* (Lakatos, ed.), North-Holland, Amsterdam, 1968, pp. 98–165; "Probability and Rationality," *Philosophical Quarterly* **11**, 1961, pp. 3–10.

A comprehensive study of many of the questions that are at issue in this chapter is Fred Schick's perceptive and penetrating article "Consistency," *Philosophical Review* **75**, 1966, pp. 467–94, in which Levi's approach is discussed.

Pierre Duhem's views are to be found in *The Aim and Structure of Physical Theory*, Princeton University Press, Princeton, New Jersey, 1954. F. P. Ramsey's are to be found in his essay "General Propositions and Causality," in *Foundations of Mathematics and Other Essays*, Routledge and Kegan Paul, London, 1931. T. Kuhn's original and controversial ideas are expressed in *The Structure of Scientific Revolutions*, University of Chicago Press, Chicago, 1962.

Bibliography

The following bibliography is intended to include as much as possible of what has been written in recent years that is of potential interest to students of Probability and Induction. There has been, of course, the problem of where to draw the line. For example, I have included a few good textbooks on probability and on statistical inference, though there would be no point in trying to include many of them. Papers by such people as R. A. Fisher and Jerzy Neyman run the spectrum from quite discursive and philosophical to highly mathematical and technical. I have attempted rather arbitrarily to choose those papers that seemed to me of greatest philosophical interest, and to leave the others out. On the other side there are many philosophical investigations in epistemology that depend on, and therefore include some discussion of, inductive inference; and there are meta-physical discussions that concern causality as it is allegedly required as a ground for the soundness of induction. In all such cases the line between what it is appropriate to include and what it is not appropriate to include, is a hard one to draw, and I have drawn it arbitrarily. I have made a serious effort, however, not to leave out anything of direct relevance to questions of probability and induction published in the last twenty years: 1948–1968.

Such a long bibliography would be hard to use, lacking some degree of guidance. I have therefore starred (*) those entries that seem to me the most significant of recent years. Many interesting and important articles and books are unstarred: either because they concern matters discussed in sources already starred, or because the matters they concern seem too specialized. I have tried to draw attention to the big books that everyone ought to know about in this field, regardless of what specific problem he happens to be interested in.

I have made use of the bibliography compiled by R. Slaght for a different purpose, and I profited from suggestions of many friends and colleagues. My greatest debt, however, is to Mrs. Ruth Spall and Mrs. Karen DeVisser for performing the miraculous transformation of a mess of three-by-five cards into an orderly and coherent list of articles and books that will, I hope, be as useful to others as it has been to me, and to Miss Donna Anderton, who performed the laborious jobs of checking incomplete references and providing cross references.

Abelson, Raziel, review of Lerner's *Evidence and Inference* in *Philosophy and Phenomenological Research*, **21**, 1960–61, pp. 413–414.

Abruzzi, Adam, "Problems of Inference in the Socio-Physical Sciences," *Journal of Philosophy*, **51**, 1954, pp. 537–549.

Achinstein, Peter, "From Success to Truth," *Analysis*, **21**, 1960–61, pp. 6–9.

Achinstein, Peter, "The Circularity of a Self-Supporting Inductive Argument," *Analysis*, **22**, 1961–62, pp. 138–141.

Achinstein, Peter, "Circularity and Induction," *Analysis*, **23**, 1962–63, pp. 123–127.

Achinstein, Peter, "Variety and Analogy in Confirmation Theory," *Philosophy of Science*, **30**, 1963, pp. 207–221.

Achinstein, Peter, "Models, Analogies, and Theories," *Philosophy of Science*, **31**, 1964, pp. 328–350.

Achinstein, Peter, "On the Meaning of Scientific Terms," *Journal of Philosophy*, **61**, 1964, pp. 497–509.

Achinstein, Peter, "The Problem of Theoretical Terms," *American Philosophical Quarterly*, **2**, 1965, pp. 193–203.

Achinstein, Peter and S. F. Barker, "On the New Riddle of Induction," *Philosophical Review*, **69**, 1960, pp. 511–522.

Ackermann, Robert, "Inductive Simplicity," *Philosophy of Science*, **28**, 1961, pp. 152–161.

Ackermann, Robert, "Some Remarks on Kyburg's Modest Proposal," *Philosophical Review*, **71**, 1962, pp. 236–240.

Ackermann, Robert, "Inductive Simplicity in Special Cases," *Synthese*, **15**, 1963, pp. 436–444.

Ackermann, Robert, *Nondeductive Inference*. New York: Dover, 1966.

Ackermann, Robert, "Discussion: Projecting Unprojectibles," *Philosophy of Science*, **33**, 1966, pp. 70–75.

Ackermann, Robert, "Conflict and Decision," *Philosophy of Science*, **34**, 1967, pp. 188–193.

Ackoff, R. and C. W. Churchman, *Methods of Inquiry*. St. Louis, Mo.: Educational Publishers, 1950.

Adams, Ernest W., "The Logic of Conditionals," *Inquiry*, **8**, 1965, pp. 166–197.

Adams, Ernest W., "Probability and the Logic of Conditionals" in Hintikka and Suppes (eds.), *Aspects of Inductive Logic*, 1966, pp. 265–316.

Agassi, Joseph, "Corroboration Versus Induction," *British Journal for the Philosophy of Science*, **9**, 1958–59, pp. 311–317.

Agassi, Joseph, "The Role of Corroboration in Popper's Methodology," *Australasian Journal of Philosophy*, **39**, 1961, pp. 82–91.

Agassi, Joseph, "Empiricism and Inductivism," *Philosophical Studies*, **14**, 1963, pp. 85–86.

Agassi, Joseph, "Analogies as Generalizations," *Philosophy of Science*, **31**, 1964, pp. 351–356.

Agassi, Joseph, "The Mystery of the Ravens," *Philosophy of Science*, **33**, 1966, pp. 395–402.

Alexander, H. Gavin, "General Statements as Rules of Inference," *Minnesota Studies in the Philosophy of Science*, II, 1958, pp. 309–329.

Alexander, H. Gavin, "The Paradoxes of Confirmation," *British Journal for the Philosophy of Science*, **9**, 1958–59, pp. 227–233.

Alexander, H. Gavin, "The Paradoxes of Confirmation—A Reply to Dr. Agassi," *British Journal for the Philosophy of Science*, **10**, 1959–60, pp. 229–234.

Alexander, H. Gavin, "Convention, Falsification, and Induction," *Proceedings of the Aristotelian Society*, Supplementary Volume XXXIV, 1960, pp. 131–144.

Ambrose, A., "The Problem of Justifying Inductive Inference," *Journal of Philosophy*, **44**, 1947, pp. 253–272.

Angel, R. B., "Explanation and Prediction, and Plea for Reason," *Philosophy of Science*, **34**, 1967, pp. 276–282.

Anscombe, F. J., "Mr. Kneale on Probability and Induction," *Mind*, **60**, 1951, pp. 299–309.

Anscombe, F. J., "Bayesian Statistics," *American Statistician*, **15**, 1961, pp. 21–24.

Anscombe, F. J., "Bayesian Inference Concerning Many Parameters, with Reference to Supersaturated Designs," *Bulletin of the International Statistical Institute*, **40**, 1963, pp. 721–733.

Arrow, Kenneth J., "Alternative Approaches to the Theory of Choice in Risk-Taking Situations," *Econometrica*, **19**, 1951, 404–437. (Reprinted: *Cowles Commission Paper* No. 51, Chicago, 1952.)

Arrow, Kenneth J., "Exposition of the Theory of Choice Under Uncertainty," *Synthese*, **16**, 1964, pp. 253–269.

Ashby, W. Ross, "Induction, Prediction, and Decision-Making in Cybernetic Systems" in Kyburg and Nagel (eds.), *Induction: Some Current Issues*, pp. 55–68.

Atkinson, R. F., "The Gambler's Fallacy—A Reply to Mr. Simopoulos," *Analysis*, **16**, 1955, pp. 66–68.

Axinn, Sidney, "Fallacy of the Single Risk," *Philosophy of Science*, **33**, 1966, pp. 154–162.

Ayer, A. J., "The Conception of Probability as a Logical Relation," Korner (ed.), *The Colston Papers*, **9**, 1957, pp. 12–17.

Ayer, A. J., "On the Probability of Particular Events," *Revue Internationale de Philosophie*, **15**, 1961, pp. 366–375.

Bar-Hillel, Yehoshua, "A Note on State Descriptions," *Philosophical Studies*, 2, 1951, pp. 72–75.

Bar-Hillel, Yehoshua, "A Note on Comparative Inductive Logic," *British Journal for the Philosophy of Science*, 3, 1952–53, pp. 308–310.

Bar-Hillel, Yehoshua, "An Examination of Information Theory," *Philosophy of Science*, 22, 1955, pp. 86–105.

Bar-Hillel, Yehoshua, "Comments on 'Degree of Confirmation' by Professor K. R. Popper," *British Journal for the Philosophy of Science*, 6, 1955–56, pp. 155–157.

Bar-Hillel, Yehoshua, "Further Comments on Probability and Confirmation," *British Journal for the Philosophy of Science*, 7, 1956–57, pp. 245–248.

Bar-Hillel, Yehoshua, "Information and Content: A Semantic Analysis," *Synthese*, 9, 1953–55, pp. 299–305.

Bar-Hillel, Yehoshua, "On an Alleged Contradiction in Carnap's Theory of Inductive Logic," *Mind*, 73, 1964, pp. 265–267.

Bar-Hillel, Yehoshua, *Language and Information*. Reading, Mass.: Addison-Wesley, 1964.

Bar-Hillel, Yehoshua, "On Alleged Rules of Detachment in Inductive Logic," Lakatos (ed.), *The Problem of Inductive Logic*, Amsterdam: North-Holland Publishing Company, 1968, pp. 120–128.

Bar-Hillel, Yehoshua and Rudolf Carnap, *An Outline of the Theory of Semantic Information*. Technical Report No. 247, Research Laboratory of Electronics, Massachusetts Institute of Technology, 1952.

Bar-Hillel, Yehoshua and Rudolph Carnap, "Semantic Information," *The British Journal for the Philosophy of Science*, 4, 1953–54, pp. 145–157.

Bar-Hillel, Yehoshua (ed.), *Logic, Methodology and Philosophy of Science*, II. Amsterdam: North-Holland Publishing Company, 1965.

Barker, S. F., *Induction and Hypothesis: A Study of the Logic of Confirmation*. Ithaca: Cornell University Press, 1957.

Barker, S. F., review of von Wright's *The Logical Problem of Induction* in *Journal of Philosophy*, 55, 1958, pp. 130–131.

Barker, S. F., review of Jeffreys' *Scientific Inference* in *Philosophical Review*, 67, 1958, pp. 404–407.

Barker, S. F., "Comments on Salmon's 'Vindication of Induction'," in Feigl and Maxwell (eds.), *Current Issues in the Philosophy of Science*, 1961, pp. 257–260.

Barker, S. F., "The Role of Simplicity in Explanation," Feigl and Maxwell (eds.), *Current Issues in the Philosophy of Science*, 1961, pp. 265–273.

Barker, S. F., "Rejoinder to Salmon" in Feigl and Maxwell (eds.), *Current Issues in the Philosophy of Science*, 1961, pp. 276–278.

Barker, S. F., "On Simplicity in Empirical Hypotheses," *Philosophy of Science*, 28, 1961, pp. 162–171.

Barker, S. F. and P. Achinstein, "On the New Riddle of Induction," *Philosophical Review*, 69, 1960, pp. 511–522.

Barnard, George A., "Statistical Inference," *Journal of the Royal Statistical Society (B)*, 11, 1949, pp. 116–149.

Barnard, George A., "Comments on Savage," in Barnard and Cox (eds.), *Foundations of Statistical Inference*, 1962, pp. 39–49.

Barnard, George A., "Logical Aspects of the Fiducial Argument," *Bulletin of the International Statistical Institute*, 40, 1963, pp. 870–883.

Barnard, George A. and D. R. Cox (eds.), *The Foundations of Statistical Inference.* New York: John Wiley and Sons, Inc., 1962.

Barnard, George A., Jenkens and Winsten, "Likelihood Inference and Time Series," *Journal of the Royal Statistical Society,* (*A*), **125**, 1962, pp. 321–327.

Barrett, W., "The Present State of the Problem of Induction," *Theoria,* **6**, 1940, pp. 151–157.

Bartlett, M. S., "Probability in Logic, Mathematics, and Science," *Dialectica,* **3**, 1949, pp. 104–113.

Bartlett, M. S., "Comments on Savage," in Barnard and Cox (eds.), *Foundations of Statistical Inference,* 1962, pp. 36–39.

Bartley, W. W., III, "A Note on Barker's Discussion of Popper's Theory of Corroboration," *Philosophical Studies,* **12**, 1961, pp. 5–10.

Bartley, W. W., III, "Goodman's Paradox: A Simple-minded Solution," *Philosophical Studies,* **19**, 1968, pp. 85–88.

Baumer, William H., "Evidence and Ideal Evidence," *Philosophy and Phenomenological Research,* **24**, 1963–64, pp. 567–572.

Baumer, William H., "Confirmation Without Paradoxes," *British Journal for the Philosophy of Science,* **15**, 1964–65, pp. 177–195.

Baumer, William H., "Invalidly Invalidating a Paradox," *Philosophical Quarterly* **15**, 1965, pp. 350–352.

Baumer, William H., "The One Systematically Ambiguous Concept of Probability," *Philosophy and Phenomenological Research,* **28**, 1967–68, pp. 264–268.

Bennet, Jonathan F., "Some Aspects of Probability and Induction (I)," *British Journal for the Philosophy of Science,* **7**, 1956–57, pp. 220–230.

Bennet, Jonathan F., "Some Aspects of Probability and Induction (II)," *British Journal for the Philosophy of Science,* **7**, 1956–57, pp. 316–322.

Berenda, C. W., "On Verifiability, Simplicity, and Equivalence," *Philosophy of Science,* **19**, 1952–53, pp. 70–76.

Bergmann, Gustav, "The Logic of Probability," *American Journal of Physics,* **9**, 1941, pp. 263–272.

Bergmann, Gustav, "Frequencies, Probabilities, and Positivism," *Philosophy and Phenomenological Research,* **6**, 1945–46, pp. 26–44.

Bergmann, Gustav, "Some Comments on Carnap's Logic of Induction," *Philosophy of Science,* **13**, 1946, pp. 71–78.

Berkson, Joseph, "Smoking and Lung Cancer," *American Statistician,* **17**, October, 1963, pp. 15–22.

Berlyne, Daniel E., "The Motivation of Inductive Behavior" in Kyburg and Nagel (eds.), *Induction: Some Current Issues,* pp. 74–92.

Beveridge, W. I. B., review of Wisdom's *Foundations of Inference in Natural Science* in *British Journal for the Philosophy of Science,* **3**, 1952–53, pp. 291–293.

Birnbaum, Allen, "Intrinsic Confidence Methods," *Bulletin de l'Institut International de Statistique,* 33ᵉ session, Paris, 1961.

Birnbaum, Allen, "Confidence Curves: An Omnibus Technique for Estimation and Testing Statistical Hypotheses," *Journal of the American Statistical Association,* **56**, June, 1961, pp. 246–249.

Birnbaum, Allan, "A Unified Theory of Estimation," *Annals of Mathematical Statistics,* **32**, 1961, pp. 112–135.

Birnbaum, Allan, "On the Foundations of Statistical Inference: Binary Experiments," *Annals of Mathematical Statistics,* **32**, 1961, pp. 414–435.

Birnbaum, Allan, "Another View on the Foundations of Statistics," *American Statistician*, **16**, 1962, pp. 17–21.

* Birnbaum, Allan, "On the Foundations of Statistical Inference," *Journal of the American Statistical Association*, **57**, 1962, pp. 269–306.

Black, Max, *Language and Philosophy*. Ithaca: Cornell University Press, 1949.

Black, Max, "The Justification of Induction," in his *Language and Philosophy*, 1949, pp. 59–88.

Black, Max, (ed.), *Philosophical Analysis*. Englewood Cliffs, N. J.: Prentice-Hall, 1963.

Black, Max, *Problems of Analysis*. Ithaca: Cornell University Press, 1950 and 1963.

Black, Max, "How Difficult Might Induction Be?," in his *Problems of Analysis*, 1954, pp. 209–225.

Black, Max, "'Pragmatic' Justifications of Induction," in his *Problems of Analysis*, 1954, pp. 157–190.

Black, Max, "Inductive Support of Inductive Rules," in his *Problems of Analysis*, 1954, pp. 191–208.

Black, Max, "Self-Supporting Inductive Arguments," *Journal of Philosophy*, **55**, 1958, pp. 718–725.

Black, Max, "Induction and Probability," Raymond Klibansky, *Philosophy in Mid-Century*, I, 1958, pp. 154–163.

Black, Max, "Can Induction be Vindicated?," *Philosophical Studies*, **10**, 1959, pp. 5–16.

Black, Max, *Models and Metaphors*. Ithaca: Cornell University Press, 1962.

Black, Max, "Self-Support and Circularity: A Reply to Mr. Achinstein," *Analysis*, **23**, 1962–63, pp. 43–44.

Black, Max, "Comments on Salmon's Paper" in Kyburg and Nagel (eds.), *Induction: Some Current Issues*, 1963, pp. 42–44.

Black, Max, "Notes on the 'Paradoxes of Confirmation'," Hintikka and Suppes (eds.), *Aspects of Inductive Logic*, 1966, pp. 175–197.

Black, Max, "The Raison d'être of Inductive Argument," *British Journal for the Philosophy of Science*, **17**, 1966–67, pp. 177–204.

Blackwell, David and Lester Dubins, "Merging of Opinions with Increasing Information," *Annals of Mathematical Statistics*, **33**, September, 1962, pp. 882–886.

* Blackwell, David and M. A. Girshick, *Theory of Games and Statistical Decisions*. New York: John Wiley and Sons, 1954.

Blom, Siri, "Concerning a Controversy on the Meaning of 'Probability'," *Theoria*, **21**, 1955, pp. 65–98.

Boden, Margaret, "The Paradox of Explanation," *Proceedings of the Aristotelian Society*, New Series, **62**, 1961–62, pp. 159–178.

Bohnert, Herbert G., "Communication by Ramsay—Sentence Clause," *Philosophy of Science*, **34**, 1967, pp. 341–347.

Bohnert, Herbert G., "In Defense of Ramsey's Elimination," *Journal of Philosophy*, **65**, 1968, pp. 275–281.

Bolker, Ethan, "A Simultaneous Axiomatization of Utility and 'Subjective Probability'," *Philosophy of Science*, **34**, 1967, pp. 333–340.

Braithwaite, Richard Bevan, *Scientific Explanation, a Study of the Function of Theory, Probability and Law in Science*. Cambridge: Cambridge University Press, 1953.

Braithwaite, Richard Bevan, "Moral Principles and Inductive Policies," *Proceedings of the British Academy*, 1950, pp. 51–68.

Braithwaite, Richard Bevan, *Theory of Games as a Tool for the Moral Philosopher*. New York: Cambridge University Press, 1955.

Braithwaite, Richard Bevan, "On Unknown Probabilities," Körner (ed.), *The Colston Papers*, **9**, 1957, pp. 3–11.

Braithwaite, Richard Bevan, "The Role of Values in Scientific Inference" in Kyburg and Nagel (eds.), *Induction: Some Current Issues*, 1963, pp. 180–193.

Braithwaite, Richard Bevan, "Why is it Reasonable to Base a Betting Rate Upon an Estimate of Chance?," *Logic, Methodology and Philosophy of Science*, Yehoshua Bar-Hillel (ed.). Amsterdam: North-Holland Publishing Company, 1965, pp. 263–274.

Broad, C. D., "The Principles of Problematic Induction," *Proceedings of the Aristotelian Society*, **28**, 1927–28, pp. 1–46.

Broad, C. D., "On the Relation Between Induction and Probability (I)," *Mind*, **27**, 1918, pp. 389–404.

Broad, C. D., "On the Relation Between Induction and Probability (II)," *Mind*, **29**, 1920, pp. 11–45.

Broad, C. D., "The Principles of Demonstrative Induction (I), (II)," *Mind*, **39**, 1930, pp. 320–317; 426–439.

Broad, C. D., review of Kneale's *Probability and Induction*, *Mind*, **59**, 1950, pp. 94–115.

Brodbeck, M., "The New Rationalism: Dewey's Theory of Induction," *Journal of Philosophy*, **46**, 1949, pp. 780–791.

Brodbeck, M., "An Analytic Principle of Induction?," *Journal of Philosophy*, **49**, 1952, pp. 747–750.

Brody, B. A., "Confirmation and Explanation," *Journal of Philosophy*, **65**, 1968, pp. 282–299.

Bronowski, Jacob, *The Common Sense of Science*. Cambridge: Harvard University Press, 1953.

Bronowski, Jacob, *Science and Human Values*. New York: J. Messner, 1956.

Bronowski, Jacob, "The Scandal of Philosophy," *British Journal for the Philosophy of Science*, **8**, 1957–58, pp. 329–334.

Brown, G. Spencer, *Probability and Scientific Inference*. New York: Longmans, Green and Company, 1957.

Brown, G. Spencer, "Randomness," *Proceedings of the Aristotelian Society*, Supplementary Volume **31**, 1957, pp. 145–150.

Bub, Jeffrey and Michael Radner, "Miller's Paradox of Information," *The British Journal for the Philosophy of Science*, **19**, 1968, pp. 63–67.

Buchdahl, G., "Convention, Falsification, and Induction," *Proceedings of the Aristotelian Society*, Supplementary Volume **34**, 1960, pp. 113–130.

Buchdahl, G., "Induction and Scientific Method," *Mind*, **60**, 1961, pp. 16–34.

Bunge, Mario, *Metascientific Queries*. Springfield, Ill.: Charles C. Thomas, 1959.

Bunge, Mario, "The Place of Induction in Science," *Philosophy of Science*, **27**, 1960, pp. 262–270.

Bunge, Mario, "The Weight of Simplicity in the Construction and Assaying of Scientific Theories," *Philosophy of Science*, **28**, 1961, pp. 120–149.

Bunge, Mario, "The Complexity of Simplicity," *Journal of Philosophy*, **59**, 1962, pp. 113–135.

Bunge, Mario, *The Myth of Simplicity*. Englewood Cliffs, N.J.: Prentice-Hall, Inc., 1963.

Bures, Charles E., "The Concept of Probability," *Philosophy of Science*, **5**, January, 1938, pp. 1–20.

Burks, Arthur W., "Peirce's Theory of Abduction," *Philosophy of Science*, **13**, 1946, pp. 301–306.

Burks, Arthur W., "Reichenbach's Theory of Probability and Induction," *Review of Metaphysics*, **4**, 1951, pp. 377–393.

Burks, Arthur W., review of Carnap's *Logical Foundations of Probability* in *Journal of Philosophy*, **48**, 1951, pp. 524–535.

* Burks, Arthur W., "The Presupposition Theory of Induction," *Philosophy of Science*, **20**, 1953, pp. 177–197.

Burks, Arthur W., "Justification in Science," in M. White (ed.), *Academic Freedom, Logic, and Religion*, 1953.

Burks, Arthur W., review of Carnap's *Continuum of Inductive Methods* in *Journal of Philosophy*, **50**, 1953, pp. 731–734.

Burks, Arthur W., "On the Presuppositions of Induction," *Review of Metaphysics*, **8**, 1954–55, pp. 574–611.

Burks, Arthur W., "On the Significance of Carnap's System of Inductive Logic for the Philosophy of Induction," Schilpp (ed.), *The Philosophy of Rudolf Carnap*, 1963, pp. 739–760.

Campbell, Keith, "One Form of Scepticism about Induction," *Analysis*, **23**, 1962–63, pp. 80–83.

Cannavo, S., "Extensionality and Randomness in Probability Sequences," *Philosophy of Science*, **33**, 1966, pp. 134–146.

Carlsson, Gösta, "Sampling, Probability and Causal Inference," *Theoria*, **18**, 1952, pp. 139–154.

Carnap, R., "Wahrheit und Bewährung," in *Induction et probabilité, Actes du congrés internationale de philosophie scientifique*. Paris: Sorbonne, **IV**, 1935, pp. 18–23.

Carnap, Rudolf, "On Inductive Logic," *Philosophy of Science*, **12**, 1945, pp. 72–97.

Carnap, Rudolf, "The Two Concepts of Probability," *Philosophy and Phenomenological Research*, **5**, 1944–45, pp. 513–532.

Carnap, Rudolf, "Remarks on Induction and Truth," *Philosophy and Phenomenological Research*, **6**, 1945–46, pp. 590–602.

Carnap, Rudolf, "Rejoinder to Mr. Kaufmann's Reply," *Philosophy and Phenomenological Research*, **6**, 1945–46, pp. 609–611.

Carnap, Rudolf, "Theory and Prediction in Science," *Science*, **104**, 1946, pp. 520–521.

Carnap, Rudolf, "Probability as a Guide in Life," *Journal of Philosophy*, **44**, 1947, pp. 141–148.

Carnap, Rudolf, "On the Application of Inductive Logic," *Philosophy and Phenomenological Research*, **8**, 1947–48, pp. 133–148.

Carnap, Rudolf, "Reply to Nelson Goodman," *Philosophy and Phenomenological Research*, **8**, 1947–48, pp. 461–462.

* Carnap, Rudolf, *The Logical Foundations of Probability*, 2nd ed. Chicago: University of Chicago Press, 1962.

Carnap, Rudolf, *The Nature and Application of Inductive-Logic*. Chicago: University of Chicago Press, 1951.

Carnap, Rudolf, "The Problem of Relations in Inductive Logic," *Philosophical Studies*, **2**, 1951, pp. 75–80.

Carnap, Rudolf, "Inductive Logic and Science," *Proceedings of the American Academy of Arts and Sciences*, **80**, 1951–54, pp. 189–197.

Carnap, Rudolf, "Meaning Postulates," *Philosophical Studies*, **3**, 1952, pp. 65–73.

* Carnap, Rudolf, *The Continuum of Inductive Methods*. Chicago: University of Chicago Press, 1952.

Carnap, Rudolf, "On the Comparative Concept of Confirmation," *British Journal for the Philosophy of Science*, **3**, 1952–53, pp. 311–318.

Carnap, Rudolf, "Remarks to Kemeny's Paper," *Philosophy and Phenomenological Research*, **13**, 1952–53, pp. 375–376.

Carnap, Rudolf, "What is Probability?," *Scientific American*, **189**, 1953, pp. 128–138.

Carnap, Rudolph and Yehoshua Bar-Hillel, "Semantic Information," *The British Journal for the Philosophy of Science*, 4, 1953–54, pp. 145–157.

Carnap, Rudolf, *Statistical and Inductive Probability*. Brooklyn, New York: The Galois Institute, 1955.

Carnap, Rudolf, "Remarks on Popper's Note on Content and Degree of Confirmation," *British Journal for the Philosophy of Science*, **7**, 1956–57, pp. 243–244.

Carnap, Rudolf, Preface to the 2nd ed. of *Logical Foundations of Probability*. Supplementary Bibliography, 1962.

Carnap, Rudolf, "The Aim of Inductive Logic," In Nagel, Suppes, and Tarski (eds.), *Logic Methodology and Philosophy of Science* (I), 1963, pp. 303–318.

Carnap, Rudolf, "Remarks on Probability," *Philosophical Studies*, **14**, 1963, pp. 65–75.

Carnap, Rudolf, "Replies and Systematic Expositions," in P. A. Schilpp (ed.), *The Philosophy of Rudolf Carnap*. La Salle, Ill.: Open Court, 1963, pp. 966–998.

Carnap, Rudolf, "Discussion: Variety, Analogy, and Periodicity in Inductive Logic," *Philosophy of Science*, **30**, 1963, pp. 222–227.

Carnap, Rudolf, "Probability and Content Measure," in Feyerabend (ed.), *Mind, Matter, and Method*, 1966, pp. 248–260.

Carnap, Rudolf, "Inductive Logic and Inductive Intuition," Imre Lakatos (ed.), *The Problem of Inductive Logic*. Amsterdam: North-Holland Publishing Company, 1968, pp. 258–267.

* Carnap, Rudolf, *Basic System of Inductive Logic*, forthcoming.

Carnap, Rudolf, and Y. Bar-Hillel, *An Outline of the Theory of Semantic Information*, Technical Report Number 247, Research Laboratory of Electronics, Massachusetts Institute of Technology, 1952.

Carnap, Rudolf and Wolfgang Stegmüller, *Induktive Logik und Wahrscheinlichkeit*. Vienna: Springer, 1959.

Carter, C. F., G. P. Meredith, and G. L. S. Shackle, *Uncertainty and Business Decisions*. Liverpool: Liverpool University Press, 1962.

Castañeda, Hector Neri, "Are Conditionals Principles of Inference?," *Analysis*, **18**, 1957–58, pp. 77–82.

Castañeda, Hector Neri, "On a Proposed Revolution in Logic," *Philosophy of Science*, **27**, 1960, pp. 279–292.

Caws, Peter, "The Paradox of Induction and the Inductive Wager," *Philosophy and Phenomenological Research*, **22**, 1961–62, pp. 512–520.

Caws, Peter, "Three Logics, or the Possibility of the Improbable," *Philosophy and Phenomenological Research*, **25**, 1964–65, pp. 516–526.

Chapman, H. Wallis, "Induction Again," *Analysis*, **7**, 1939–40, pp. 73–74.

Chapman, H. Wallis, "Mr. Urmson on the Word 'Probable'," *Analysis*, **8**, 1947–48, pp. 71–76.

Chatalian, George, "Probability: Inductive versus Deductive," *Philosophical Studies*, **3**, 1952, pp. 49–56.

Chatalian, George, "Induction and the Problem of the External World," *Journal of Philosophy*, **49**, 1952, pp. 601–607.

Cheng, Chung-Ing, "Requirements for the Validity of Induction, an Examination of Charles Peirce's Theory," *Philosophy and Phenomenological Research*, **28**, 1968, pp. 392–402.

* Chernoff, Herman, and Lincoln E. Moses, *Elementary Decision Theory*. New York: John Wiley and Sons, Inc., 1959.

Chin, Y. L., "The Principle of Induction and the A Priori," *Journal of Philosophy*, **37**, 1940, pp. 178–187.

Chisholm, Roderick, "Epistemic Statements and the Ethics of Belief," *Philosophy and Phenomenological Research*, **16**, 1955–56, pp. 447–460.

Chisholm, Roderick, "Evidence as Justification," *Journal of Philosophy*, **58**, 1961, pp. 739–748.

Church, Alonzo, "On the Concept of a Random Sequence," *Bulletin of the American Mathematical Society*, **46**, 1940, pp. 130–135.

Churchman, C. West, "Probability Theory," *Philosophy of Science*, **12**, 1945, pp. 147–173.

Churchman, C. West, "Statistics, Pragmatics, Induction," *Philosophy of Science*, **15**, 1948, pp. 249–268.

Churchman, C. West, *Theory of Experimental Inference*. New York: Macmillan, 1948.

Churchman, C. West, "A Critique of Scientific Critiques," *Review of Metaphysics*, **7**, 1953–54, pp. 89–97.

Churchman, C. West, "A Pragmatic Theory of Induction," in Frank (ed.) *The Validation of Scientific Theories*, pp. 18–24.

Churchman, C. West, "Science and Decision Making," *Philosophy of Science*, **23**, 1956, pp. 247–249.

Churchman, C. West, *Prediction and Optimal Decision*. Englewood Cliffs, N.J.: Prentice-Hall, 1961.

Churchman, C. West, and R. Ackoff, *Methods of Inquiry*. St. Louis, Mo.: Educational Publishers, 1950.

Clendinnen, F. John, "Katz on the Vindication of Induction," *Philosophy of Science*, **32**, 1965, pp. 370–376.

Clendinnen, F. John, "Induction and Objectivity," *Philosophy of Science*, **33**, 1966, pp. 215–229.

Clopper, C. J. and E. S. Pearson, "The Use of Confidence or Fiducial Limits Illustrated in the Case of a Binomial," *Biometrika*, 26, 1934, pp. 404–413.

Coburn, Robert C., "A Defect in Harrod's Inductive Justification of Memory," *Philosophical Studies*, **11**, 1960, pp. 81–85.

Coburn, Robert C., "Braithwaite's Inductive Justification of Induction," *Philosophy of Science*, **28**, 1961, pp. 65–71.

Cohen, John, and Mark Hansel, *Risk and Gambling: the Study of Subjective Probability*. New York: Philosophical Library, Inc., 1956.

Cohen, L. J., "What Has Confirmation to Do with Probabilities?," *Mind*, **75**, 1966, pp. 463–481.

Cohen, L. J., "A Logic for Evidential Support I," *British Journal for the Philosophy of Science*, **17**, 1966–67, pp. 21–43.

Cohen, L. J., "The Logic of Evidential Support II," *British Journal for the Philosophy of Science*, **17**, 1966–67, pp. 105–126.

Cohen, L. J., "Discussion: Confirmation Still without Paradoxes," *British Journal of the Philosophy of Science*, **19**, 1968–69, pp. 57–71.

Cohen, Morris R., and Ernest Nagel, *An Introduction to Logic and Scientific Method*. New York: Harcourt, Brace and Company, 1934.

Collins, Arthur W., "The Use of Statistics in Explanation," *British Journal for the Philosophy of Science*, **17**, 1966–67, pp. 127–140.

Colodny, Robert G. (ed.), *Frontiers of Science and Philosophy*. Pittsburgh: University of Pittsburgh Press, 1962.

Colodny, Robert G. (ed.), *Beyond the Edge of Certainty: Essays in Contemporary Science and Philosophy*. Englewood Cliffs, N.J.: Prentice-Hall, 1965.

Colodny, Robert G. (ed.), *Mind and Cosmos: Essays in Contemporary Science and Philosophy*. Pittsburgh: University of Pittsburgh Press, 1966.

Cooley, J. C., "Professor Goodman's 'Fact, Fiction and Forecast'," *Journal of Philosophy*, **54**, 1957, pp. 293–311.

Cooley, J. C., "A Somewhat Adverse Reply to Professor Goodman," *Journal of Philosophy*, **55**, 1958, pp. 159–166.

* Cooley, J. C., "Toulmin's Revolution in Logic," *Journal of Philosophy*, **56**, 1959, pp. 297–319.

Copeland, A. H., "Predictions and Probabilities," *Erkenntnis*, **6**, 1936–37, pp. 189–203.

Copeland, A. H., "Consistency of the conditions determining kollektivs," *Transactions of the American Mathematical Society*, **42**, 1937, pp. 333–357.

Copeland, A. H., "The Role of Observations in a Formal Theory of Probability," *Erkenntnis*, **9**, 1939–40, pp. 159–163.

Copeland, A. H., "Postulates for the Theory of Probability," *American Journal of Mathematics*, **63**, 1941, pp. 741–762.

Copeland, A. H., "Statistical Induction and the Foundations of Probability," *Theoria*, **28**, 1962, pp. 27–44 and pp. 87–109.

Copeland, A. H., Sr., "Mathematical Proof and Experimental Proof," *Philosophy of Science*, **33**, 1966, pp. 303–316.

Cooper, Neil, "The Concept of Probability," *British Journal for the Philosophy of Science*, **16**, 1965–66, pp. 226–238.

Cox, D. R., "Some Problems Connected with Statistical Inference," *Annals of Mathematical Statistics*, **29**, 1958, pp. 357–372.

Cox, D. R., "Comments on Savage," in Barnard (ed.), *Foundations of Statistical Inference*, 1962, pp. 49–53.

Cox, R. T., "Probability, Frequency, and Reasonable Expectation," *American Journal of Physics*, **14**, 1946, pp. 1–13.

* Cox, R. T., *The Algebra of Probable Inference*. Baltimore: Johns Hopkins Press, 1961.

Cramér, Harald, *Mathematical Methods of Statistics*. Princeton: Princeton University Press, 1951.

* Cramér, Harald, *The Elements of Probability Theory*. New York: John Wiley and Sons, 1955.

Crawshay, William Rupert, "Equivocal Confirmation," *Analysis*, **11**, 1950–51, pp. 73–79.

Creed, Isabel, "The Justification of the Habit of Induction," *Journal of Philosophy*, **37**, 1940, pp. 85–97.

Crossley, J. N., and M. A. E. Dummett (eds.), *Formal Systems and Recursive Functions*. Amsterdam: North-Holland Publishing Company, 1965.

Crossley, J. N. (ed.), *Sets, Models, and Recursion Theory*. Amsterdam, North-Holland Publishing Company, 1967.

Crow, C., "Some Remarks on Induction," *Synthese*, **15**, 1963, pp. 379–387.

Cunningham, M. A., "The Justification of Induction," *Analysis*, **7**, 1939–1940, pp. 13–19.

Cunningham, R. L., "Inductive Ascent the Same as Inductive Descent?," *Mind*, **72**, 1963, pp. 598.

Danielson, Sven, "Modal Logic Based on Probability Theory," *Theoria*, **33**, 1967, pp. 189–197.

Danto, Arthur, and Sidney Morgenbesser (eds.), *Philosophy of Science*. New York: Meridian Books, 1960.

Dantzig, D. van, "Carnap's Foundation of Probability Theory," *Synthese*, **8**, 1953, pp. 459–470.

Dantzig, D. van, "Some Informal Information on 'Information'," *Synthese*, **9**, 1953–55, pp. 137–144.

Darlington, Jared, "On the Confirmation of Laws," *Philosophy of Science*, **26**, 1959, pp. 14–24.

Darlington, Jared, "Reply to Linhart," *Philosophy of Science*, **26**, 1959, pp. 363.

Darwin, C. G., "Logic and Probability in Physics," *Philosophy of Science*, **6**, No. 1, January, 1939, pp. 48–64.

Das, R., "Induction and Non-Instantial Hypothesis," *British Journal for the Philosophy of Science*, **8**, 1957–58, pp. 317–325.

Davidson, Donald, "Actions, Reasons and Causes," *Journal of Philosophy*, **60**, 1963, pp. 685–700.

Davidson, Donald, "Emeroses by Other Names," *Journal of Philosophy*, **63**, 1966, pp. 778–780.

Davidson, Donald, "Causal Relations," *The Journal of Philosophy*, **64**, 1967, pp. 691–703.

Davidson, Donald, and Patrick Suppes, "A Finitistic Axiomatization of Subjective Probability and Utility," *Econometrica, Journal of the Econometric Society*, **24**, July, 1956, pp. 264–275.

Davidson, Donald, Patrick Suppes, and Sidney Siegel, *Decision Making: An Experimental Approach*. Stanford: Stanford University Press, 1957.

Day, John P., review of von Wright's *Logical Problem of Induction*, in *Philosophy*, **35**, 1960, pp. 77–80.

Day, John P., *Inductive Probability*. New York: Humanities Press, 1961.

Dietl, Paul, "Paresis and the Alleged Asymmetry between Explanation and Prediction," *British Journal for the Philosophy of Science*, **17**, 1966–67, pp. 313–318.

Doob, J. L., "Probability and Statistics," *Transactions of the American Mathematical Society*, **36**, 1934, pp. 759–775.

Doob, J. L., "Probability as Measure," *Annals of Mathematical Statistics*, **12**, 1941, pp. 206–214.

Dotterer, Ray H., "Ignorance and Equal Probability," *Philosophy of Science*, **8**, 1941, pp. 297–303.

Dubins, Lester and David Blackwell, "Merging of Opinions with Increasing Information," *Annals of Mathematical Statistics*, 33, September, 1962, pp. 882–886.

Dubins, Lester E., and Leonard J. Savage, *How to Gamble If You Must; Inequalities for Stochastic Processes*. New York: McGraw-Hill, 1965.

Ducasse, C. J., "Some Observations Concerning the Nature of Probability," *Journal of Philosophy*, **38**, 1941, pp. 393–403.

Ducasse, C. J., "Probability," *Journal of Philosophy*, **58**, 1941, pp. 393–403.

Ducasse, C. J., "Deductive Probability Arguments," *Philosophical Studies*, **4**, 1953, pp. 29–31.

Dummett, M. A. E., and J. N. Crossley (eds.), *Formal Systems and Recursive Functions*. Amsterdam: North-Holland Publishing Company, 1965.

Eaton, Ralph M., *General Logic. An Introductory Survey*. New York: Charles Scribner's Sons, 1931.

Edwards, Paul, "Russell's Doubts about Induction," *Mind*, **58**, 1949, pp. 141–163.

* Edwards, Lindeman, and Savage, "Bayesian Statistical Inference for Psychological Research," *Psychological Review*, **70**, 1963, pp. 193–242.

Ehrenfest-Afanasjewa, Tatiana, "On the Use of the Notion 'Probability' in Physics," *American Journal of Physics*, **26**, 1958, pp. 388–392.

Ellis, Brian, "A Vindication of Scientific Inductive Practices," *American Philosophical Quarterly*, **2**, 1965, pp. 296–304.

Emmerich, David S., and James G. Greeno, "Some Decision Factors in Scientific Investigation," *Philosophy of Science*, **33**, 1966, pp. 262–270.

Ennis, Robert H., "Enumerative Induction and Best Explanation," *Journal of Philosophy*, **65**, 1968, pp. 523–529.

Ewing, A. C., "Causality and Induction," *Philosophy and Phenomenological Research*, **12**, 1951–52, pp. 465–485.

Ezorsky, Gertrude, "On Verifying Universal Empirical Propositions," *Analysis*, **26**, 1965–66, pp. 110–112.

Fain, Haskell, "The Very Thought of Grue," *Philosophical Review*, **76**, 1967, pp. 61–73.

Feibleman, James R., "Pragmatism and Inverse Probability," *Philosophy and Phenomenological Research*, **5**, 1944–45, pp. 309–319.

Feibleman, James K., "On the Theory of Induction," *Philosophy and Phenomenological Research*, **14**, 1953–54, pp. 332–342.

Feibleman, James K., "The Logical Structure of the Scientific Method," *Dialectica*, **13**, 1959, pp. 208–225.

Feigl, Herbert, "The Logical Character of the Principle of Induction," *Philosophy of Science*, **1**, 1934, pp. 20–29.

* Feigl, Herbert, "De Principiis Non Disputandum...?," in Black (ed.), *Philosophical Analysis*, 1950, pp. 113–147.

Feigl, Herbert, "Confirmability and Confirmation," *Revue Internationale de Philosophie*, **5**, 1951, pp. 268–279.

Feigl, Herbert, "Scientific Method without Metaphysical Presuppositions," *Philosophical Studies*, 5, 1954, pp. 17–29.

Feigl, Herbert, "Some Major Issues and Developments in the Philosophy of Science," in *Minnesota Studies in the Philosophy of Science*, I, 1956, pp. 3–37.

Feigl, Herbert, "On the Vindication of Induction," *Philosophy of Science*, 28, 1961, pp. 212–216.

Feigl, Herbert, and Michael Scriven (eds.), *Minnesota Studies in the Philosophy of Science, I; the Foundations of Science and the Concepts of Psychology and Psychoanalysis.* Minneapolis: University of Minnesota Press, 1962.

Feigl, Herbert, Michael Scriven, and Grover Maxwell (eds.), *Concepts, Theories, and the Mind-Body Problem, Minnesota Studies in the Philosophy of Science*, II. Minneapolis: University of Minnesota Press, 1958.

Feigl, Herbert, and Wilfrid Sellars (eds.), *Readings in Philosophical Analysis.* New York: Appleton-Century Crofts, 1949.

Feigl, Herbert, and Grover Maxwell (eds.), *Current Issues in the Philosophy of Science.* New York: Holt, Rinehart and Winston, 1961.

Feigl, Herbert, and Grover Maxwell (eds.), *Scientific Explanation, Space, and Time, Minnesota Studies in the Philosophy of Science*, III. Minneapolis: University of Minnesota Press, 1962.

Feller, William, *An Introduction to Probability Theory and its Applications*, 2nd ed. New York: John Wiley and Sons, 1957.

Fenstad, J. E., "Representations of Probabilities Defined on First Order Language," in J. N. Crossley (ed.), *Sets, Models and Recursion Theory.* Amsterdam: North-Holland Publishing Company, 1967, pp. 156–172.

Fenstad, J. E., review of Hintikka and Suppes (eds.), *Aspects of Inductive Logic* in *Synthese*, 17, 1967, pp. 449–460.

Feuer, Lewis S., "The Principle of Simplicity," *Philosophy of Science*, 24, 1957, pp. 109–122.

Feyerabend, Paul K., "Comments on Hanson's 'Is there a logic of discovery'," in Feigl and Maxwell, *Current Issues in the Philosophy of Science*, 1961, pp. 35–39.

Feyerabend, Paul K., "A Note on the Problem of Induction," *Journal of Philosophy*, 61, 1964, pp. 349–353.

Feyerabend, Paul K., and Grover Maxwell, *Mind, Matter, and Method; Essays in Honor of Herbert Feigl.* Minneapolis: University of Minnesota Press, 1966.

Finch, Henry Albert, "Validity Rules for Proportionally Quantified Syllogisms," *Philosophy of Science*, 24, 1957, pp. 1–18.

Finch, Henry Albert, "An Explanation of Counterfactuals by Probability Theory," *Philosophy and Phenomenological Research*, 18, 1957–58, pp. 368–378.

Finch, Henry Albert, "Due Care in Explicating Counterfactuals: A Reply to Mr. Jeffrey," *Philosophy and Phenomenological Research*, 20, 1959–60, p. 117.

Finch, Henry, "Confirming Power of Observations Metricized for Decisions Among Hypotheses," *Philosophy of Science*, 27, 1960, pp. 293–307, pp. 391–404.

Findlay, J. N., "Probability without Nonsense," *Philosophical Quarterly*, 2, 1952, pp. 218–239.

Finetti, Bruno de, "Sul significato Doggetivo della probabilita," *Fundamenta Mathematica*, 17, 1931, pp. 298–329.

Finetti, B. de, "La logique de la Probabilité," in *Induction et probabilité, Actes du congrès internationale de philosophie scientifique.* Paris: Sorbonne, IV, 1935, pp. 31–39.

Finetti, B. di, "La logique de la Probabilité," in *Induction et probabilité*, 1935, pp. 31–39.

* Finetti, B. de, "La Prevision: ses lois logiques, ses sources subjectives," *Annales de l'Institut Henri Poincaré*, **7**, 1937, pp. 1–68.

Finetti, B. de, "La vrai et la probable," *Dialectica*, **3**, 1949, pp. 78–92.

Finetti, B. de, "Foundations of Probability," Klibansky (ed.), *Philosophy in Mid-Century*, I, 1958, pp. 140–147.

Finetti, B. de, "La probabilita e la statistica nei rapporti con l'induzione, seconde i diversi punti di vista," *Induzione e Statistica*. Rome: Instituto Matematico Dell' Universita, 1963.

* Finetti, B. de, "Foresight: Its Logical Laws, Its Subjective Sources," in Kyburg and Smokler (eds.), *Studies in Subjective Probability*, 1964, pp. 93–158.

Firth, Roderick, "Coherence, Certainty, and Epistemic Priority," *Journal of Philosophy*, **61**, 1964, pp. 547–557.

Fisher, R. A., "The Conditions Under Which Chi Square Measures the Discrepancy Between Observation and Hypothesis," *Journal of the Royal Statistical Society*, **87**, Part III, 1924, pp. 442–450.

Fisher, R. A., *Statistical Methods for Research Workers*. New York: Hafner Publishing Company, 1963.

Fisher, R. A., "Theory of Statistical Estimation," *Proceedings of the Cambridge Philosophical Society*, **22**, Part 5, 1925, pp. 700–725.

Fisher, R. A., "Inverse Probability," *Proceedings of the Cambridge Philosophical Society*, **26**, Part 4, 1930, pp. 528–535.

Fisher, R. A., "Probability, Likelihood, and Quantity of Information in the Logic of Uncertain Inference," *Proceedings of the Royal Society*, A, **146**, 1934, pp. 1–8.

Fisher, R. A., "The Fiducial Argument in Statistical Inference," *Annals of Eugenics*, **6**, Part 4, 1935, pp. 391–398.

Fisher, R. A., *Induction et probabilité*, *Actes du Congress internationale de philosophie scientifique*. Paris: Sorbonne, IV, 1935.

Fisher, R. A., *The Design of Experiments*. Edinburgh: Oliver and Boyd, Limited, 1935.

Fisher, R. A., "The Logic of Inductive Inference," *Journal of the Royal Statistical Society*, **98**, Part I, 1935, pp. 39–54.

Fisher, R. A., "Uncertain Inference," *Proceedings of the American Academy of Arts and Science*, **71**, Number 4, 1936, pp. 245–258.

Fisher, R. A., "Statistical Methods and Scientific Inference," *Journal of the Royal Statistical Society*, B, **17**, 1955, pp. 69–78.

* Fisher, R. A., *Statistical Methods and Scientific Inference*. New York: Hafner Publishing Company, 1956.

Fisk, Milton, "Falsifiability and Corroboration." *Philosophical Studies*, **9**, 1959, pp. 49–65.

Fisk, Milton, Review of Day's *Inductive Probability* in *Philosophical Studies*, **11**, 1961–62.

Fitch, F. B., "Justification in Science," in M. White (ed.), *Academic Freedom, Logic and Religion*. Philadelphia: University of Pennsylvania Press, 1953, pp. 99–107.

Flew, Anthony (ed.), *Logic and Language*. New York: Philosophical Library, 1951.

Flew, Anthony, review of Brown's *Probability and Scientific Inference* in *Philosophy*, **9**, 1959, pp. 380–381.

Fogelin, Robert J., "Inferential Constructions," *American Philosophical Quarterly*, **4**, 1967, pp. 15–27.

Frank, Philipp G. (ed.), *The Validation of Scientific Theories*. Boston: Beacon Press, 1954.

Frank, Philipp G., "The Variety of Reasons for the Acceptance of Scientific Theories," in Frank, *The Validation of Scientific Theories*, pp. 3–18.

Frank, Philipp G., *Philosophy of Science: The Link between Science and Philosophy*. Englewood Cliffs, N. J.: Prentice-Hall, 1957.

Fraser, D. A. S., "On the Definition of Fiducial Probability," *Bulletin of the International Statistical Institute*, **40**, 1963, pp. 842–856.

Fraser, D. A. S., *The Structure of Inference*. New York: John Wiley and Sons, 1968.

Freudenthal, Hans, "Is there a Specific Problem of Application for Probability?," *Mind*, **50**, 1941, pp. 367–373.

Freudenthal, Hans, "Models in Applied Probability," *Synthese*, **12**, 1960, pp. 202–212.

Freudenthal, Hans, "Abus philosophiques de la statistique," *Revue de Metaphysique et de Morale*, **67**, 1962, pp. 237–246.

Freudenthal, Hans, "Realistic Models in Probability," in Imre Lakatos (ed.), *The Problem of Inductive Logic*. Amsterdam: North-Holland Publishing Company, 1968, pp. 1–14.

Freund, John E., "On the Confirmation of Scientific Theories," *Philosophy of Science*, **17**, 1950, pp. 87–94.

Freund, John E., "On the Problem of Confirmation," *Methods*, **3**, 1951, pp. 33–42.

Freund, John E., *Modern Elementary Statistics*. Englewood Cliffs, N.J.: Prentice-Hall, 1952.

Fritz, Charles A., "What is Induction?," *Journal of Philosophy*, **57**, 1960, pp. 126–138.

Fry, Thornton C., "A Mathematical Theory of Rational Inference: A Nonmathematical Discussion of Bayes' Theorem," *Scripta Mathematica*, **2**, pp. 205–221.

Gaifman, H., "Concerning Measures on First-Order Calculi," in *Israel Journal of Mathematics*, **2**, pp. 1–18.

Georgescu-Roegen, Nicholas, "The End of the Probability Syllogism?," *Philosophical Studies*, **5**, 1954, pp. 31–32.

Gibbons, P. C., "On the Severity of Tests," *Australasian Journal of Philosophy*, **40**, 1962, pp. 79–82.

Girshick, M. A. and David Blackwell, *Theory of Games and Statistical Decisions*. New York: John Wiley and Sons, 1954.

Goldberg, Samuel, *Probability: An Introduction*. Englewood Cliffs, N.J.: Prentice-Hall, 1960.

Good, I. J., *Probability and the Weighing of Evidence*. London: C. Griffin, 1950.

Good, I. J., "Rational Decisions," *Journal of the Royal Statistical Society*, Series B, **14**, 1952, pp. 107–114.

Good, I. J., "Kinds of Probability," *Science*, **129**, 1959, pp. 443–446.

Good, I. J., "The Paradox of Confirmation," *British Journal for the Philosophy of Science*, **11**, 1960–61, pp. 145–149.

Good, I. J., "The Paradox of Confirmation (II)," *British Journal for the Philosophy of Science*, **12**, 1961–62, pp. 63–64.

Good, I. J., "Subjective Probability as a Measure of a Non-Measurable Set," in Nagel, Suppes, and Tarski (eds.), *Logic, Methodology and Philosophy of Science* (I), pp. 319–329.

Good, I. J., "On the Principle of Total Evidence," *British Journal for the Philosophy of Science*, **17**, 1966–67, pp. 319–321.

Good, I. J., "The White Shoe is a Red Herring," *British Journal for the Philosophy of Science*, **17**, 1966–67, p. 322.

Goodman, Nelson, "A Query on Confirmation," *Journal of Philosophy*, **43**, 1946, pp. 383–385.

Goodman, Nelson, "The Logical Simplicity of Predicates," *Journal of Symbolic Logic*, **14**, 1949, pp. 32–41.

Goodman, Nelson, "An Improvement in the Theory of Simplicity, *Journal of Symbolic Logic*, **14**, 1949, pp. 228–229.

Goodman, Nelson, "Sense and Certainty," *Philosophical Review*, **61**, 1952, pp. 160–167.

Goodman, Nelson, "New Notes on Simplicity," *Journal of Symbolic Logic*, **17**, 1952, pp. 189–191.

Goodman, Nelson, "Axiomatic Measurement of Simplicity," *Journal of Philosophy*, **52**, 1955, pp. 709–722.

Goodman, Nelson, *Fact, Fiction, and Forecast*. Cambridge: Harvard University Press, 1955.

Goodman, Nelson, "The Test of Simplicity," *Science*, **128**, 1958, pp. 1064–1069.

Goodman, Nelson, "Recent Developments in the Theory of Simplicity," *Philosophy and Phenomenological Research*, **19**, 1958–59, pp. 429–446.

Goodman, Nelson, "Positionality and Pictures," *Philosophical Review*, **69**, 1960, pp. 523–525.

Goodman, Nelson, "Safety, Strength, Simplicity," *Philosophy of Science*, **28**, 1961, pp. 150–151.

Goodman, Nelson, "Comments on 'The New Riddle of Induction'," *Journal of Philosophy*, **63**, 1966, pp. 328–331.

Goodman, Nelson, "Two Replies," *Journal of Philosophy*, **64**, 1967, pp. 286–287.

Goodstein, L., "On von Mises Theory of Probability," *Mind*, **49**, 1940, pp. 58–62.

Gordon, Robert Dean, "Inverse Probability and Modern Statisticians," *Philosophy of Science*, **7**, 1940, pp. 389–399.

Goudge, Th. A., "Peirce's Treatment of Induction," *Philosophy of Science*, **7**, 1940, pp. 56–68.

Grandy, Richard E., "Some Comments on Confirmation and Selective Confirmation," *Philosophical Studies*, **18**, 1967, pp. 19–24.

Greeno, James G., and David S. Emmerich, "Some Decision Factors in Scientific Investigation," *Philosophy of Science*, **33**, 1966, pp. 262–270.

Gregg, John R., and F. T. C. Harris (eds.), *Form and Strategy in Science: Studies Dedicated to J. H. Woodger on the Occasion of his Seventieth Birthday*. Dordrecht, Holland: D. Reidel Publishing Company, 1964.

Gross, Edward, "Toward a Rationale for Science," *Journal of Philosophy*, **54**, 1957, pp. 829–838.

Guenther, William C., *Concepts of Statistical Inference*. New York: McGraw-Hill, 1965.

Hacking, Ian, "Guessing by Frequency," *Proceedings of the Aristotelian Society*, **64**, 1963–64, pp. 55–70.

Hacking, Ian, review of Leblanc's *Statistical and Inductive Probabilities*, *Philosophical Quarterly*, **14**, 1964, p. 281.

* Hacking, Ian, *Logic of Statistical Inference*. Cambridge: Cambridge University Press, 1965.

Hacking, Ian, "Salmon's Vindication of Induction," *Journal of Philosophy*, **62**, 1965, pp. 260–266.

Hacking, Ian, "Salmon's Vindication," *Philosophy of Science*, **32**, 1965, pp. 269–271.

Hacking, Ian, "On the Foundations of Statistics," *British Journal for the Philosophy of Science*, **15**, 1964–65, pp. 1–26.

Hacking, Ian, review of Kyburg and Smokler (eds.), *Studies in Subjective Probability*, *British Journal for the Philosophy of Science*, **16**, 1965–66, pp. 334–339.

Hacking, Ian, review of Isaac Levi's *Gambling with Truth*, *Synthese*, **17**, 1967, pp. 444–447.

Hacking, Ian, "Slightly More Realistic Personal Probability," *Philosophy of Science*, **34**, 1967, pp. 311–325.

Hacking, Ian, "On Falling Short of Strict Coherence," *Philosophy of Science*, **35**, 1968, pp. 284–286.

Hailperin, Theodore, "Foundations of Probability in Mathematical Logic," *Philosophy of Science*, **4**, 1937, Supplement Number 2, pp. 125–150.

Hallden, Sören, "Preference Logic and Theory Choice," *Synthese*, **16**, 1966, pp. 307–320.

Hallden, Sören, "On Preference, Probability, and Learning," *Synthese*, **16**, 1966, pp. 307–320.

Halmos, P. R., "The Foundations of Probability," *The American Mathematical Monthly*, **51**, 1944, pp. 497–510.

Hamblin, C. L., "The Modal 'Probably'," *Mind*, **68**, 1959, pp. 234–240.

Hamlyn, D. W., review of Harrod's *Foundations of Inductive Logic*, in *Philosophy*, **33**, 1958, pp. 369–370.

Hammerton, M., "Bayesian Statistics and Popper's Epistemology," *Mind*, **77**, 1968, pp. 109–112.

Hanen, Marsha, "Goodman, Wallace, and the Equivalence Condition," *Journal of Philosophy*, **58**, 1966, pp. 271–280.

Hansel, Mark and John Cohen, *Risk and Gambling: the Study of Subjective Probability*. New York: Philosophical Library, Inc., 1956.

* Hanson, Norwood Russell, *Patterns of Discovery*. Cambridge: Cambridge University Press, 1958.

Hanson, Norwood Russell, "The Logic of Discovery," *Journal of Philosophy*, **55**, 1958, pp. 1073–1089.

Hanson, Norwood Russell, "More on 'The Logic of Discovery'," *Journal of Philosophy*, **57**, 1960, pp. 182–186.

Hanson, Norwood Russell, "Is there a Logic of Scientific Discovery," *Australasian Journal of Philosophy*, **38**, 1960, pp. 91–100.

Hanson, Norwood Russell, "Is there a Logic of Discovery," in Feigl and Maxwell (eds.), *Current Issues in the Philosophy of Science*, pp. 20–35.

Hanson, Norwood Russell, "Good Inductive Reasons," *Philosophical Quarterly*, **11**, 1961, pp. 123–134.

Hanson, Norwood Russell, "The Idea of a Logic of Discovery," *Dialectica*, **4**, 1965–66, pp. 48–61.

Hanson, Norwood Russell, "An Anatomy of Discovery," *Journal of Philosophy*, **64**, 1967, pp. 321–352.

Harman, Gilbert, "How Belief is Based on Inference," *Journal of Philosophy*, **61**, 1964, pp. 353–359.

Harman, Gilbert, "The Inference to the Best Explanation," *Philosophical Review*, **74**, 1965, pp. 88–95.

Harman, Gilbert, "Lehrer on Knowledge," *Journal of Philosophy*, **63**, 1966, pp. 241–247.

Harman, Gilbert, "Unger on Knowledge," *Journal of Philosophy*, **64**, 1967, pp. 390–395.

Harman, Gilbert, "Detachment, Probability, and Maximum Likelihood," *Nous*, **1**, 1967, pp. 401–411.

Harman, Gilbert, "Enumerative Induction as Inference to the Best Explanation," *Journal of Philosophy*, **65**, 1968, pp. 529–533.

Harman, Gilbert, "Knowledge, Inference, and Explanation," *American Philosophical Quarterly*, **5**, 1968, pp. 164–173.

Harman, Gilbert H., "Introduction: A Discussion of the Relevance of the Theory of Induction (with a Digression to the Effect that neither Deductive Logic nor the Probability Calculus has anything to do with Inference)" in Swain (ed.), *Induction, Acceptance and Rational Belief.*

Harper, William and Henry E. Kyburg, Jr., "Discussion: The Jones Case," *British Journal for the Philosophy of Science*, **19**, 1968, pp. 247–258.

Harrah, David, "A Logic of Questions and Answers," *Philosophy of Science*, **28**, 1961, pp. 40–46.

Harré, R., "Dissolving the 'Problem' of Induction," *Philosophy*, **32**, 1957, pp. 58–64.

Harré, R., "Simplicity as a Criterion of Induction," *Philosophy*, **34**, 1959, pp. 229–234.

Harré, R., review of Barker's *Induction and Hypothesis*, *Mind*, **71**, 1962, pp. 412–420.

Harré, R., review of J. J. Katz's *The Problem of Induction and its Solution*, *Mind*, **73**, 1964, pp. 457–458.

Harris, F. T. C. and John R. Gregg (eds.), *Form and Strategy in Science: Studies Dedicated to J. H. Woodger on the Occasion of his Seventieth Birthday.* Dordrecht, Holland: D. Reidel Publishing Company, 1964.

Harrod, Roy F., "Induction and Probability," *Philosophy*, **26**, 1951, pp. 37–52.

Harrod, Roy F., *Foundations of Inductive Logic.* New York: Harcourt, Brace and World, 1956.

Harrod, Roy F., "New Argument for Induction: Reply to Professor Popper," *British Journal for the Philosophy of Science*, **10**, 1960, pp. 309–312.

Harrod, Roy F., "The General Structure of Inductive Argument," *Proceedings of the Aristotelian Society*, **61**, 1960–61, pp. 41–56.

Harsanyi, John C., "Popper's Improbability Criterion for the Choice of Scientific Hypotheses," *Philosophy*, **35**, 1960, pp. 332–340.

Hartley, H. O., "In Dr. Bayes; Consulting Room," *American Statistician*, **17**, 1963, pp. 22–24.

Hawkins, David, "Existential and Epistemic Probability," *Philosophy of Science*, **10**, 1943, pp. 255–261.

Hay, William H., "Professor Carnap and Probability," *Philosophy of Science*, **19**, 1952, pp. 170–177.

Hay, William H., review of Carnap's *Continuum of Inductive Methods*, in *Philosophical Review*, **62**, 1953, pp. 468–472.

Hay, William H., review of Wright's *Treatise on Probability and Induction* in *Journal of Philosophy*, **50**, 1953, pp. 782–788.

Hayek, F., "Degree of Explanation," *British Journal for the Philosophy of Science*, **6**, 1955–56, pp. 209–225.

Heidelberger, Herbert, "Knowledge, Certainty and Probability," *Inquiry*, **6**, 1963, pp. 242–250.

Heidelberger, Herbert, "Probability and Knowledge: A Reply to Miss Weyland," *Inquiry*, **6**, 1963, pp. 417–418.

Helmer, Olaf, and Paul Oppenheim, "A Syntactical Definition of Probability and Degree of Confirmation," *Journal of Symbolic Logic*, **10**, 1945, pp. 25–60.

Hempel, C. G., "On the Logical Form of Probability Statements," *Erkenntnis*, **7**, 1937–38, pp. 154–160.

Hempel, C. G., "Supplementary Remarks on the Form of Probability-Statements, Suggested by the Discussion," *Erkenntnis*, **7**, 1937–38, pp. 360–363.

Hempel, C. G., "A Purely Syntactical Definition of Confirmation," *Journal of Symbolic Logic*, **8**, 1943, pp. 122–143.

* Hempel, C. G., "Studies in the Logic of Confirmation," *Mind*, **54**, 1945, pp. 1–26, pp. 97–121.

Hempel, C. G., "The Theoretician's Dilemma," in Feigl (ed.), *Minnesota Studies in the Philosophy of Science*, **2**, 1958, pp. 37–98.

Hempel, C. G., "Empirical Statements and Falsifiability," *Philosophy*, **33**, 1958, pp. 342–348.

* Hempel, C. G., "Deductive-Nomological vs. Statistical Explanation," in Feigl (ed.), *Minnesota Studies in the Philosophy of Science*, III, pp. 98–169.

Hempel, C. G., "Inductive Inconsistencies," *Logic and Language*, 1962, pp. 128–158. Also in *Synthese* **12**, 1960, pp. 439–469.

Hempel, C. G., "Coherence and Morality," *Journal of Philosophy*, **62**, 1965, pp. 539–542.

Hempel, C. G., *Aspects of Scientific Explanation*. New York: The Free Press, 1965.

Hempel, C. G., "Aspects of Scientific Explanation," in *Aspects of Scientific Explanation*. New York: The Free Press, 1965, pp. 331–496.

Hempel, C. G., "Recent Problems of Induction," in Colodny (ed.), *Mind and Cosmos*, III. Pittsburgh: University of Pittsburgh Press, 1966.

Hempel, C. G., "The White Shoe: No Red Herring," *British Journal for the Philosophy of Science*, **18**, 1967–68, pp. 239–240.

Hempel, C. G., "Maximal Specificity and Lawlikeness in Probabilistic Explanation," *Philosophy of Science*, **35**, 1968, pp. 116–133.

Hempel, C. G., "On a Claim by Skyrms Concerning Lawlikeness and Confirmation," *Philosophy of Science*, **35**, 1968, pp. 274–278.

Hempel, C. G., and Paul Oppenheim, "A Definition of 'Degree of Confirmation'," *Philosophy of Science*, **12**, 1945, pp. 98–115.

Hempel, C. G., and Paul Oppenheim, "Studies in the Logic of Explanation," *Philosophy of Science*, **15**, 1948, pp. 135–175.

Hesse, Mary B., review of Jeffreys' *Scientific Inference*, *Philosophy*, **34**, 1959, pp. 66–68.

Hesse, Mary B., "Subjunctive Conditionals," *Proceedings of the Aristotelian Society*, Supplementary Volume **36**, 1962, pp. 201–214.

Hesse, Mary B., "Analogy and Confirmation Theory," *Philosophy of Science*, **31**, 1964, pp. 319–327.

Hesse, Mary B., "The Explanatory Function of Metaphor," in Yehoshua Bar-Hillel (ed.), *Logic, Methodology and Philosophy of Science* (II). Amsterdam: North-Holland Publishing Company, 1965, pp. 249–259.

Hesse, Mary B., "Consilience of Inductions," in Imre Lakatos (ed.), *The Problem of Inductive Logic*. Amsterdam: North-Holland Publishing Company, 1968, pp. 232–257.

Hesse, Mary B., "A Self-Correcting Observation Language," in B. Van Rootselaar and J. F. Staal (eds.), *Logic, Methodology and Philosophy of Science, III*. Amsterdam: North-Holland Publishing Company, 1968, pp. 297–310.

Hillman, Donald J., "The Measurement of Simplicity," *Philosophy of Science*, **29**, 1962, pp. 225–252.

Hillman, Donald J., "The Probability of Induction," *Philosophical Studies*, **14**, 1965, pp. 51–56.

Hilpinen, Risto, "On Inductive Generalization in Monadic First-Order Logic with Identity," in Hintikka and Suppes (eds.), *Aspects of Inductive Logic*, 1966, pp. 133–154.

* Hilpinen, Risto, "Rules of Acceptance and Inductive Logic," *Acta Philosophica Fennica*, **21**, Amsterdam: North-Holland Publishing Company, 1968.

Hilpinen, Risto and Jaakko Hintikka, "Knowledge, Acceptance, and Inductive Logic," in Hintikka and Suppes (eds.), *Aspects of Inductive Logic*, 1966, pp. 1–20.

Hintikka, Jaakko, *Knowledge and Belief: An Introduction to the Logic of the Two Notions*. Ithaca: Cornell University Press, 1962.

Hintikka, Jaakko, "Towards a Theory of Inductive Generalization," in Yehoshua Bar-Hillel (ed.), *Logic, Methodology and Philosophy of Science, II*. Amsterdam: North-Holland Publishing Company, 1964, pp. 274–288.

Hintikka, Jaakko, "On a Combined System of Inductive Logic," *Studia Logico-Mathematica et Philosophica in Honorem Rolf Nevanlinna*, Acta Philosophica Fennica, **18**, 1965, pp. 21–35.

Hintikka, Jaakko, "Distributive Normal Forms in First-Order Logic," in Crossley (ed.), *Formal Systems*, 1965, pp. 48–91.

* Hintikka, Jaakko, "A Two-Dimensional Continuum of Inductive Methods," in Hintikka and Suppes (eds.), *Aspects of Inductive Logic*, 1966, pp. 113–132.

Hintikka, Jaakko, "Induction by Enumeration and Induction by Elimination," in Imre Lakatos (ed.), *The Problem of Inductive Logic*. Amsterdam: North-Holland Publishing Company, 1968, pp. 191–216.

Hintikka, Jaakko, "The Varieties of Information and Scientific Explanation," in B. Van Rootselaar and J. F. Staal (eds.), *Logic, Methodology and Philosophy of Science, III*. Amsterdam: North-Holland Publishing Company, 1968, pp. 311–332.

Hintikka, Jaakko, and Risto Hilpinen, "Knowledge, Acceptance, and Inductive Logic," in Hintikka and Suppes (eds.), *Aspects of Inductive Logic*, 1966, pp. 1–20.

Hintikka, Jaakko, and J. Pietarinen, "Semantic Information and Inductive Logic," in Hintikka and Suppes (eds.), *Aspects of Inductive Logic*, 1966, pp. 96–112.

Hintikka, Jaakko, and Patrick Suppes (eds.), *Aspects of Inductive Logic*. Amsterdam: North-Holland Publishing Company, 1966.

Hirst, review of Barker's *Induction and Hypothesis* in *Philosophical Quarterly*, **10**, 1960, pp. 375–376.

Hjorth, Sune, "The Meanings of Probability Statements," *Theoria*, **25**, 1959, pp. 27–30.

Hodges, J. L., Jr., and E. L. Lehmann, *Basic Concepts of Probability and Statistics*. San Francisco: Holden-Day, Inc., 1964.

Hofstadter, Albert, "Quine's View of Knowledge: The Myth of the Whole," *Journal of Philosophy*, **51**, 1954, pp. 397–417.

Hooker, C. A., "Craigian Transcriptionism," *American Philosophical Quarterly*, **5**, 1968, pp. 152–163.

Hooker, C. A., "Goodman, 'Grue' and Hempel," *Philosophy of Science*, **35**, 1968, pp. 232–247.

Hooker, C. A., and D. Stove, "Relevance and the Ravens," *British Journal for the Philosophy of Science*, **18**, 1967–68, pp. 305–315.

Hopf, E., "On Causality, Statistics, and Probability," *Journal of Mathematics and Physics*, **13**, 1934, pp. 51–102.

Hosiasson, Janina, "Why Do We Prefer Probabilities Relative to Many Data?," *Mind*, **40**, 1931, pp. 23–36.

Hosiasson, Janina, "La théorie des probabilités est-elle une logique généralisée?," *Actes du congrès internationale de philosophie scientifique*, Paris, 1936, pp. 58–64.

Hosiasson, Janina, "On Confirmation," *Journal of Symbolic Logic*, **5**, 1940, pp. 133–148.

Hosiasson, Janina, "Induction et Analogie," *Mind*, **50**, 1941, p. 351–365.

Hotelling, Harold, "The Statistical Method and the Philosophy of Science," *American Statistician*, **12**, 1958, pp. 9–14.

Huff, Darrell, *How to Lie with Statistics*. New York: W. W. Norton, 1954.

Hullett, James, and Robert Schwartz, "Grue: Some Remarks," *Journal of Philosophy*, **58**, 1966, pp. 259–271.

Hume, *A Treatise of Human Nature*. Oxford: Oxford University Press, 1960.

Humphreys, Willard C., "Statistical Ambiguity and Maximal Specificity," *Philosophy of Science*, **35**, 1968, pp. 112–115.

Hutten, E. H., "Induction as a Semantic Problem," *Analysis*, **10**, 1949–50, pp. 126–136.

Hutten, E. H., "Probability-Sentences," *Mind*, **61**, 1952, pp. 38–56.

Hutten, E. H., Review of Day's *Inductive Probability*, *Mind*, **71**, 1962, p. 583.

Issman, S., "Les problèmes de la deduction logique et des inférences inductives," *Revue Internationale de Philosophie*, **13**, 1959, pp. 132–134.

Jardine, R., "The Resolution of the Confirmation Paradox," *Australasian Journal of Philosophy*, **43**, 1965, pp. 359–368.

Jeffrey, Richard C., "Valuation and Acceptance of Scientific Hypotheses," *Philosophy of Science*, **23**, 1956, pp. 237–246.

Jeffrey, Richard C., "A Note on Finch's 'An Explication of Counterfactuals by Probability Theory'," *Philosophy and Phenomenological Research*, **20**, 1959, p. 116.

Jeffrey, Richard C., "Comments on Leblanc Paper," in Kyburg and Nagel (eds.), *Induction: Some Current Issues*, pp. 18–21.

Jeffrey, Richard C., "Popper on the Rule of Succession," *Mind*, **73**, 1964, p. 129.

Jeffrey, Richard C., "New Foundations for Bayesian Decision Theory," Yehoshua Bar-Hillel (ed.), *Logic, Methodology and Philosophy of Science, II.* Amsterdam: North-Holland Publishing Company, 1964, pp. 289–300.

* Jeffrey, Richard C., *The Logic of Decision.* New York: McGraw-Hill, 1965.

Jeffrey, Richard C., "Ethics and the Logic of Decision," *Journal of Philosophy*, **62**, 1965, pp. 528–539.

Jeffrey, Richard C., "Solving the Problem of Measurement," *Journal of Philosophy*, **58**, 1966, pp. 400–401.

Jeffrey, Richard C., "Goodman's Query," *Journal of Philosophy*, **63**, 1966, pp. 281–283.

Jeffrey, Richard C., review of Isaac Levi's *Gambling with Truth*, in *Journal of Philosophy*, **65**, 1968, pp. 313–322.

Jeffrey, Richard C., "Probable Knowledge," in Imre Lakatos (ed.), *The Problem of Inductive Logic.* Amsterdam: North-Holland Publishing Company, 1968, pp. 166–190.

Jeffrey, Richard C., "Dracula Meets Wolfman: Acceptance vs. Partial Belief" in Swain (ed.), *Induction, Acceptance and Rational Belief.*

* Jeffreys, Harold, *Scientific Inference.* Cambridge: Cambridge University Press, 1957.

Jeffreys, Harold, "The Problem of Inference," *Mind*, **45**, 1936, pp. 324–333.

Jeffreys, Harold, *Theory of Probability.* Oxford: Oxford University Press, 1939.

Jeffreys, Harold, "Bertrand Russell on Probability," *Mind*, **59**, 1950, pp. 313–319.

Jeffreys, Harold, review of von Wright's *A Treatise on Induction and Probability* in *British Journal for the Philosophy of Science*, **3**, 1952–53, pp. 276–277.

Jeffreys, Harold, "The Present Position in Probability Theory," *British Journal for the Philosophy of Science*, **5**, 1954–55, pp. 275–289.

Jones, Robert M., "The Non-Reducibility of Koopman's Theorem of Probability in Carnap's System for MC," *Philosophy of Science*, **32**, 1965, pp. 368–369.

Jourdain, P. E. B., "Causality, Induction, and Probability," *Mind*, **28**, 1919, pp. 162–179.

Juhos, Bela, "Deduktion, Induktion und Wahrscheinlichkeit," *Methodos*, **6**, 1954, pp. 259–276.

Kac, Mark, *Probability and Related Topics in Physical Sciences.* New York: Interscience, 1959.

Kac, Mark, *Statistical Independence in Probability, Analysis, and Number Theory.* Rahway, N.J.: Mathematical Association of America, 1959.

Kading, Daniel, "Concerning Mr. Feigl's 'Vindication' of Induction," *Philosophy of Science*, **27**, 1960, pp. 405–407.

Kadish, Mortimer, "Note on the Grounds of Evidence," *Journal of Philosophy*, **46**, 1949, pp. 229–243.

Kahane, Howard, "Nelson Goodman's Entrenchment Theory," *Philosophy of Science*, **32**, 1965, pp. 377–383.

Kahane, Howard, "Reply to Ackermann," *Philosophy of Science*, **34**, 1967, pp. 184–187.

Kahane, Howard, "Baumer on the Confirmation Paradoxes," *British Journal for the Philosophy of Science*, **18**, 1967–68, pp. 52–56.

Katz, Jerrold J., *The Problem of Induction and Its Solution*. Chicago: University of Chicago Press, 1962.

Kaufmann, Felix, "The Logical Rules of Scientific Procedure," *Philosophy and Phenomenological Research*, **2**, 1941–42, pp. 457–471.

Kaufmann, Felix, "Scientific Procedure and Probability," *Philosophy and Phenomenological Research*, **6**, 1945–46, pp. 47–66.

Kaufmann, Felix, "On the Nature of Inductive Inference," *Philosophy and Phenomenological Research*, **6**, 1945–46, pp. 602–609.

Keene, G. B., "Randomness," *Proceedings of the Aristotelian Society*, Supplementary Volume **31**, 1957, pp. 151–160.

Keene, G. B., "Confirmation and Corroboration," *Mind*, **70**, 1961, pp. 85–87.

Keene, G. B., "Mill's Method of Hypothesis," *Filosofia*, Supplementary Volume **13**, 1962, pp. 595–598.

Kemble, Edwin C., "The Probability Concept," *Philosophy of Science*, **8**, 1941, pp. 204–232.

Kemble, Edwin C., "Is the Frequency Theory of Probability Adequate for all Scientific Purposes?," *American Journal of Physics*, **10**, 1942, pp. 6–16.

Kemeny, John G., review of Carnap's *Logical Foundations of Probability* in *Journal of Symbolic Logic*, **16**, 1951, pp. 205–207.

Kemeny, John G., review of Carnap's *Logical Foundations of Probability* in *Review of Metaphysics*, **5**, 1951–52, pp. 145–156.

Kemeny, John G., "Extension of the Methods of Inductive Logic," *Philosophical Studies*, **3**, 1952, pp. 38–42.

Kemeny, John G., "A Contribution to Inductive Logic," *Philosophy and Phenomenological Research*, **13**, 1952–53, pp. 371–374.

Kemeny, John G., "A Logical Measure Function," *Journal of Symbolic Logic*, **18**, 1953, pp. 289–308.

Kemeny, John G., review of Wright's *A Treatise on Induction and Probability* in *Philosophical Review*, **62**, 1953, pp. 93–101.

Kemeny, John G., "The Use of Simplicity in Induction," *Philosophical Review*, **62**, 1953, pp. 391–408.

Kemeny, John G., "Two Measures of Complexity," *Journal of Philosophy*, **52**, 1955, pp. 722–733.

Kemeny, John G., "Fair Bets and Inductive Probabilities," *Journal of Symbolic Logic*, **20**, 1955, pp. 263–273.

Kemeny, John G., *A Philosopher Looks at Science*. Princeton, N.J.: D. Van Nostrand, 1959.

* Kemeny, John G., "Carnap's Theory of Probability and Induction," in Schilpp (ed.), *The Philosophy of Rudolf Carnap*, 1963, pp. 711–738.

Kemeny, John G., and Paul Oppenheim, "Degree of Factual Support," *Philosophy of Science*, **19**, 1952, pp. 307–324.

Kessen, William, "Comments on Berlyne's Paper," in Kyburg and Nagel (eds.), *Induction: Some Current Issues*, pp. 94–97.

* Keynes, John Maynard, *A Treatise on Probability*. London: Macmillan, 1952.

Khatchadourian, Haig, "Some Metaphysical Presuppositions of Science," *Philosophy of Science*, **22**, 1955, pp. 194–204.

Kim, Jaegwon, "Inference, Explanation, and Prediction," *Journal of Philosophy*, **61**, 1964, pp. 360–368.

King-Farlow, John, "Toulmin's Analysis of Probability," *Theoria*, **29**, 1963, pp. 12–26.

Klibansky, Raymond, *Philosophy in Mid-Century*, Part I, *Logic*, 1958.

Kneale, William, *Probability and Induction*. Oxford: Oxford University Press, 1949.

Kneale, William, "Probability and Induction," *Mind*, **60**, 1951, pp. 310–317.

Kneale, William, "Some Aspects of Probability and Induction: A Reply to Mr. Bennet," *British Journal for the Philosophy of Science*, **8**, 1957–58, pp. 57–63.

Kneebone, George T., "Frequency Theory of Induction," *Proceedings of the Aristotelian Society*, **50**, 1949–50, pp. 27–42.

Kneebone, George T., "Induction and Probability," *Philosophy*, **26**, 1951, pp. 261–262.

* Kolmogoroff, A. N., *Foundations of the Theory of Probability*. New York: Chelsea, 1950.

* Koopman, B. O., "The Axioms and Algebra of Intuitive Probability," *Annals of Mathematics*, **41**, 1940, pp. 269–292.

Koopman, B. O., "The Bases of Probability," *Bulletin of the American Mathematical Society*, **46**, 1940, pp. 763–774.

Koopman, B. O., "Intuitive Probabilities and Sequences," *Annals of Mathematics*, **42**, 1941, pp. 169–187.

Korner, Stephen (ed.), *The Colston Papers*, **9**, *Observation and Interpretation: A Symposium of Philosophers and Scientists*. London: Butterworths Scientific Publications, 1957.

Koslow, Arnold, review of Jeffreys' *Scientific Inference* in *The Journal of Philosophy*, **57**, 1960, pp. 384–391.

Kotarbinska, Janina, "The Controversy: Deductivism versus Inductivism," in Nagel (ed.), *Logic, Methodology and Philosophy of Science*, I, 1961, pp. 265–274.

Kraft, Charles H., and John W. Pratt and A. Seidenberg, "Intuitive Probability on Finite Sets," *Annals of Mathematical Statistics*, 30, 1959, pp. 408–419.

Kraft, Victor, "The Problem of Induction," in Feyerabend (ed.), *Mind, Matter, Method*, 1966, pp. 306–318.

Krauss, Peter and Dana Scott, "Assigning Probabilities to Logical Formulas," in Hintikka and Suppes (eds.), *Aspects of Inductive Logic*. Amsterdam: North-Holland Publishing Company, 1966, pp. 219–264.

Kuhn, Thomas S., "Historical Structure of Scientific Discovery," *Science*, **136**, 1962, pp. 760–764.

Kuhn, Thomas S., *The Structure of Scientific Revolutions*. Chicago: University of Chicago Press, 1962.

Kyburg, Henry E., Jr., "The Justification of Induction," *Journal of Philosophy*, **53**, 1956, pp. 392–400.

Kyburg, Henry E., Jr., "R. B. Braithwaite on Probability and Induction," *British Journal for the Philosophy of Science*, **9**, 1958–59, pp. 203–220.

Kyburg, Henry E., Jr., "Demonstrative Induction," *Philosophy and Phenomenological Research*, **21**, 1960–61, pp. 80–92.

Kyburg, Henry E., Jr., "Probability and Rationality," *The Philosophical Quarterly*, **11**, 1961, pp. 3–10.

* Kyburg, Henry E., Jr., *Probability and the Logic of Rational Belief.* Middletown, Conn.: Wesleyan University Press, 1961.

Kyburg, Henry E., Jr., "A Modest Proposal Concerning Simplicity," *The Philosophical Review*, **70**, 1961, pp. 390–395.

Kyburg, Henry E., Jr., review of C. West Churchman's *Prediction and Optimal Decision* in *Journal of Philosophy*, **59**, 1962, pp. 549–554.

Kyburg, Henry E., Jr., "Probability and Randomness," *Theoria*, **29**, 1963, pp. 27–55.

Kyburg, Henry E., Jr., review of Rudolf Carnap's *Logical Foundations of Probability*, 2nd ed., *Journal of Philosophy*, **60**, 1963, pp. 362–364.

Kyburg, Henry E., Jr., review of Pap's *Introduction to the Philosophy of Science* in *Journal of Philosophy*, **60**, 1963, pp. 358–362.

Kyburg, Henry E., Jr., review of Leblanc's *Statistical and Inductive Probabilities*, in *American Mathematical Monthly*, **70**, 1963, pp. 1022–1023.

Kyburg, Henry E., Jr., "Logical and Fiducial Probability," *Bulletin of the International Statistical Institute*, **40**, Ottawa, 1963, pp. 884–901.

Kyburg, Henry E., Jr., "Comments on Braithwaite Paper," in Kyburg and Nagel (eds.), *Induction: Some Current Issues*, pp. 196–199.

Kyburg, Henry E., Jr., "A Further Note on Rationality and Consistency," *Journal of Philosophy*, **60**, 1963, pp. 463–465.

Kyburg, Henry E., Jr., "Probability, Rationality, and a Rule of Detachment," Yehoshua Bar-Hillel (ed.), *Logic, Methodology and Philosophy of Science*, II. Amsterdam: North-Holland Publishing Company, 1964, pp. 301–310.

Kyburg, Henry E., Jr., "Recent Work in Inductive Logic," *American Philosophical Quarterly*, **1**, 1964, pp. 1–39.

Kyburg, Henry E., Jr., "Comments on Salmon's 'Inductive Evidence'," *American Philosophical Quarterly*, **2**, 1965, pp. 10–12.

Kyburg, Henry E., Jr., "Salmon's Paper," *Philosophy of Science*, **32**, 1965, pp. 147–151.

Kyburg, Henry E., Jr., "Probability and Decision," *Philosophy of Science*, **33**, 1966, pp. 250–261.

Kyburg, Henry E., Jr., review of Schilpp (ed.), *The Philosophy of Rudolf Carnap* in *The Journal of Philosophy*, **65**, 1968, pp. 503–515.

Kyburg, Henry E., Jr., "The Rule of Detachment in Inductive Logic," in Lakatos (ed.), *The Problem of Inductive Logic*. Amsterdam: North-Holland Publishing Company, 1968, pp. 98–165.

Kyburg, Henry E., Jr., "Bets and Beliefs," *American Philosophical Quarterly*, **5**, 1968, pp. 54–63.

Kyburg, Henry E., Jr., review of Hintikka and Suppes (eds.), *Aspects of Inductive Logic* in *Philosophical Review*, **77**, 1968, pp. 526–528.

Kyburg, Henry E., Jr., review of Jeffrey's *The Logic of Decision* in *Philosophical Review*, **77**, 1968, pp. 250–253.

Kyburg, Henry E., Jr., *Probability Theory*. Englewood Cliffs, N.J.: Prentice-Hall, 1969.

Kyburg, Henry E., Jr., "Conjunctivitis" in Swain (ed.), *Induction, Acceptance and Rational Belief.*

Kyburg, Henry E., Jr., and E. Nagel (eds.), *Induction: Some Current Issues*. Middletown, Conn.: Wesleyan University Press, 1963.

Kyburg, Henry E., Jr., and Howard Smokler (eds.), *Studies in Subjective Probability*. New York: John Wiley and Sons, 1964.

Kyburg, Henry E., Jr., and William Harper, "Discussion: The Jones Case," *British Journal for the Philosophy of Science*, **19**, 1968–69, pp. 247–258.

Laer, P. Henry Van, *Philosophy of Science*. Pittsburgh: Duquesne Studies, 1956.

Lakatos, Imre (ed.), *The Problem of Inductive Logic*. Amsterdam: North-Holland Publishing Company, 1968.

Lakatos, Imre, and Alan Musgrave (eds.), *Problems in the Philosophy of Science*. Amsterdam: North-Holland Publishing Company, 1968.

Lakatos, Imre, "Changes in the Problem of Inductive Logic," in Imre Lakatos (ed.), *The Problem of Inductive Logic*. Amsterdam: North-Holland Publishing Company, 1968, pp. 315–417.

LeBlanc, Hugues, "Evidence logique et degré de confirmation," *Revue Philosophique de Louvain*, **52**, 1954, pp. 619–625.

LeBlanc, Hugues, "Two Probability Concepts," *Journal of Philosophy*, **53**, 1956, pp. 679–688.

LeBlanc, Hugues, "On Logically False Evidence Statements," *Journal of Symbolic Logic*, **22**, 1957, pp. 345–349.

LeBlanc, Hugues, "On Chances and Estimated Chances of Being True," *Revue Philosophique de Louvain*, **57**, 1959, pp. 225–239.

LeBlanc, Hugues, "On So-called Degrees of Confirmation," *British Journal for the Philosophy of Science*, **10**, 1959–60, pp. 312–315.

LeBlanc, Hugues, "A New Interpretation of $c(h, e)$," *Philosophy and Phenomenological Research*, **21**, 1960–61, pp. 373–376.

LeBlanc, Hugues, "On Requirements for Conditional Probability," *Journal of Symbolic Logic*, **25**, 1960, pp. 238–242.

LeBlanc, Hugues, "Probabilities as Truth Value Estimates," *Philosophy of Science*, **28**, 1961, pp. 414–417.

LeBlanc, Hugues, "The Problem of the Confirmation of Laws," *Philosophical Studies*, **12**, 1961, pp. 81–84.

LeBlanc, Hugues, "Statistical and Inductive Probabilities," in Kyburg and Nagel (eds.), *Induction: Some Current Issues*, pp. 3–16.

LeBlanc, Hugues, *Statistical and Inductive Probabilities*. Englewood Cliffs, N.J.: Prentice-Hall, 1962.

LeBlanc, Hugues, "That Positive Instances are No Help," *Journal of Philosophy*, **60**, 1963, pp. 453–462.

LeBlanc, Hugues, "A Revised Version of Goodman's Paradox on Confirmation," *Philosophical Studies*, **14**, 1963, pp. 49–51.

LeBlanc, Hugues, "On Requirements for Conditional Probability Functions," *Journal of Symbolic Logic*, **25**, 1966, pp. 238–242.

Lee, Harold N., "An Epistemological Analysis of Induction," in *Tulane Studies in Philosophy*, II. New Orleans: Tulane University, 1953, pp. 83–94.

* Lehmann, E. L., *Testing Statistical Hypotheses*. New York: John Wiley and Sons, Inc., 1959.

Lehmann, E. L. and J. L. Hodges, Jr., *Basic Concepts of Probability and Statistics*. San Francisco: Holden-Day, Inc., 1964.

Lehman, R. Sherman, "On Confirmation and Rational Betting," *Journal of Symbolic Logic*, **20**, 1955, pp. 251–262.

Lehrer, Keith, "Descriptive Completeness and Inductive Methods," *Journal of Symbolic Logic*, **28**, 1963, pp. 157–160.

Lehrer, Keith, "Knowledge and Probability," *Journal of Philosophy*, **61**, 1964, pp. 368–372.

Lehrer, Keith, "Knowledge, Truth and Evidence," *Analysis*, **25**, 1964–65, pp. 168–175.

Lehrer, Keith, "Letter: On Knowledge and Probability," *Journal of Philosophy*, **62**, 1965, pp. 67–68.

Lehrer, Keith, Richard Roelofs, and Marshall Swain, "Reason and Evidence: An Unsolved Problem," *Ratio*, **9**, 1967, pp. 38–48.

Lehrer, Keith, "Justification, Explanation, and Induction," in Swain (ed.), *Induction, Acceptance and Rational Belief.*

Lenz, John W., "Carnap on Defining 'Degrees of Confirmation'," *Philosophy of Science*, **23**, 1956, pp. 230–236.

Lenz, John W., "Problems for the Practicalists' Justification of Induction," *Philosophical Studies*, **9**, 1958, pp. 4–8.

Lerner, Daniel (ed.), *Evidence and Inference*. Glencoe, Ill.: The Free Press, 1959.

Lev, Joseph and Helen Walker, *Statistical Inference*. New York: Holt, Rinehart and Winston, 1953.

Levi, Isaac, review of Harrod's *Foundations of Inductive Logic* in *Journal of Philosophy*, **55**, 1958, pp. 209–212.

Levi, Isaac, "Must the Scientist Make Value Judgements?," *Journal of Philosophy*, **57**, 1960, pp. 345–357.

Levi, Isaac, "Decision Theory and Confirmation," *Journal of Philosophy*, **58**, 1961, pp. 614–625.

Levi, Isaac, "On the Seriousness of Mistakes," *Philosophy of Science*, **29**, 1962, pp. 47–65.

Levi, Isaac, "Corroboration and Rules of Acceptance," *British Journal for the Philosophy of Science*, **13**, 1962–63, pp. 307–313.

Levi, Isaac, review of H. LeBlanc's *Statistical and Inductive Probabilities* in *Journal of Philosophy*, **60**, 1963, p. 21.

Levi, Isaac, "Belief and Action," *The Monist*, **48**, 1963–64, pp. 306–316.

Levi, Isaac, "Deductive Cogency in Inductive Inference," *Journal of Philosophy*, **62**, 1965, pp. 68–77.

Levi, Isaac, "Hacking Salmon on Induction," *Journal of Philosophy*, **62**, 1965, pp. 481–487.

Levi, Isaac, "On Potential Surprise," *Ratio*, **8**, 1966, pp. 107–129.

Levi, Isaac, "Utility and Acceptance of Hypotheses," in Sidney Morgenbesser (ed.), *Philosophy of Science Today*, New York: Basic Books, 1967.

* Levi, Isaac, *Gambling with the Truth: An Essay on Induction and the Aims of Science*. New York: Alfred A. Knopf, 1967.

Levi, Isaac, "Probability Kinematics," *British Journal for the Philosophy of Science*, **18**, 1967–68, pp. 197–209.

Levi, Isaac, "Information and Inference," *Synthese*, **17**, 1969, pp. 369–391.

Levi, Isaac, "Putnam's Three Truth Values," *Philosophical Studies*, **10**, 1959, pp. 65–69.

Levi, Isaac, "Probability and Evidence," in Swain (ed.), *Induction, Acceptance and Rational Belief.*

Levi, Isaac, and Sidney Morgenbesser, "Belief and Disposition," *American Philosophical Quarterly*, **1**, 1964, pp. 221–232.

Lévy, Paul, "Le fondement du calcul des probabilités," *Revue de Metaphysique*, **59**, 1954, pp. 164–179.

Lewis, C. I., *An Analysis of Knowledge and Valuation*. LaSalle, Ill.: Open Court, 1946.

Lewis, H. D. (ed.), *Contemporary British Philosophy*. New York: Macmillan, 1956.

Lewy, Casimir, "On the Justification of Induction," *Analysis*, **6**, 1939, pp. 87–90.

Lindeman, Edwards, and Savage, "Bayesian Statistical Inference for Psychological Research," *Psychological Review*, 70, 1963, pp. 193–242.

Lindley, D. V., "Statistical Inference," *Journal of the Royal Statistical Society*, B, **15**, 1953, pp. 30–76.

Lindley, D. V., "A Statistical Paradox," *Biometrika*, **44**, 1957, pp. 187–192.

Lindley, D. V., *Introduction to Probability and Statistics: Part 1, Probability*. Cambridge: Cambridge University Press, 1965.

Lindley, D. V., *Introduction to Probability and Statistics: Part 2, Inference*. Cambridge: Cambridge University Press, 1965.

Linhart, H., "Darlington's 'On the Confirmation of Laws'," *Philosophy of Science*, **26**, 1949, p. 362.

Llewelyn, J. E., "Unquantified Inductive Generalizations," *Analysis*, **22**, 1961–62, pp. 134–137.

Lucas, J. R., "The One Concept of Probability," *Philosophy and Phenomenological Research*, **26**, 1965–66, pp. 180–199.

* Luce, R. Duncan, and Howard Raiffa, *Games and Decisions: Introduction and Critical Survey*. New York: John Wiley and Sons, 1957.

Mace, Cecil Alec (ed.), *British Philosophy in Midcentury*. London: Allen and Unwin, 1957.

Machol, R. E. (ed.), *Recent Developments in Information and Decision Processes*. New York: Macmillan, 1962.

Mackie, J. L., "The Paradox of Confirmation," *British Journal for the Philosophy of Science*, **13**, 1962–63, pp. 265–277.

Mackie, J. L., "Miller's So-called Paradox of Information," *British Journal for the Philosophy of Science*, **17**, 1966–67, pp. 144–147.

Madden, Edward H., "Aristotle's Treatment of Probability and Signs," *Philosophy of Science*, **24**, 1957, pp. 167–172.

Madden, Edward H., review of Wright's *Logical Problem of Induction* in *Philosophy and Phenomenological Research*, **18**, 1957–59, pp. 550–551.

Madden, Edward H., "The Riddle of Induction," *Journal of Philosophy*, **55**, 1958, pp. 705–718.

Mahalanobis, P. C., "The Foundations of Statistics," *Dialectica*, **8**, 1954, pp. 95–111.

Malinovich, S., "The Verification of Universal Empirical Propositions," *Analysis*, **25**, 1964–65, pp. 202–204.

Margenau, Henry, "Probability, Many-Valued Logics, and Physics," *Philosophy of Science*, **6**, 1939, pp. 65–87.

Margolis, J., "The Demand for a Justification of Induction," *Synthese*, **11**, 1959, pp. 259–264.

Margolis, J., "'Entitled to Assert'," *Synthese*, **17**, 1967, pp. 292–298.

Martin, Richard M., "A Formalization of Inductive Logic," *Journal of Symbolic Logic*, **23**, 1958, pp. 251–256.

Martin, Richard M., *Intension and Decision*. Englewood Cliffs, N.J.: Prentice-Hall, 1963.

Massey, Gerald J., "Hempel's Criterion of Maximal Specificity," *Philosophical Studies*, **19**, 1968, pp. 43–47.

Mathers, Ruth Anne, "A Note on R. H. Vincent's Cognitive Sensibilities," *Philosophical Studies*, **14**, 1963, pp. 75–77.

Matson, W. I., "Against Induction and Empiricism," *Proceedings of the Aristotelian Society*, New Series, **62**, 1961–62, pp. 143–158.

Maxwell, Grover, "An 'Analytic' Vindication of Induction," *Philosophical Studies*, **12**, 1961, pp. 43–45.

Maxwell, Grover and Herbert Feigl (eds.), *Current Issues in the Philosophy of Science*. New York: Holt, Rinehart, and Winston, 1961.

Maxwell, Grover and Paul K. Feyerabend, *Mind, Matter, and Method; Essays in Honor of Herbert Feigl*. Minneapolis: University of Minnesota Press, 1962.

Maxwell, Grover, Herbert Feigl, and Michael Scriven (eds.), *Minnesota Studies in the Philosophy of Science*, I. *the Foundations of Science and the Concepts of Psychology and Psychoanalysis*. Minneapolis: University of Minnesota Press, 1962.

Maxwell, Grover, Herbert Feigl, and Michael Scriven, *Concepts, Theories, and the Mind-Body Problem, Minnesota Studies in the Philosophy of Science*. II. Minneapolis: University of Minnesota Press, 1958.

Maxwell, Grover and Herbert Feigl (eds.), *Scientific Explanation, Space, and Time, Minnesota Studies in the Philosophy of Science*, III. Minneapolis: University of Minnesota Press, 1962.

Mayberry, Thomas C., "Donald Williams on Induction," *Journal of Thought*, **3**, 1968, pp. 204–211.

Mayo, Bernard, "Probability: A Rejoinder to Mr. Urmson," *Analysis*, **8**, 1947–48, pp. 30–32.

Mays, W., "Probability Models and Thought and Learning Processes," *Synthese*, **15**, 1963, pp. 204–221.

McLendon, Hiram J., "Has Russell Answered Hume?," *Journal of Philosophy*, **49**, 1952, pp. 145–159.

McNabb, D. G. C., "Hume on Induction," *Revue Internationale de Philosophie*, **6**, 1952, pp. 184–198.

Mellor, D. H., "Experimental Error and Deducibility," *Philosophy of Science*, **32**, 1965, pp. 105–122.

Mellor, D. H., "Connectivity, Chance and Ignorance," *British Journal for the Philosophy of Science*, **16**, 1965–66, pp. 209–225.

Mellor, D. H., "Inexactness and Explanation," *Philosophical Studies*, **33**, 1966, pp. 345–359.

Mellor, D. H., "Imprecision and Explanation," *Philosophy of Science*, **34**, 1967, pp. 1–9.

Menger, Karl, "On the Relation Between the Calculus of Probability and Statistics," *Notre Dame Mathematical Lecture*, **4**, 1944, pp. 44–53.

Menger, Karl, "Random Variables from the Point of View of a General Theory of Variables," *Proceedings of the Third Berkeley Symposium on Mathematical Statistics and Probability*, **2**, 1954, pp. 215–229.

Meredith, G. P., C. F. Cater, and G. L. S. Shackle, *Uncertainty and Business Decisions*. Liverpool: Liverpool University Press, 1962.

Michalos, Alex, "Two Theorems on Degree of Confirmation," *Ratio*, 7, 1965, pp. 196–198.

Michalos, Alex, "Estimated Utility and Corroboration," *British Journal for the Philosophy of Science*, 16, 1965–66, pp. 327–331.

Michalos, Alex, review of Hacking's *Logic of Statistical Inference* in *Dialectica*, 5, 1966–67, pp. 647–649.

Michalos, Alex, "Descriptive Completeness and Linguistic Variance," *Dialogue*, 6, 1967–68, pp. 224–228.

Mill, John Stuart, *A System of Logic, Ratiocinative and Inductive, Being a Connected View of the Principles of Evidence and the Methods of Scientific Investigations*, 2 vols. London: Longman's, 1868. New York: Harper and Brothers, 1900, 8th ed.

Miller, David, "A Paradox of Information," *British Journal for the Philosophy of Science*, 17, 1966–67, pp. 59–61.

Miller, David, "On the So-Called So-Called Paradox: A Reply to Professor J. L. Mackie," *British Journal for the Philosophy of Science*, 17, 1966–67, pp. 147–149.

Miller, David, "The Straight and Narrow Rule of Induction, a Reply to Dr. Bub and Mr. Radner," *British Journal for the Philosophy of Science*, 19, 1968, pp. 145–152.

Minas, J. Sayer, "Comment on Richard C. Jeffrey's 'Ethics and the Logic of Decision'," *Journal of Philosophy*, 62, 1965, pp. 542–544.

Mises, Richard von, "On the Foundations of Probability and Statistics," *Annals of Mathematical Statistics*, 12, 1941, p. 191–205.

Mises, Richard von, "Comments on D. Williams' Paper," *Philosophy and Phenomenological Research*, 6, 1945–46, pp. 45–46.

Mises, Richard von, "Comments on Donald Williams' Reply," *Philosophy and Phenomenological Research*, 6, 1945–46, pp. 611–613.

* Mises, Richard von, *Probability, Statistics, and Truth*. New York: Macmillan, 1957.

Moore, Asher, "The Principle of Induction," *Journal of Philosophy*, 49, 1952, pp. 741–747.

Moore, Asher, "The Principle of Induction (II): A Rejoinder to Miss Brodbeck," *Journal of Philosophy*, 49, 1952, pp. 750–758.

Morgenbesser, Sidney, "A Note on Justification," *Journal of Philosophy*, 58, 1961, pp. 748–749.

Morgenbesser, Sidney, "Goodman and the Ravens," *Journal of Philosophy*, 59, 1962, pp. 493–495.

Morgenbesser, Sidney and Arthur Danto (eds.), *Philosophy of Science*. New York: Meridian Books, 1960.

Morgenbesser, Sidney and Isaac Levi, "Belief and Disposition," *American Philosophical Quarterly*, 1, 1964, pp. 221–232.

Morgenbesser, Sidney (ed.), *Philosophy of Science Today*. New York: Basic Books, 1967.

Morgenstern, Oskar and John von Neumann, *Theory of Games and Economic Behavior*. Princeton: Princeton University Press, 1944. New York: John Wiley and Sons, 1964.

Moses, Lincoln E. and Herman Chernoff, *Elementary Decision Theory*. New York: John Wiley and Sons, Inc., 1959.

Mosteller, Frederick, and David Wallace, *Inference and Disputed Authorship: The Federalist*. Reading, Mass.: Addison-Wesley, 1964.

Mundle, C. W. K., "Probability and Scientific Inference," *Philosophy*, **34**, 1959, pp. 150–154.

Musgrave, Alan and Imre Lakatos (eds.), *Problems in the Philosophy of Science*. Amsterdam: North-Holland Publishing Company, 1968.

Myhill, John, "On the Concept of a Random Sequence," *Journal of Symbolic Logic*, **16**, 1951, p. 236.

Nagel, Ernest, "The Meaning of Probability," *Journal of the American Statistical Association*, **31**, 1936, pp. 10–26.

Nagel, Ernest, "Probability and the Theory of Knowledge," *Philosophy of Science*, **6**, 1939, pp. 212–253.

* Nagel, Ernest, "Principles of the Theory of Probability," *International Encyclopedia of Unified Science*. Chicago: University of Chicago Press, 1949.

Nagel, Ernest, "Jeffreys' Theory of Probability," *Journal of Philosophy*, **37**, 1940, pp. 524–528.

Nagel, Ernest, "Probability and Non-demonstrative Inference," *Philosophy and Phenomenological Research*, **5**, 1944–45, pp. 485–507.

Nagel, Ernest, "Is the LaPlacean Theory of Probability Tenable?," *Philosophy and Phenomenological Research*, **6**, 1945–46, pp. 614–618.

Nagel, Ernest, review of Carnap's "On Inductive Logic," *Journal of Symbolic Logic*, **11**, 1946, pp. 19–23.

Nagel, Ernest, "Kneale's Probability and Induction," *Journal of Philosophy*, **47**, 1950, pp. 545–551.

Nagel, Ernest, "Reichenbach's Theory of Probability," *Journal of Philosophy*, **47**, 1950, pp. 551–555.

Nagel, Ernest, *The Structure of Science*. New York: Harcourt, Brace and World, 1961.

Nagel, Ernest, "Carnap's Theory of Induction," in Schilpp (ed.), *The Philosophy of Rudolf Carnap*. LaSalle, Ill.: Open Court, 1963, pp. 785–826.

Nagel, Ernest and Morris Cohen, *An Introduction to Logic and Scientific Method*. New York: Harcourt, Brace and Company, 1934.

Nagel, Suppes, and Tarski (eds.), *Logic, Methodology and Philosophy of Science, I*. Stanford: Stanford University Press, 1962.

Nagel, E. and Henry E. Kyburg, Jr., *Induction: Some Current Issues*. Middletown, Connecticut: Wesleyan University Press, 1963.

Nelson, E. J., "Professor Reichenbach on Induction," *Journal of Philosophy*, **33**, 1936, pp. 577–580.

Nelson, E. J., "The Ground of Induction: A Review," *Philosophy and Phenomenological Research*, **9**, 1948–49, pp. 139–143.

Nelson, E. J., "Causal Necessity and Induction," *Proceedings of the Aristotelian Society*, New Series, **64**, 1963–64, pp. 289–300.

Nelson, John O., "The Confirmation of Hypotheses," *Philosophical Review*, **67**, 1958, pp. 95–100.

Nelson, John O., "Are Inductive Generalizations Quantifiable?," *Analysis*, **22**, 1961–62, pp. 59–65.

Nelson, John O., "Logical Notation and Indoor Ornithology," *Ratio*, **10**, 1968, pp. 169–172.

* Neumann, John von, and Oskar Morgenstern, *Theory of Games and Economic Behavior*. Princeton: Princeton University Press, 1944. New York: John Wiley and Sons, 1964.

Neyman, Jerzy, "Outline of a Theory of Statistical Estimation Based on the Classical Theory of Probability," *Philosophical Transactions of the Royal Society*, A, **236**, 1937, pp. 333–380.

Neyman, Jerzy, "Fiducial Argument and the Theory of Confidence Intervals," *Biometrika*, **32**, 1941, pp. 128–150.

* Neyman, Jerzy, "Basic Ideas and Some Recent Results of the Theory of Testing Statistical Hypotheses," *Journal of the Royal Statistical Society*, **105**, 1942, pp. 292–327.

Neyman, Jerzy, "Raisonnement inductif ou comportement inductif," *Proceedings of the International Statistical Conference*, 3, 1947, pp. 423–433.

Neyman, Jerzy, *First Course in Probability and Statistics*. New York: Henry Holt and Company, 1950.

Neyman, Jerzy, *Lectures and Conferences on Mathematical Statistics and Probability*, 2nd ed. Washington: United States Department of Agriculture, 1952.

Neyman, Jerzy, "The Problem of Inductive Inference," *Communications on Pure and Applied Mathematics*, **8**, 1955, pp. 13–45.

* Neyman, Jerzy, "'Inductive Behavior' as a Basic Concept of Philosophy of Science," *Review of the International Statistical Institute*, **25**, 1957, pp. 7–22.

Neyman, Jerzy, and E. S. Pearson, "The Testing of Statistical Hypotheses in Relation to Probabilities A Priori," *Proceedings of the Cambridge Philosophical Society*, **29**, 1932–33, pp. 492–510.

Neyman, Jerzy, and E. S. Pearson, "On the Problem of the Most Efficient Tests of Statistical Hypotheses," *Philosophical Transactions of the Royal Society*, A, **231**, 1933, pp. 289–337.

Neyman, Jerzy, and E. S. Pearson, "Contributions to the Theory of Testing Statistical Hypotheses," *Statistical Research Memoirs*, **1**, 1936, pp. 1–37; **2**, 1938, pp. 25–57.

Nicod, Jean, *Foundations of Geometry and Induction*. New York: The Humanities Press, 1950.

Nielsen, Harry A., "Sampling and the Problem of Induction," *Mind*, **68**, 1959, pp. 474–481.

Nowak, Stefan, "Some Problems of Causal Interpretation of Statistical Relationships," *Philosophy of Science*, **27**, 1960, pp. 23–38.

Nyman, Alf, "Induction et Intuition," *Theoria*, **19**, 1953, pp. 21–41.

O'Connor, John, "Differential Properties and Goodman's Riddle," *Analysis*, **28**, 1967–68, p. 59.

Ofsti, Audin, "Some Problems of Counter-inductive Policy as Opposed to Inductive," *Inquiry*, **5**, 1962, pp. 267–282.

Oliver, James Willard, "Deduction and the Statistical Syllogism," *Journal of Philosophy*, **50**, 1953, pp. 805–807.

Oliver, W. Donald, "A Re-examination of the Problem of Induction," *Journal of Philosophy*, **49**, 1952, pp. 769–780.

Oppenheim, Paul and Olaf Helmer, "A Syntactical Definition of Probability and Degree of Confirmation," *Journal of Symbolic Logic*, **10**, 1945, pp. 25–60.

Oppenheim, Paul and C. G. Hempel, "A Definition of Degree of Confirmation," *Philosophy of Science*, **12**, 1945, pp. 98–115.

Oppenheim, Paul and C. G. Hempel, "Studies in the Logic of Explanation," *Philosophy of Science*, **15**, 1948, pp. 135–175.

Oppenheim, Paul and John G. Kemeny, "Degree of Factual Support," *Philosophy of Science*, **19**, 1952, pp. 307–324.

Ore, Oystein, "Pascal and the Invention of Probability Theory," *American Mathematical Monthly*, **67**, 1960, pp. 409–418.

O'Toole, Edward J., "A Note on Probability," *Philosophical Studies* (Dublin), **11**, 1961–62, pp. 112–127.

Pakswer, S., "Information, Entropy, and Inductive Logic," *Philosophy of Science*, **21**, 1954, pp. 254–259.

Palmieri, L. E., "Confirmation, Intention, and Language," *Methodos*, **11**, 1959, pp. 33–40.

Palmieri, L. E., "Induction, Deduction, and Certainty," *Methodos*, **11**, 1959, pp. 169–172.

Pap, Arthur, *An Introduction to the Philosophy of Science*. New York: The Free Press of Glencoe, 1962.

Parzen, Emanuel, *Modern Probability Theory and its Applications*. New York: John Wiley and Sons, 1960.

Passmore, J. A., "Popper's Account of Scientific Method," *Philosophy*, **35**, 1960, pp. 326–331.

Pearson, E. S., and C. J. Clopper, "The Use of Confidence or Fiducial Limits Illustrated in the Case of a Binomial," *Biometrika*, **26**, 1934, pp. 404–413.

Pearson, Karl, "The Fundamental Problem of Practical Statistics," *Biometrika*, **13**, 1920, pp. 1–16.

Pearson, E. S. and Jerzy Neyman, "The Testing of Statistical Hypotheses in Relation to Probabilities A Priori," *Proceedings of the Cambridge Philosophical Society*, **29**, 1932–33, pp. 492–510.

Pearson, E. S. and Jerzy Neyman, "On the Problem of the Most Efficient Tests of Statistical Hypotheses," *Philosophical Transactions of the Royal Society*, A, **231**, 1933, pp. 289–337.

Pearson, E. S. and Jerzy Neyman, "Contributions to the Theory of Testing Statistical Hypotheses," *Statistical Research Memoirs*, **1**, 1936, pp. 1–37; **2**, 1938, pp. 25–57.

Peirce, Charles Saunders, "The Probability of Induction," 1878. Reprinted in *Collected Papers*, II, pp. 415–432.

Peirce, Charles Saunders, "A Theory of Probable Inference," 1883. Reprinted in *Collected Papers*, II, pp. 433–477.

Peirce, Charles Saunders, *Collected Papers* ed. by Charles Hartshorne and Paul Weiss. Cambridge: Harvard University Press, 1932–33.

Peirce, C. S., *The Philosophy of Peirce: Selected Writings*, ed. Buchler. New York: Harcourt, Brace and Company, 1950.

Pettijohn, William C., "Salmon on 'the Short Run'," *Philosophy of Science*, **23**, 1956, p. 149.

Pfeiffer, Paul E., *Concepts of Probability Theory*. New York: McGraw-Hill, 1965.

Pietarinen, J. and Jaakko Hintikka, "Semantic Information and Inductive Logic," in Hintikka and Suppes (eds.), *Aspects of Inductive Logic*, 1966, pp. 96–112.

Polanyi, Michael, *Personal Knowledge*. Chicago: University of Chicago Press, 1958.

Pollock, John L., "Counter-Induction," *Inquiry*, **5**, 1962, pp. 284–294.

Pollock, John L., "Non-analytic Implication," *Inquiry*, **10**, 1967, pp. 196–203.

Polya, G., "Heuristic Reasoning and the Theory of Probability," *American Mathematical Monthly*, **41**, 1941, pp. 450–465.

Polya, G., "On Patterns of Plausible Inference," in *Courant Anniversary Volume*, 1948, pp. 277–288.

Polya, G., *Mathematics and Plausible Reasoning*. Princeton: Princeton University Press, 1954.

Popper, Karl R., "A Set of Independent Axioms for Probability," *Mind*, **47**, 1938, pp. 275–277.

Popper, Karl R., "Degree of Confirmation," *British Journal for the Philosophy of Science*, **5**, 1954–55, pp. 143–149.

* Popper, Karl R., "Two Autonomous Axiom Systems for the Calculus of Probabilities," *British Journal for the Philosophy of Science*, **6**, 1955–56, pp. 51–57.

Popper, Karl R., "'Content' and 'Degree of Confirmation': A Reply to Dr. Bar-Hillel," *British Journal for the Philosophy of Science*, **6**, 1955–56, pp. 157–163.

Popper, Karl R., "Three Views Concerning Human Knowledge" in Lewis (ed.), *Contemporary British Philosophy*. New York: Macmillan, 1956, pp. 355–388.

Popper, Karl R., "Reply to Professor Carnap," *British Journal for the Philosophy of Science*, **7**, 1956–57, pp. 244–245.

Popper, Karl R., "Adequacy and Consistency: A Second Reply to Dr. Bar-Hillel," *British Journal for the Philosophy of Science*, **7**, 1956–57, pp. 249–256.

Popper, Karl R., "A Second Note on Degree of Confirmation," *British Journal for the Philosophy of Science*, **7**, 1956–57, pp. 350–353.

Popper, Karl R., "Probability Magic or Knowledge Out of Ignorance," *Dialectica*, **11**, 1957, pp. 354–373.

* Popper, Karl R., "The Propensity Interpretation of the Calculus of Probability and the Quantum Theory," in Körner (ed.), *The Colston Papers*, **9**, 1957, pp. 65–70.

Popper, Karl R., "The Aim of Science," *Ratio*, **1**, 1957–58, pp. 24–35.

Popper, Karl R., "A Third Note on Degree of Corroboration or Conformation," *British Journal for the Philosophy of Science*, **8**, 1957–58, pp. 294–302.

Popper, Karl R., "On Mr. Harrod's New Argument for Induction," *British Journal for the Philosophy of Science*, **9**, 1958–59, pp. 221–224.

Popper, Karl R., *The Logic of Scientific Discovery*. London: Hutchinson and Company, 1959.

Popper, Karl R., "The Propensity Interpretation of Probability," *British Journal for the Philosophy of Science*, **10**, 1959–60, pp. 25–42.

Popper, Karl R., "Probabilistic Independence and Corroboration by Empirical Tests," *British Journal for the Philosophy of Science*, **10**, 1959–60, pp. 315–318.

Popper, Karl R., "On Carnap's Version of Laplace's Rule of Succession," *Mind*, **71**, 1962, pp. 69–73.

Popper, Karl R., "On the Sources of Knowledge and Ignorance," in *Conjectures and Refutations*. London: Routledge and Kegan Paul, 1963, pp. 23–30.

Popper, Karl R., "Truth, Rationality, and the Growth of Scientific Knowledge," in *Conjectures and Refutations*. London: Routledge and Kegan Paul, 1963, pp. 215–250.

Popper, Karl R., "The Demarcation Between Science and Metaphysics," in *Conjectures and Refutations*. London: Routledge and Kegan Paul, 1963, pp. 253–292.

Popper, Karl R., "Science: Conjectures and Refutations," in *Conjectures and Refutations*. London: Routledge and Kegan Paul, 1963, pp. 23–30.

Popper, Karl R., "The Demarcation Between Science and Metaphysics," in Schilpp (ed.), *The Philosophy of Rudolf Carnap*. LaSalle, Ill.: Open Court, 1963, pp. 183–226.

Popper, Karl R., "Creative and Non-creative Definitions in the Calculus of Probability," *Synthese*, **15**, 1963, pp. 167–186.

* Popper, Karl R., *Conjectures and Refutations*. London: Routledge and Kegan Paul, 1963.

Popper, Karl R., "Creative and Non-creative Definitions in the Calculus of Probability," in Gregg and Harris (eds.), *Form and Strategy in Science*. Dordrecht, Holland: D. Reidel Publishing Company, 1964, pp. 171–190.

Popper, Karl R., "A Comment on Miller's New Paradox of Information," *British Journal for the Philosophy of Science*, **17**, 1966–67, pp. 61–69.

Popper, Karl R., "A Paradox of Zero Information," *British Journal for the Philosophy of Science*, **17**, 1966–67, pp. 141–143.

Popper, Karl R., "The Mysteries of Udolpho: A Reply to Professors Jeffrey and Bar-Hillel," *Mind*, **76**, 1967, pp. 103–110.

Popper, Karl R., "Epistemology without a Knowing Subject," in B. Van Rootselaar and J. F. Staal (eds.), *Logic, Methodology and Philosophy of Science*, III. Amsterdam: North-Holland Publishing Company, 1968, pp. 333–373.

Post, H. R., "Simplicity in Scientific Theories," *British Journal for the Philosophy of Science*, **11**, 1960–61, pp. 32–41.

Putnam, Hilary, "A Definition of Degree of Confirmation for Very Rich Languages," *Philosophy of Science*, **23**, 1956, pp. 58–62.

Putnam, Hilary, "Degree of Confirmation and Inductive Logic," in Schilpp (ed.), *The Philosophy of Rudolf Carnap*. LaSalle, Ill.: Open Court, 1963, pp. 761–784.

Quine, Willard Van Orman, *Mathematical Logic*. Cambridge: Harvard University Press, 1951 (revised edition).

Quine, Willard Van Orman, *From a Logical Point of View*. Cambridge: Harvard University Press, 1953.

Quine, Willard Van Orman, "The Scope and Language of Science," *British Journal for the Philosophy of Science*, **8**, 1957–58, pp. 1–17.

Quine, Willard Van Orman, *Word and Object*. New York: John Wiley and Sons, 1960.

Radner, Michael and Jeffrey Bub, "Miller's Paradox of Information," *The British Journal for the Philosophy of Science*, **19**, 1968, pp. 63–67.

* Raiffa, Howard, and Robert Schlaifer, "Applied Statistical Decision Theory," Division of Research, Harvard Business School, 1961.

Raiffa, Howard and R. Duncan Luce, *Games and Decisions: Introduction and Critical Survey*. New York: John Wiley and Sons, 1957.

* Ramsey, Frank P., *The Foundations of Mathematics*, ed. by Braithwaite. London: Routledge and Kegan Paul, 1950.

Ramsey, Frank P., "Truth and Probability," in Ramsey, *The Foundations of Mathematics*, pp. 156–198.

Ramsey, Frank P., "Further Considerations," in Ramsey, *The Foundations of Mathematics*, pp. 199–211.

Ramsey, Frank P., "Probability and Partial Belief," in Ramsey, *The Foundations of Mathematics*, pp. 256–257.

Ramsey, Frank P., "General Propositions and Causality," in *Foundations of Mathematics and Other Essays*. London: Routledge and Kegan Paul, 1931, pp. 237–255.

Reichenbach, Hans, "Die logischen Grundlagen des Wahrscheinlichkeitsbegriffs," *Erkenntnis*, **3**, 1932–1933, pp. 401–425. English translation: "The Logical Foundations of the Concept of Probability," in Feigl, *Readings in Philosophical Analysis*.

Reichenbach, Hans, "On Probability and Induction," *Philosophy of Science*, **5**, 1938, pp. 21–45.

Reichenbach, Hans, "On the Justification of Induction," *Journal of Philosophy*, **37**, 1940, pp. 97–103.

Reichenbach, Hans, "Philosophical Foundations of Probability," *Proceedings of the Berkeley Symposium on Probability and Statistics*. Berkeley: University of California Press, 1943, pp. 1–20.

Reichenbach, Hans, "Reply to Donald C. Williams' Criticism of the Frequency View of Probability," *Philosophy and Phenomenological Research*, **5**, 1945, pp. 508–512.

* Reichenbach, Hans, *The Theory of Probability*. Berkeley and Los Angeles: University of California Press, 1949.

Reichenbach, Hans, "A Conversation Between Bertrand Russell and David Hume," *Journal of Philosophy*, **46**, 1949, pp. 545–549.

Rescher, Nicholas, "Can There Be Random Individuals?," *Analysis*, **18**, 1957–58, pp. 114–117.

Rescher, Nicholas, "A Contribution to Modal Logic," *Review of Metaphysics*, **12**, 1958, pp. 186–199.

Rescher, Nicholas, "Theory of Evidence," *Philosophy of Science*, **25**, 1958, pp. 83–94.

Rescher, Nicholas, "The Problem of a Logical Theory of Belief Statements," *Philosophy of Science*, **27**, 1960, pp. 88–95.

Rescher, Nicholas, "A Problem in the Theory of Numerical Estimation," *Synthese*, **12**, 1960, pp. 34–39.

Rescher, Nicholas, "Plausible Implication," *Analysis*, **21**, 1960–61, pp. 128–135.

Rescher, Nicholas, "On the Probability of Non-recurring Events," in Feigl and Maxwell (eds.), *Current Issues in the Philosophy of Science*. New York: Holt, Rinehart and Winston, 1961, pp. 228–237.

Rescher, Nicholas, "The Concept of Randomness," *Theoria*, **27**, 1961, pp. 1–11.

Rescher, Nicholas, "Non-deductive Rules of Inference and Problems in the Analysis of Inductive Reasoning," *Synthese*, **13**, 1961, pp. 242–251.

Rescher, Nicholas, "A Probabilistic Approach to Modal Logic," *Acta Philosophica Fennica*, **16**, 1963, pp. 215–226.

Rescher, Nicholas, "Discrete State Systems, Markov Chains, and Problems in the Theory of Scientific Explanation and Prediction," *Philosophy of Science*, **30**, 1963, pp. 325–345.

Rescher, Nicholas, *Hypothetical Reasoning*. Amsterdam: North-Holland Publishing Company, 1964.

Rescher, Nicholas, "Notes on Preference, Utility, and Cost," *Synthese*, **16**, 1966, pp. 332–343.

Rescher, Nicholas, and Brian Skyrms, "A Methodological Problem in the Evaluation of Explanation," *Nous*, **2**, 1968, pp. 121–129.

Resnick, Lawrence, "Confirmation and Hypothesis," *Philosophy of Science*, **26**, 1959, pp. 25–30.

Ritchie, A. D., "The Gambler's Fallacy," *Analysis*, **15**, 1954, p. 47.

Robbins, Herbert, and Ester Samuel, "Testing Statistical Hypotheses—the 'Compound' Approach" in Machol (ed.), *Recent Developments in Information and Decision Processes*. New York: Macmillan, 1962, pp. 63–70.

Robbins, Herbert, "A New Approach to a Classical Statistical Decision Problem," in Kyburg and Nagel (eds.), *Induction: Some Current Issues*. Middletown, Conn.: Wesleyan University Press, 1963, pp. 101–110.

Robinson, Richard E., "Measurement and Statistics: Towards a Clarification of the Theory of 'Permissible Statistics'," *Philosophy of Science*, **32**, 1965, pp. 229–243.

Roelofs, Richard, Keith Lehrer, and Marshall Swain, "Reason and Evidence: An Unsolved Problem," *Ratio*, **9**, 1967, pp. 38–48.

Rosett, Richard N., "Gambling and Rationality," *Journal of Political Economy*, **73**, 1965, pp. 595–607.

Rosthal, Robert, review of Barker's *Induction and Hypothesis* in *Philosophy and Phenomenological Research*, **19**, 1958–59, pp. 123–124.

Rozeboom, William W., "Ontological Induction and the Logical Typology of Scientific Variables," *Philosophy of Science*, **28**, 1961, pp. 337–377.

Rozeboom, William W., "Why I Know So Much More Than You Do," *American Philosophical Quarterly*, **4**, 1967, pp. 281–290.

Rozeboom, William W., "New Dimensions of Confirmation," *Philosophy of Science*, **35**, 1968, pp. 134–155.

Rudner, Richard S., "The Scientist *Qua* Scientist Makes Value Judgements," *Philosophy of Science*, **20**, 1953, pp. 1–6.

Rudner, Richard S., "Value Judgements in the Acceptance of Theories," in Frank (ed.), *The Validation of Scientific Theories*. Boston: Beacon Press, 1954, pp. 24–28.

Rudner, Richard S., "Comments on Salmon's 'Vindication of Induction'," in Feigl and Maxwell (eds.), *Current Issues in the Philosophy of Science*. New York: Holt, Rinehart and Winston, 1961, pp. 262–264.

Rudner, Richard S., "An Introduction to Simplicity," *Philosophy of Science*, **28**, 1961, pp. 109–119.

Russell, Bertrand, *Human Knowledge, Its Scope and Limits*. New York: Simon and Schuster, 1948.

Russell, L. J., review of Carnap's *Continuum of Inductive Methods* in *Philosophy*, **28**, 1953, pp. 272–273.

* Ryle, Gilbert, "'If,' 'So,' and 'Because'," in Black (ed.), *Philosophical Analysis*. Englewood Cliffs, N.J.: Prentice-Hall, 1950, pp. 302–318.

Ryle, Gilbert, "Predicting and Inferring" in Körner (ed.), *The Colston Papers*, **9**, 1957, pp. 165–170.

Ryle, Gilbert, "Comment on Mr. Achinstein's Paper," *Analysis*, **21**, 1960–61, pp. 9–11.

Ryle, Gilbert, "Induction and Hypothesis," *Proceedings of the Aristotelian Society, Supplementary Volume* **16**, 1937, pp. 36–62.

Rynin, David, "Probability and Meaning," *Journal of Philosophy*, **44**, 1947, p. 589.

Rynin, David, "Evidence," *Synthese*, **12**, 1960, pp. 6–24.

Salmon, Wesley, "The Frequency Interpretation and Antecedent Probabilities," *Philosophical Studies*, **4**, 1953, pp. 44–48.

Salmon, Wesley, "The Uniformity of Nature," *Philosophy and Phenomenological Research*, **14**, 1953, pp. 39–48.

Salmon, Wesley, "The Short Run," *Philosophy of Science*, **22**, 1955, pp. 214–221.

Salmon, Wesley, "Regular Rules of Induction," *Philosophical Review*, **65**, 1956, pp. 385–388.

Salmon, Wesley, "Reply to Pettijohn," *Philosophy of Science*, **23**, 1956, pp. 150–151.

Salmon, Wesley, "The Predictive Inference," *Philosophy of Science*, **24**, 1957, pp. 180–190.

Salmon, Wesley, "Should We Attempt to Justify Induction?" *Philosophical Studies*, **8**, 1957, pp. 33–48.

Salmon, Wesley, review of Barker's *Induction and Hypothesis* in *Philosophical Review*, **68**, 1959, pp. 247–253.

Salmon, Wesley, "Barker's Theory of the Absolute," *Philosophical Studies*, **10**, 1959, pp. 50–53.

Salmon, Wesley, "On Vindicating Induction," in Kyburg and Nagel (eds.) *Induction: Some Current Issues*. Middletown, Conn.: Wesleyan University Press, 1963, pp. 27–41.

Salmon, Wesley, "Vindication of Induction," in Feigl and Maxwell (eds.), *Current Issues in the Philosophy of Science*. New York: Holt, Rinehart and Winston, 1961, pp. 245–257.

Salmon, Wesley, "Rejoinder to Barker," in Feigl and Maxwell (eds.), *Current Issues in the Philosophy of Science*. New York: Holt, Rinehart and Winston, 1961, pp. 260–262.

Salmon, Wesley, review of Day's *Inductive Probability* in *Philosophical Review*, **72**, 1963, pp. 392–396.

Salmon, Wesley, "What Happens in the Long Run?," *Philosophical Review*, **74**, 1965, pp. 373–378.

Salmon, Wesley, "The Status of Prior Probabilities in Statistical Explanation," *Philosophy of Science*, **32**, 1965, pp. 137–146.

Salmon, Wesley, "Reply to Kyburg," *Philosophy of Science*, **32**, 1965, pp. 152–154.

Salmon, Wesley, "The Concept of Inductive Evidence," *American Philosophical Quarterly*, **2**, 1965, pp. 1–6.

Salmon, Wesley, "Rejoinder to Barker and Kyburg," *American Philosophical Quarterly*, **2**, 1965, pp. 13–16.

Salmon, Wesley, "Consistency, Transitivity, and Inductive Support," *Ratio*, **7**, 1965, pp. 164–169.

Salmon, Wesley, "The Foundations of Scientific Inference," in Colodny (ed.), *Mind and Cosmos: Essays in Contemporary Science and Philosophy*. Pittsburgh: University of Pittsburgh Press, 1966, pp. 135–275.

Salmon, Wesley, "Use, Mention, and Linguistic Invariance," *Philosophical Studies*, **17**, 1966, pp. 13–18.

Salmon, Wesley, *The Foundations of Scientific Inference*. Pittsburgh: University of Pittsburgh Press, 1966.

Salmon, Wesley, "Carnap's Inductive Logic," *Journal of Philosophy*, **64**, 1967, pp. 725–739.

* Salmon, Wesley, "The Justification of Inductive Rules of Inference" in Imre Lakatos (ed.), *The Problem of Inductive Logic*. Amsterdam: North-Holland Publishing Company, 1968, pp. 24–43.

Salmon, Wesley, "Who Needs Inductive Acceptance Rules" in Lakatos (ed.), *The Problem of Inductive Logic*. Amsterdam: North-Holland Publishing Company, 1968, pp. 139–144.

Samuel, Ester and Herbert Robbins, "Testing Statistical Hypotheses—the 'Compound' Approach," in Machol (ed.), *Recent Developments in Information and Decision Processes*. New York: Macmillan, 1962, pp. 63–70.

Sass, Louis D., "The Justification of Induction," *Analysis*, **7**, 1939–40, pp. 56–60.

* Savage, Leonard J., *Foundations of Statistics*. New York: John Wiley and Sons, 1954.

Savage, Leonard J., "The Foundations of Statistics Reconsidered," *Proceedings of the Fourth [1960] Berkeley Symposium on Mathematics and Probability*. Berkeley: University of California Press, 1961, pp. 575–585.

Savage, Leonard J., "Subjective Probability and Statistical Practice," in Savage *et al.*, *Foundations of Statistical Inference*. New York: John Wiley and Sons, 1962, pp. 9–35.

Savage, Leonard J. and Lester E. Dubins, *How to Gamble if You Must; Inequalities for Stochastic Processes*. New York: McGraw-Hill, 1965.

Savage, Edwards, and Lindeman, "Bayesian Statistical Inference for Psychological Research," *Psychological Review*, **70**, 1963, pp. 193–242.

Savage, Leonard J., "Implications of Personal Probability for Induction," *Journal of Philosophy*, **58**, 1966, pp. 593–607.

Savage, Leonard J., "Difficulties in the Theory of Personal Probability," *Philosophy of Science*, **34**, 1967, pp. 305–310.

Savage, Leonard J., et al, *The Foundations of Statistical Inference*. New York: John Wiley and Sons, 1962. (Also listed under Barnard and Cox, eds.)

Schagrin, Morton L., "An Analytic Justification of Induction," *British Journal for the Philosophy of Science*, **14**, 1963–64, pp. 343–344.

Scheffler, Israel, "On Justification and Commitment," *Journal of Philosophy*, **51**, 1954, pp. 180–190.

Scheffler, Israel, "Explanation, Prediction, and Abstraction," *British Journal for the Philosophy of Science*, **7**, 1956–57, pp. 293–309.

Scheffler, Israel, "Inductive Inference: A New Approach," *Science*, **127**, 1958, pp. 177–181.

Scheffler, Israel, "A Note on Confirmation," *Philosophical Studies*, **11**, 1960, pp. 21–23.

Scheffler, Israel, "A Rejoinder on Confirmation," *Philosophical Studies*, **12**, 1961, pp. 19–20.

Scheffler, Israel, *The Anatomy of Inquiry*. New York: Alfred A. Knopf, 1963.

Scheffler, Israel, *Conditions of Knowledge: An Introduction to Epistemology and Education*. Chicago: Scott, Foresman and Company, 1966.

Scheffler, Israel, "Reflections on the Ramsey Method," *Journal of Philosophy*, **65**, 1968, pp. 269–274.

Schick, Frederick, "Rationality and Consistency," *Journal of Philosophy*, **60**, 1963, pp. 5–19.

Schick, Frederick, review of Katz's *The Problem of Induction and its Solution* in *Journal of Philosophy*, **60**, 1963, pp. 453–462.

* Schick, Frederick, "Consistency," *Philosophical Review*, **75**, 1966, pp. 467–495.

Schick, Frederick, review of Jeffrey's *The Logic of Decision* in *Journal of Philosophy*, **58**, 1966, pp. 396–400.

Schick, Frederick, "Three Logics of Belief," in Swain (ed.), *Induction, Acceptance and Rational Belief*.

Schilpp, Paul Arthur (ed.), *The Philosophy of Rudolf Carnap*. LaSalle, Ill.: Open Court, 1963.

Schlaifer, Robert and Howard Raiffa, *Applied Statistical Decision Theory*. *Division of Research*, Harvard Business School, 1961.

Schlesinger, George, "The Probability of the Simple Hypothesis," *American Philosophical Quarterly*, **4**, 1967, pp. 152–158.

Schoenberg, Judith, "Confirmation by Observation and the Paradox of the Ravens," *British Journal for the Philosophy of Science*, **15**, 1964–65, pp. 200–212.

Schon, Donald, "Comments on Mr. Hanson's 'The Logic of Discovery'," *Journal of Philosophy*, **56**, 1959, pp. 500–503.

Schwartz, Robert and James Hullett, "Grue: Some Remarks," *Journal of Philosophy*, **58**, 1966, pp. 259–271.

* Scott, Dana, and Peter Krauss, "Assigning Probabilities to Logical Formulas" in Hintikka and Suppes (eds.), *Aspects of Inductive Logic*. Amsterdam: North-Holland Publishing Company, 1966, pp. 219–264.

Scriven, Michael, "The Principle of Inductive Simplicity," *Philosophical Studies*, **6**, 1955, pp. 26–30.

Scriven, Michael, Herbert Feigl, and Grover Maxwell (eds.), *Minnesota Studies in the Philosophy of Science*, I: *the Foundations of Science and the Concepts of Psychology and Psychoanalysis*. Minneapolis: University of Minnesota Press, 1962.

Scriven, Michael, Herbert Feigl, and Grover Maxwell, *Concepts, Theories, and the Mind-Body Problem, Minnesota Studies in the Philosophy of Science*, II. Minneapolis: University of Minnesota Press, 1958.

Sellars, Wilfrid and Herbert Feigl, (eds.), *Readings in Philosophical Analysis*. New York: Appleton-Century Crofts, 1949.

Sellars, Wilfrid, "Inference and Meaning," *Mind*, **62**, 1953, pp. 313–338.

Sellars, Wilfrid, "Counterfactuals, Dispositions, and the Causal Modalities," in Feigl, Scrivens, and Maxwell (eds.), *Minnesota Studies in the Philosophy of Science*, II. Minneapolis: University of Minnesota Press, 1957, pp. 225–303.

Sellars, Wilfrid, "Induction as Vindication," *Philosophy of Science*, **31**, 1964, pp. 197–231.

Shackle, G. L. S., *Expectation in Economics*, 2nd. ed. Cambridge: Cambridge University Press, 1952.

Shackle, G. L. S., *Decision, Order and Time*. Cambridge: Cambridge University Press, 1961.

Shackle, G. L. S., C. F. Carter, and Meredith, G. P., *Uncertainty and Business Decisions*. Liverpool: Liverpool University Press, 1962.

Sharpe, R. A., "Validity and the Paradox of Confirmation," *Philosophical Quarterly*, **14**, 1964, pp. 170–173.

Shiman, Paul L., "Comments on Ashby Paper," in Kyburg and Nagel (eds.), *Induction: Some Current Issues*. Middletown, Conn.: Wesleyan University Press, 1963, pp. 68–70.

Shimony, Abner, "Braithwaite on Scientific Method," *Review of Metaphysics*, **7**, 1953–54, pp. 644–660.

* Shimony, Abner, "Coherence and the Axioms of Confirmation," *Journal of Symbolic Logic*, **20**, 1955, pp. 1–28.

Shimony, Abner, "Amplifying Personal Probability Theory: Comments on L. J. Savage's 'Difficulties in the Theory of Personal Probability,'" *Philosophy of Science*, **34**, 1967, pp. 326–332.

Siegel, Sidney, Donald Davidson, and Patrick Suppes, *Decision Making: An Experimental Approach*. Stanford: Stanford University Press, 1957.

Silvers, Stuart, "Some Comments on Quine's Analysis of Simplicity," *Philosophy of Science*, **31**, 1964, pp. 59–61.

Simon, Herbert A., Prediction and Hindsight as Confirmatory Evidence," *Philosophy of Science*, **22**, 1955, pp. 227–230.

Simon, Herbert A., "On Judging the Plausibility of Theories," in B. Van Rootselaar and J. F. Staal (eds.), *Logic, Methodology and Philosophy of Science, III*. Amsterdam: North-Holland Publishing Company, 1968, pp. 439–459.

Simopoulos, John C., "The Gambler's Fallacy—A Further Note," *Analysis*, **15**, 1955, pp. 94–96.

Skyrms, Brian, "On Failing to Vindicate Induction," *Philosophy of Science*, **32**, 1965, pp. 253–268.

Skyrms, Brian, *Choice and Chance: An Introduction to Inductive Logic*. Belmont, Calif.: Dickenson Publishing Company, 1966.

Skyrms, Brian, "Nomological Necessity and the Paradoxes of Confirmation," *Philosophy of Science*, **33**, 1966, pp. 230–249.

Skyrms, Brian, "The Explication of '*x* Knows That *p*'," *Journal of Philosophy*, **64**, 1967, pp. 373–389.

Skyrms, Brian and Nicholas Rescher, "A Methodological Problem in the Evaluation of Explanation," *Nous*, **2**, 1968, pp. 121–129.

Slaght, Ralph L., "Induction, Acceptance, and Rational Belief: A Selected Bibliography," in Swain (ed.), *Induction, Acceptance and Rational Belief*.

Sleigh, Robert C., Jr., "A Note on Some Epistemic Principles of Chisholm and Martin," *Journal of Philosophy*, **61**, 1964, pp. 216–218.

Sleigh, Robert C., Jr., "A Note on Knowledge and Probability," *Journal of Philosophy*, **61**, 1964, p. 478.

Sloman, A., "Rules of Inference, or Suppressed Premisses?," *Mind*, **73**, 1964, pp. 84–96.

Slote, Michael Anthony, "Some Thoughts on Goodman's Riddle," *Analysis*, **27**, 1966–67, pp. 128–132.

Small, Kenneth, "Professor Goodman's Puzzle," *Philosophical Review*, **70**, 1961, pp. 544–552.

Smart, J. J. C., "Excogitation and Induction," *Australasian Journal of Philosophy*, **28**, 1950, pp. 191–199.

* Smith, Cedric A. B., "Consistency in Statistical Inference and Decision," *The Journal of the Royal Statistical Society*, B, **23**, 1961, pp. 1–37.

Smith, Cedric A. B., "Comments on Savage," in Savage et al, *Foundations of Statistical Inference*, 1962, pp. 58–62.

Smith, Cedric A. B., "Personal Probability and Statistical Analysis," *The Journal of the Royal Statistical Society*, A, **128**, 1965, pp. 469–489.

Smokler, Howard, "Consistency and Rationality: A Comment," *Journal of Philosophy*, **62**, 1965, pp. 77–80.

Smokler, Howard, "Goodman's Paradox and the Problem of Rules of Acceptance," *American Philosophical Quarterly*, **3**, 1966, pp. 71–76.

Smokler, Howard, "Informational Content: A Problem of Definition," *Journal of Philosophy*, **63**, 1966, pp. 201–211.

* Smokler, Howard, "The Equivalence Condition," *American Philosophical Quarterly*, **4**, 1967, pp. 300–307.

Smokler, Howard, "Conflicting Conceptions of Confirmation," *Journal of Philosophy*, **65**, 1968, pp. 300–312.

Smokler, Howard and Henry E. Kyburg, Jr. (eds.), *Studies in Subjective Probability*. New York: John Wiley and Sons, 1964.

Smullyan, Arthur, "The Concept of Empirical Knowledge," *Philosophical Review*, **65**, 1956, pp. 362–370.

Smullyan, Arthur, *Fundamentals of Logic*. Englewood Cliffs, N.J.: Prentice-Hall, Inc., 1962.

Sneed, Joseph D., "Entropy, Information, and Decision," *Synthese*, **17**, 1967, pp. 329–407.

Somezi, Vittorio, "Can Induction Be Mechanized?," *Methodos*, **7**, 1955, pp. 147–151.

Sosa, E., "The Analysis of 'Knowledge That *p*'," *Analysis*, **25**, 1964, pp. 1–8.

Spilsbury, R. J., "A Note on Induction," *Mind*, **58**, 1949, pp. 215–217.

Spilsbury, R. J., review of Churchman's *Theory of Experimental Inference* in *Mind*, **59**, 1950, pp. 115–116.

Staal, J. F. and B. Van Rootselaar (eds.), *Logic, Methodology and the Philosophy of Science*, III. Amsterdam: North-Holland Publishing Company, 1968.

Stalnaker, Robert C., "A Theory of Conditionals," *Studies in Logical Theory*, N. Rescher (ed.), *American Philosophical Quarterly Monograph Series*, **2**, 1968, pp. 98–112.

Stegmüller, W., "Explanation, Scientific Systematization and Non-explanatory Information," *Ratio*, **8**, 1966, pp. 1–24.

Stegmüller, W., and R. Carnap, *Induktive Logik und Wahrscheinlichkeit*, Vienna: Springer, 1959.

Stenner, Alfred J., "A Note on 'Grue'," *Philosophical Studies*, **18**, 1967, pp. 76–78.

Stewart, John P. and John Sweigart, Jr., "Another Look at Fact, Fiction, and Forecast," *Philosophical Studies*, **10**, 1959, pp. 81–89.

Stocker, Michael, "Knowledge, Causation, and Decision," *Nous*, **2**, 1968, pp. 65–73.

Stoothoff, R. H., review of Day's *Inductive Probability* in *Philosophical Quarterly*, **13**, 1963, pp. 87–88.

Stoothof, R. H., review of Katz's *The Problem of Induction and Its Solution* in *Philosophical Quarterly*, **15**, 1965, pp. 85–86.

Stopes-Roe, Harry V., "Recipes and Induction: Ryle v. Achinstein," *Analysis*, **21**, 1960–61, pp. 115–120.

Stove, D. C., review of Goodman's *Fact, Fiction, and Forecast* in *Australasian Journal of Philosophy*, **33**, 1955, pp. 128–132.

Stove, D. C., review of Harrod's *Foundations of Inductive Logic* in *Australasian Journal of Philosophy*, **36**, 1958, pp. 71–79.

Stove, D. C., "Popperian Confirmation and the Paradox of the Ravens," *Australasian Journal of Philosophy*, **37**, 1959, pp. 149–155.

Stove, D. C., "A Reply to Mr. Watkins," *Australasian Journal of Philosophy*, **38**, 1960, pp. 51–54.

Stove, D. C., review of Popper's *Logic of Scientific Discovery* in *Australasian Journal of Philosophy*, **38**, 1960, pp. 173–187.

Stove, D. C., "Hempel and Goodman on the Ravens," *Australasian Journal of Philosophy*, **43**, 1965, pp. 300–310.

Stove, D. C., "Hume, Probability, and Induction," *Philosophical Review*, **74**, 1965, pp. 160–177.

Stove, D. C., "Hempel's Paradox," *Dialectica*, **4**, 1965–66, pp. 444–455.

Stove, D. C., "On Logical Definitions of Confirmation," *British Journal for the Philosophy of Science*, **16**, 1965–66, pp. 265–272.

Stove, D. C., "Hempel's Paradox," *Dialogue*, **4**, 1966, p. 446.

Stove, D. and C. A. Hooker, "Relevance and the Ravens," *British Journal for the Philosophy of Science*, **18**, 1967–68, pp. 305–315.

Strawson, Peter F., *Introduction to Logical Theory*. London: Methuen and Company, Ltd. New York: John Wiley and Sons, 1952.

Strawson, Peter F., "On Justifying Induction," *Philosophical Studies*, **9**, 1958, pp. 20–21.

Stuart, A., "Some Remarks on Sampling with Unequal Probabilities," *Bulletin of the International Statistical Institute*, **40**, 1963, pp. 773–780.

Suppes, Patrick, "Nelson Goodman on the Concept of Logical Simplicity," *Philosophy of Science*, **23**, 1956, pp. 153–159.

Suppes, Patrick, Donald Davidson, and Sidney Siegel, *Decision Making: An Experimental Approach*. Stanford: Stanford University Press, 1957.

Suppes, Patrick, "Some Open Problems in the Foundations of Subjective Probability," in R. E. Machol (ed.), *Information and Decision Processes*. New York: John Wiley and Sons, 1960, pp. 162–169.

Suppes, Patrick, "The Philosophical Significance of Decision Theory," *Journal of Philosophy*, **58**, 1961, pp. 605–614.

Suppes, Patrick, "Concept Formation and Bayesian Decisions," in Hintikka and Suppes (eds.), *Aspects of Inductive Logic*. Amsterdam: North-Holland Publishing Company, 1966, pp. 21–48.

Suppes, Patrick, "Probabilistic Inference and the Concept of Total Evidence," in Hintikka and Suppes (eds.), *Aspects of Inductive Logic*. Amsterdam: North-Holland Publishing Company, 1966, pp. 50–65.

Suppes, Patrick, "A Bayesian Approach to the Paradoxes of Confirmation," in Hintikka and Suppes (eds.), *Aspects of Inductive Logic*. Amsterdam: North-Holland Publishing Company, 1966, pp. 199–207.

Suppes, Patrick and Jaakko Hintikka (eds.), *Aspects of Inductive Logic*. Amsterdam: North-Holland Publishing Company, 1966.

Suppes, Patrick, "Probabilistic Inference and the Concept of Total Evidence," Technical Report 94, March 1966, "Psychology Series," Stanford.

Suppes, Patrick, and Donald Davidson, "A Finitistic Axiomatization of Subjective Probability and Utility," *Econometrica*, **24**, 1956, pp. 264–275.

Suppes, Patrick, Donald Davidson, and Sidney Siegel, *Decision Making: An Experimental Approach*. Stanford: Stanford University Press, 1957.

Suppes, Nagel, and Tarski (eds.), *Logic, Methodology and Philosophy of Science*, I. Stanford: Stanford University Press, 1962.

Suppes, Patrick and Jaakko Hintikka (eds.), *Aspects of Inductive Logic*. Amsterdam: North-Holland Publishing Company, 1966.

Svenonius, Lars, "Definability and Simplicity," *Journal of Symbolic Logic*, **20**, 1955, pp. 235–250.

Swain, Marshall, Keith Lehrer, and Richard Roelofs, "Reason and Evidence: An Unsolved Problem," *Ratio*, **9**, 1967, pp. 38–48.

Swain, Marshall, "The Consistency of Rational Belief," in Swain (ed.), *Induction, Acceptance and Rational Belief*.

Swain, Marshall (ed.), *Induction, Acceptance, and Rational Belief*. Dordrecht, Holland: Reidel Publishing Company, 1969.

Sweigart, John W., Jr., and John P. Stewart, "Another Look at Fact, Fiction and Forecast," *Philosophical Studies*, **10**, 1959, pp. 81–89.

Swinbourne, R. G., "Grue," *Analysis*, **28**, 1967–68, pp. 123–128.

Szaniawski, Klemens, "The Value of Perfect Information," *Synthese*, **17**, 1967, pp. 408–424.

Tarski, Alfred, *Introduction to Logic and to the Methodology of Deductive Sciences*. New York: Oxford University Press, 1965.

Tarski, Nagel, and Suppes (eds.), *Logic, Methodology and Philosophy of Science*, I. Stanford: Stanford University Press, 1962.

Thomson, Judith Jarvis, "Grue," *Journal of Philosophy*, **63**, 1966, pp. 289–309.

Thomson, Judith Jarvis, "More Grue," *Journal of Philosophy*, **63**, 1966, pp. 528–534.

Tintner, Gerhard, "The Theory of Choice under Subjective Risk and Uncertainty," *Econometrica*, **9**, 1941, pp. 298–304.

Tintner, Gerhard, "A Contribution to the Non-Static Theory of Choice," *Quarterly Journal of Economics*, **56**, 1942, pp. 274–306.

Tintner, Gerhard, "Foundations of Probability and Statistical Inference," *Journal of the Royal Statistical Society*, A, **112**, 1949, pp. 251–286.

Todd, William, "Counterfactual Conditions and the Presuppositions of Induction," *Philosophy of Science*, **31**, 1964, pp. 101–110.

Todd, William, "Probability and the Theorem of Confirmation," *Mind*, **76**, 1967, pp. 260–263.

Törnebohm, Håkan, *Information and Confirmation*. Göteborg: *Acta Universitatis Gothoburgensis*, 1964.

Törnebohm, Håkan, "Two Measures of Evidential Strength," in Hintikka and Suppes (eds.), *Aspects of Inductive Logic*. Amsterdam: North-Holland Publishing Company, 1966, pp. 81–95.

Toulmin, Stephen, "Probability," *Proceedings of the Aristotelian Society*, Supplementary Volume **24**, 1950, pp. 27–62.

Toulmin, Stephen, "What Kind of Discipline Is Logic?," *Actes du XIème congrès international de philosophie*, V. Amsterdam: North-Holland Publishing Company, 1953, pp. 7–11.

Toulmin, Stephen, *The Philosophy of Science*. London: Hutchinson's University Library. New York: Longmans, Green and Company, 1953.

* Toulmin, Stephen, *The Uses of Argument*. Cambridge: Cambridge University Press, 1958.

Tukey, John W., "Some Examples with Fiducial Relevance," *Annals of Mathematical Statistics*, **28**, 1957, pp. 687–695.

Tukey, John W., "Conclusions versus Decisions," *Technometrics*, **2**, 1960, pp. 423–433.

Tuomela, Raimo, "Inductive Generalization in an Ordered Universe," in Hintikka and Suppes (eds.), *Aspects of Inductive Logic*. Amsterdam: North-Holland Publishing Company, 1966, pp. 155–174.

Tuomela, Raimo, *The Application Process of a Theory with Special Reference to Some Behavioral Theories*. Helsinki: Suomalainen Tiedeakatemia, 1968.

Ullian, Joseph, "Luck, License, and Lingo," *Journal of Philosophy*, **58**, 1961, pp. 731–738.

Ullian, Joseph, "More on 'Grue' and Grue," *Philosophical Review*, **70**, 1961, pp. 386–389.

Unger, Peter, "Experience and Factual Knowledge," *Journal of Philosophy*, **64**, 1967, pp. 152–173.

Unger, Peter, "An Analysis of Factual Knowledge," *Journal of Philosophy*, **65**, 1968, pp. 157–170.

Urmson, J. O., "Two of the Senses of 'Probable'," *Analysis*, **8**, 1947, pp. 9–16.

Van Rootselaar, B., and J. F. Staal (eds.), *Logic, Methodology and Philosophy of Science*, III. Amsterdam: North-Holland Publishing Company, 1968.

Venn, John, *The Logic of Chance*. London and Cambridge: Macmillan, 1866.

Verhagen, A. M. W., "The Notion of Induced Probability in Statistical Inference," *Commonwealth Scientific and Industrial Research Organization, Australia 1966*, Paper 21.

Vickers, John M., "Some Remarks on Coherence and Subjective Probability," *Philosophy of Science*, **32**, 1965, pp. 32–38.

Vickers, John M., "Some Features of Theories of Belief," *Journal of Philosophy*, **63**, 1966, pp. 197–201.

Vickers, John M., "Characteristics of Projectible Predicates," *Journal of Philosophy*, **64**, 1967, pp. 280–286.

Vigier, Jean-Paul, "The Concept of Probability in the Frame of the Probabilistic and the Causal Interpretation of Quantum Mechanics," Körner (ed.), *The Colston Papers*, **9**, pp. 71–77.

Villegas, C., "On Qualitative Probability σ-algebras," *Annals of Mathematical Statistics*, **35**, 1964, pp. 1787–1796.

Vincent, R. H., "A Note of Some Quantitative Theories of Confirmation," *Philosophical Studies*, **12**, 1961, pp. 91–92.

Vincent, R. H., "Popper on Qualitative Confirmation and Disconfirmation," *Australasian Journal of Philosophy*, **40**, 1962, pp. 159–166.

Vincent, R. H., "The Paradox of Ideal Evidence," *Philosophical Review*, **71**, 1962, pp. 497–503.

Vincent, R. H., "On My Cognitive Sensibility," *Philosophical Studies*, **14**, 1963, pp. 77–79.

Vincent, R. H., "Corroboration and Probability," *Dialectica*, **2**, 1963–64, pp. 194–205.

Vincent, R. H., review of Leblanc's *Statistical and Inductive Probabilities* in *Dialectica*, **2**, 1963–64, pp. 475–480.

Vincent, R. H., "The Problem of the Unexamined Individual," *Mind*, **73**, 1964, pp. 550–556.

Vincent, R. H., "The Paradoxes of Confirmation," *Mind*, **73**, 1964, pp. 273–279.

Wald, Abraham, "Die Widerspruchsfreiheit des Kollektivebegriffs der Wahrscheinlichkeits rechnung," *Ergebnisse eines mathematische Kolloquiums*, **8**, 1937, pp. 38–72.

Wald, A., "Contributions to the Theory of Statistical Estimation and Testing Hypotheses," *Annals of Mathematical Statistics*, **10**, 1939, pp. 299–326.

* Wald, A., *Statistical Decisions Functions.* New York: John Wiley and Sons, 1950.

Wald, A., *On the Principles of Statistical Inference.* South Bend, Ind.: University of Notre Dame Press, 1942.

Walk, Kurt, "Simplicity, Entropy, and Inductive Logic" in Hintikka and Suppes (eds.), *Aspects of Inductive Logic.* Amsterdam: North-Holland Publishing Company, 1966, pp. 66–80.

Walker, Edwin Ruthven, "Verification and Probability," *Journal of Philosophy*, **44**, 1947, pp. 701–710.

Walker, Helen, and Joseph Lev, *Statistical Inference.* New York: Holt, Rinehart and Winston, 1953.

Wallace, David L., and Frederick Mosteller, *Inference and Disputed Authorship: The Federalist.* Reading, Mass.: Addison-Wesley, 1964.

Wallace, John R., "Lawlikeness = Truth," *Journal of Philosophy*, **58**, 1966, pp. 780–781.

Wallace, John R., "Goodman, Logic, Induction," *Journal of Philosophy*, **63**, 1966, pp. 310–328.

Warnock, G. J., review of Popper's *Logic of Scientific Discovery* in *Mind*, **69**, 1960, pp. 99–101.

Watanabe, S., "A Mathematical Explication of Inductive Inference," *Colloquium on the Foundations of Mathematics, Mathematical Machines, and Their Applications*, 1962.

Watkins, J. W. N., "Decisions and Uncertainty," *British Journal for the Philosophy of Science*, **6**, 1955–56, pp. 66–78.

Watkins, J. W. N., "Between Analytic and Empirical," *Philosophy*, **32**, 1957, pp. 112–131.

Watkins, J. W. N., "A Rejoinder to Professor Hempel's Reply," *Philosophy*, **33**, 1958, pp. 349–355.

Watkins, J. W. N., "Mr. Stove's Blunders," *Australasian Journal of Philosophy*, **37**, 1959, pp. 240–241.

Watkins, J. W. N., "Confirmation without Background Knowledge," *British Journal for the Philosophy of Science*, **10**, 1959–60, pp. 318–320.

Watkins, J. W. N., "A Reply to Mr. Stove's Reply," *Australasian Journal of Philosophy*, **38**, 1960, pp. 54–58.

Watkins, J. W. N., "Professor Scheffler's Note," *Philosophical Studies*, **12**, 1961, pp. 16–19.

Watling, J., review of Goodman's *Fact, Fiction, and Forecast* in *Mind*, **65**, 1956, pp. 267–273.

Weyl, Hermann, *Philosophy of Mathematics and Natural Science.* Princeton: Princeton University Press, 1949.

Weyland, F., "A Note on 'Knowledge, Certainty, and Probability'," *Inquiry*, **7**, 1964, p. 417.

Wheatley, Jon, "Entrenchment and Engagement," *Analysis*, **27**, 1966–67, pp. 119–127.

White, Morton, "Probability and Confirmation," *Journal of Philosophy*, **36**, 1939, pp. 323–328.

White, Morton (ed.), *Academic Freedom, Logic, and Religion*. Philadelphia: University of Pennsylvania Press, 1953.

Whiteley, C. H., "On the Justification of Induction," *Analysis*, **7**, 1939–40, pp. 68–72.

Whitely, C. H., "More About Probability," *Analysis*, **8**, 1947–48, pp. 76–80.

Whitely, C. H., review of Wisdom's *Foundations of Inference in the Natural Sciences* in *Mind*, **62**, 1953, pp. 113–114.

Wilks, S. S., "Shortest Average Confidence Intervals from Large Samples," *Annals of Mathematical Statistics*, **9**, 1938, pp. 166–175.

Wilks, S. S., *Elementary Statistical Analysis*. Princeton: Princeton University Press, 1958.

Wilks, S. S., *Mathematical Statistics*. New York: John Wiley and Sons, 1962.

Will, Frederick L., "Donald Williams' Theory of Induction," *Philosophical Review*, **57**, 1948, pp. 231–247.

Will, Frederick L., "Generalization and Evidence," in Black (ed.), *Philosophical Analysis*. Englewood Cliffs, N.J.: Prentice-Hall, Inc., 1963, pp. 359–386.

Will, Frederick L., "Kneale's Theories of Probability and Induction," *Philosophical Review*, **63**, 1954, pp. 19–42.

Will, Frederick L., "The Justification of Theories," *Philosophical Review*, **64**, 1955, pp. 370–388.

Will, Frederick L., "Justification and Induction," *Philosophical Review*, **68**, 1959, pp. 359–372.

Will, Frederick L., "The Preferability of Probable Beliefs," *Journal of Philosophy*, **62**, 1965, pp. 57–67.

Will, Frederick L., "Consequences and Confirmation," *Philosophical Review*, **75**, 1966, pp. 34–58.

Williams, Donald C., "On the Derivation of Probabilities from Frequencies," *Philosophy and Phenomenological Research*, **5**, 1944–45, pp. 449–484.

Williams, Donald C., "The Challenging Situation in the Philosophy of Probability," *Philosophy and Phenomenological Research*, **6**, 1945–46, pp. 67–86.

Williams, Donald C., "The Problem of Probability," *Philosophy and Phenomenological Research*, **6**, 1945–46, pp. 619–622.

Williams, Donald C., *The Ground of Induction*. Cambridge: Harvard University Press, 1947.

Williams, Donald C., review of Reichenbach's *Theory of Probability* in *Philosophy and Phenomenological Research*, **11**, 1950–51, pp. 252–257.

Williams, Donald C., "Professor Carnap's Philosophy of Probability," *Philosophy and Phenomenological Research*, **13**, 1952–53, pp. 103–121.

Williams, Donald C., "The External World and Mr. Chatalian," *Journal of Philosophy*, **50**, 1953, pp. 13–18.

Williams, Donald C., "Mr. Chatalian on Probability and Deduction," *Philosophical Studies*, **4**, 1953, pp. 28–29.

Williams, Donald C., "On the Direct Probability of Inductions," *Mind*, 62, 1953, pp. 465–483.

Williams, J. S., "The Role of Probability in Fiducial Inference," *Sankhya: The Indian Journal of Statistics*, A, 28, 1966, pp. 271–296.

Williams, P. M., "The Structure of Acceptance and its Evidential Basis," *British Journal for the Philosophy of Science*, 19, 1968–69, pp. 325–344.

Wilson, P. R., "On the Confirmation Paradox," *British Journal for the Philosophy of Science*, 15, 1964–65, pp. 196–200.

Wilson, P. R., "A New Approach to the Confirmation Paradox," *Australasian Journal of Philosophy*, 42, 1964, pp. 393–401.

Wilson, P. R., "On the Argument by Analogy," *Philosophy of Science*, 31, 1964, pp. 34–39.

Wisdom, John, "A Note on Probability," in Black (ed.), *Philosophical Analysis*. Englewood Cliffs, N.J.: Prentice-Hall, Inc., 1963, pp. 387–393.

Wisdom, John, *Foundations of Inference in Natural Science*. London: Methuen and Company, 1952.

Wisdom, John, "A Reply to Dr. Das's Criticisms," *British Journal for the Philosophy of Science*, 8, 1957–58, pp. 325–328.

Workman, Rollin, "The Logical Status of the Principle of Induction," *Synthese* 13, 1961, pp. 68–74.

Workman, Rollin, "Two Extralogical Uses of the Principle of Induction," *Philosophical Studies*, 13, 1962, pp. 27–32.

Wright, G. H. von, "On Probability," *Mind*, 49, 1940, pp. 265–283.

Wright, G. H. von, "Carnap's Theory of Probability," *Philosophical Review*, 60, 1951, pp. 362–374.

Wright, G. H. von, *Über Wahrscheinlichkeit, eine Logische und Philosophische Untersuchung*. Helsinki, 1945.

* Wright, G. H. von, *A Treatise on Induction and Probability*. New York: Harcourt, Brace and World, 1951.

Wright, G. H. von, *The Logical Problem of Induction*, 2nd rev. ed. New York: Macmillan, 1957.

Wright, G. H. von, "A New System of Modal Logic," in *Logical Studies*. London: Routledge and Kegan Paul, 1957, pp. 89–126.

Wright, G. H. von, *Logical Studies*. London: Routledge and Kegan Paul, 1957.

Wright, G. H. von, "Remarks on the Epistemology of Subjective Probability," in Nagel, Suppes, and Tarski (eds.), *Logic, Methodology and Philosophy of Science*, I. Stanford: Stanford University Press, 1962, pp. 330–339.

Wright, G. H. von, *The Logic of Preference*. Edinburgh: Edinburgh University Press, 1963.

* Wright, G. H. von, "The Paradoxes of Confirmation," in Hintikka and Suppes (eds.), *Aspects of Inductive Logic*. Amsterdam: North-Holland Publishing Company, 1966, pp. 208–219.

Zaragüeta, Bengoechea J., "La fonction estamative dans l'induction empirique," *Revue Philosophique de Louvain*, 49, 1951, pp. 198–201.

Symposium: Salmon, Barker, Kyburg, "Inductive Evidence," *American Philosophical Quarterly*, 2, 1965, pp. 265–280.

Carnap Festschrift. *Logic and Language*. Dordrecht, Holland: D. Reidel Publishing Company, 1962.

Suggested Answers to Selected
Exercises from the Text

Chapter 1

The answers to the exercises in Chapter One all require essay or discussion by the student and are therefore not provided.

Chapter 2

8. $\binom{10}{4}(\frac{1}{2})^4(\frac{1}{2})^6 = 0.2051$

9. $\binom{10}{4}(\frac{1}{2})^4(\frac{1}{2})^6 + \binom{10}{5}(\frac{1}{2})^5(\frac{1}{2})^5 + \binom{10}{6}(\frac{1}{2})^5(\frac{1}{2})^5 = 0.6563$

10. $\frac{10!}{10!\,0!}(\frac{1}{2})^0(\frac{1}{2})^{10} = 0.00098$

12. $\frac{6}{36} = 0.1667$

13. $\left(\frac{13}{52}\right)\left(\frac{12}{51}\right) = 0.0588$

Chapter 3

1. No. There is a reason to suppose that one of the outcomes (namely, one head and one tail) is twice as probable as each of the other two (equally probable) outcomes, since it may arise in two ways: #1 coin head and #2 coin tail, or #1 coin tail and #2 coin head.
4. Yes. The die is apparently unbiased, so we have reason to believe that each of the six clear-cut alternatives will occur with approximately equal frequency, about 1/6 in the long run.
7. One-eighth = 0.125. The principle of indifference is not appropriate for horse races, since many factors (e.g., speed of horses, skill of riders) render false the claim that all alternatives are equally probable.
8. Yes. One can deny that $P(H_i) = P(H)$ where $i = 1$, and thus deny that the conditions of the example satisfy the antecedent of Theorem 12.

Chapter 4

9.
(a) An empirical interpretation of this statement is appropriate when "a" is construed as "any arbitrary" but does not, of course, assert that on any particular throw of die "six" will result.
(b) An empirical interpretation seems inappropriate here, since presumably one is speaking only about a particular day. But it is also true that good reasons which one might offer for making the statement would entail that other days which are like tomorrow in the relevant aspects are also days for which the probability is 0.4 that it will rain.
(c) Here again, it appears that one is speaking only of a particular Christmas, and not of Christmases in general, or of future days of a certain sort, preceded by days with weather like today's, and so forth, but the reasons one might adduce for the statement may indeed have such consequences.
(d) In this statement we are not speaking of any tosses of a coin but of exactly the next ten, so the applicability of empirical interpretation seems doubtful. But it is because of the projected frequency of heads for random tosses of the coin that we make the statement, and there is a plausible case to be made that the next ten tosses of the coin are a random sample of all possible tosses of the coin.
(e) The empirical interpretation seems more appropriate here than in (d) because the statement is not about any particular thousand tosses but rather about any arbitrary (random) thousand tosses of the coin, and this statement is based upon the frequency one projects for an infinite possible set of tosses of the coin.
(f) This statement appears to refer only to a particular train and not to any set of events, so the empirical interpretation seems inappropriate. Nevertheless, one might regard the arrival of the 6:20 to Boston today as a random member of the set of all events described as the arrival of the 6:20 to Boston, and so construe the frequentist view as more appropriate than otherwise, although this interpretation seems a bit strained.
(g) If "a" is construed as "any," the same considerations mentioned in (d) should apply to this statement as well.

(h) This statement does not have the generality of the previous similar claim, and it is difficult indeed to make plausible any empirical interpretation, unless one claims that the two nations are random instances of the general terms in (f); such a claim, although dubious, is arguable.

Chapter 5

1. $c^{\dagger}(Pa, t) = \frac{1}{2}$
   $c^{*}(Pa, t) = \frac{1}{2}$

   It does not matter what tautology of L you choose since any two tautologies in L are logically equivalent; they have the same measure, 1; they hold in all state and structure descriptions.

   $c^{\dagger}(Pa, Pb) = \frac{1}{2}$
   $c^{*}(Pa, Pb) = \frac{3}{5}$
   $c^{\dagger}((x)(Px \supset Qx), Pa \ \& \ Qa) = \frac{9}{16}$
   $c^{*}((x)(Px \supset Qx), Pa \ \& \ Qa) = \frac{4}{5}$

4. The value of $c(h, e)$ remains unchanged when new individual constants are added if no quantifiers occur in h or e; if quantifiers occur as in 1–3 above, the value of $c(h, e)$ decreases. The addition of new predicates leaves the value of the confirmation function unchanged.

9. If $\lambda = 0$, we have a rule which identifies the probability of h_j with the relative frequency of P_j among the sample of s individuals. This rule violates A-6 since the rule asserts that $c(h, e) = 1$ and h is not a logical consequence of e.

10. $\lambda = 0$ violates A-12 since $\lambda = 0$ yields $c^{\dagger}$, and $c^{\dagger}$ is inconsistent with A-12.

Chapter 6

5. The conditional probability that I should attach to the hypothesis that I have urn I, on the information given, is

$$P(H_1/E) = \frac{\frac{3}{4} \times (\frac{1}{3})^4}{\frac{3}{4} \times (\frac{1}{3})^4 + \frac{1}{4} \times (\frac{2}{3})^4} = \frac{3}{19} = 0.1579$$

When I actually draw the four black balls, my degree of belief in H_I should be 0.1579. If it remains 0.75, I have ignored evidence that should have caused me to change my degree of belief. In light of the evidence, my beliefs are not consistent through time.

6. The conditional probability that the Yankees will win the series, given that they win the first game, is

$$Cr(H/E) = \frac{0.6 \times 0.5}{0.4} = 0.75$$

If they win the first game and your belief that they will go on to win the series is 0.3, your beliefs are not consistent through time and either (i) your belief is irrational or (ii) you have gained some other new evidence (e.g., an injury to a player) which has caused you to change your belief.

7. Coherence requires that my belief in E satisfy the probability calculus:

$$0.2 = \frac{0.4 \times \mathrm{Cr}(E/H)}{\mathrm{Cr}(E)} \quad \text{(Bayes' Thm.)}$$

$$0.5 = \frac{0.4 \times \mathrm{Cr}(\bar{E}/H)}{1 - \mathrm{Cr}(E)} \quad \text{(Bayes' Thm. and Thm. 3)}$$

Since $\mathrm{Cr}(E/H) = 1 - \mathrm{Cr}(E/H)$, we may solve these simultaneous equations and determine that

$$\mathrm{Cr}(E) = \tfrac{1}{3} = 0.3333$$

If my belief in E becomes 0.7 then, according to Jeffrey, my conditional beliefs should remain constant and my belief that the team will win should become

$$\mathrm{Cr}_2(H) = (0.2 \times 0.7) + (0.5 \times 0.3) = 0.29$$

If my eggs are overdone and my coffee is cold and this causes my belief in H to change to 0.2, Jeffrey would say that I have changed my belief for the wrong reasons. In this case, however, I would have to change my conditional beliefs or be inconsistent.

Chapter 7

1. The card is a random member, relative to what we know about it so far, of the set of cards in the deck with respect to being a spade, and also a random member, relative to what we know about it so far, of the set of cards drawn from ordinary well-shuffled decks of cards with respect to being a spade. It can be a random member of both these sets because the definition of randomness is satisfied in each case; in particular, clause 4 (a) is satisfied. The card drawn is not a random member of the set of cards in the top half of the deck because clause 2 is not satisfied; it is not a random member of the set of cards drawn by John in the afternoon because we do not know that clause 3 is satisfied. The probability that the card is a spade is $\tfrac{1}{4} + \epsilon$; the probability that the card is drawn from the top half of the deck is 1 since we know that it is drawn from the top half of the deck.

2. The probability that a and b are both hearts is $(1/4 + \epsilon) \times (1/4 + \epsilon) = 1/16 + \epsilon/2 + \epsilon^2$. The probability that either a or b is a heart or both are hearts is

$$\binom{2}{1}\left(\frac{1}{4} + \epsilon\right)^1\left(\frac{3}{4} - \epsilon\right)^1 + \binom{2}{2}\left(\frac{1}{4} + \epsilon\right)^2 \times 1 = \frac{7}{16} + \frac{3\epsilon}{2} - \epsilon^2$$

8. There are, of course, many things we might know about John that would prevent his being a random member of the population. We might know something of his family background, his education, his job, his income, etc. Knowing any of these facts would place John in a group which itself has a measure of the subset of people with I.Q's less than 100. Each of these sets would probably have a measure different from that of the population as a whole, and informa-

tion about each of them would be relevant to our assignment of probability to the hypothesis that John has an I.Q. less than 100.

Chapter 8

2. All the Americans I know belong to families with incomes of more than $3000 per year; John is an American; therefore, John probably belongs to a family with income more than $3000. Almost all Americans belong to families with incomes of more than $3000; John is an American; therefore, it is reasonable to believe that John belongs to a family with income more than $3000 per year.

4. One might argue in a particular case that the sample was not random, or fair, or representative of the population, especially if the sample were extremely small or if it were known to have been selected by a procedure that might reasonably be expected to produce a different proportion of C's than occur in the entire population (e.g., if a sample to determine men's leisure activities consisted entirely of married men). One might, of course, deny that any conclusion about the population is warranted unless the sample is very large— 50% or more of the population.

6. An enthymematic deductive argument can be construed as an inductive argument. An enthymeme is not explicitly deductive unless the missing premise is supplied. If the supplied premise is such that the premises entail the conclusion, the argument is deductive and valid; but we could always supply a premise such that the premises do not entail the conclusion but merely offer good warrant for it. Whenever the latter course is taken the argument is inductive, so an enthymematic deductive argument can always be construed as an inductive argument.

Chapter 9

1. If F is a necessary condition of G then

   1. $(x)(\sim Fx \supset \sim Gx)$, which is equivalent to
   2. $(x)(Gx \supset Fx)$
   3. Since $(x)(Fx) \supset (x)(Fx \vee F'x)$,
   4. $(x)(Gx \supset Fx \vee F'x)$, which is equivalent to
   5. $(x)(\sim [Fx \vee F'x] \supset \sim Gx)$

   4 and 5 state that $F \vee F'$ is a necessary condition of G; this shows that if F is a necessary condition of G, so is $(F \vee F')$.

3. An experiment in which D (lack of heat) is produced for a particular plant would eliminate D as a possible sufficient condition for wilting if the particular plant did not wilt. If any particular plant which wilts does not have A (lack of water) or, stated differently, if any plant which does not have lack of water wilts, A is eliminated as a possible necessary condition for wilting.

5. The total list of possible sufficient conditions for #3 is

Ax	Ax & Bx	Bx & Dx	Ax & Bx & Cx
Bx	Ax & Cx	$Cx \vee Dx$	Ax & Bx & Dx
Cx	Ax & Dx		Ax & Bx & $(Cx \vee Dx)$
Dx	Bx & Cx		

If all but one of these is eliminated, that one remaining is Ax & Bx & $(Cx \lor Dx)$.

9. An exception arises to the claim that the elimination of all sufficient conditions but one leaves the conjunction of all the conditions as a sufficient condition, when two of the conditions are mutually contradictory. In that case, as in #5, the elimination of all conditions but one leaves the remaining condition as the conjunction of all the conditions but the two which are contradictory, conjoined with the disjunction of these two conditions.

Chapter 10

The questions for this chapter all require somewhat lengthy discussion or explanation, and are therefore left to the reader.

Chapter 11

1.

	Level of Significance	Probability of Type II Error	Power of Test
Test I	0.01	0.08	0.92
Test II	0.98	0.94	0.06

3. Consider test T: Reject H_1 when both A's are B's.
   Level of significance of

$$T = \binom{2}{2}(\tfrac{1}{10})^2(\tfrac{9}{10})^0 = 0.01$$

   Power of test against

$$H_2 = 1 - \binom{2}{0}(\tfrac{2}{3})^0(\tfrac{1}{3})^2 + \binom{2}{1}(\tfrac{2}{3})^1(\tfrac{1}{3})^1$$

$$= 0.666$$

   Power of test against

$$H_3 = 1 - \binom{2}{0}(\tfrac{1}{2})^0(\tfrac{1}{2})^2 + \binom{2}{1}(\tfrac{1}{2})(\tfrac{1}{2}) = 0.25$$

5. Expected loss of S^* if $\tfrac{3}{4}$ are defective is

$$\binom{4}{1}(\tfrac{3}{4})^1(\tfrac{1}{4})^3 = (\tfrac{3}{64} \times 10) + (\tfrac{61}{64} \times 5) = \tfrac{335}{64} = 5.2344$$

   Expected loss of S^* if $\tfrac{1}{3}$ are defective is

$$\binom{4}{1}(\tfrac{1}{3})^1(\tfrac{2}{3})^3 = (\tfrac{32}{81} \times 0) + (\tfrac{49}{81} \times 8) = 4.8395$$

   Clearly, S^* is dominated by a mixed strategy which uses S_1 half the time and S_2 the remainder, and there are other calculable mixtures of S_1 and S_2 which also dominate S^*.

Chapter 12

Since almost all of the questions for this chapter are of the essay or discussion variety, these questions are left as exercises for the reader and answers are not supplied.

Chapter 13

2. The range of relevance of the generalization in the example is likely to be taken as the set of all birds, although it might be taken as any set of which the set of all birds is a subset.
3. In general one determines what the range of relevance of a generalization is taken to be within a specific inquiry by examining the background statistical assertion generalized. One cannot assume that the most natural range of relevance is the intended one; apart from the examination of the background statistical assertion, there really is no way of determining the intended range of relevance of the generalization.
4. One way to avoid the lottery paradox is to deny that the conjunction of two acceptable hypotheses is itself always acceptable. This proposal strikes some writers as unacceptable or at least counter-intuitive, but it has the consequence of avoiding some paradoxes that might otherwise arise. Moreover, the proposal can be seen as reasonable in accounting for why we might say that it is reasonable for a man to accept each of his beliefs as probably true, and yet reasonable for him to believe that among his many beliefs some are probably false. Some further sources for discussion of the lottery paradox are mentioned in the bibliography for Chapter 13.

Chapter 14

2. The question is which of the three viruses is a necessary condition of the common cold—i.e., for which one it is true that if the virus is not present the cold will not occur. The ultimate partition, U_e, consists of the three statements:

Virus A will be present

Virus B will be present

Virus C will be present

The total set of relevant answers, M_e, is

Either A or B or C will be present (S_e)

Either A or B will be present

Either A or C will be present

Either B or C will be present

A will be present

B will be present

C will be present

A and B and C will be present (C_e)

$$P(H_A, e) = \frac{0.5 \times 0.1}{0.5 \times 0.1 + 0.3 \times 0.4 + 0.2 \times 0.2} = \frac{0.05}{0.19} = 0.2632$$

$$P(H_B, e) = \frac{0.3 \times 0.4}{0.19} = 0.6316$$

$$P(H_C, e) = \frac{0.2 \times 0.1}{0.19} = 0.1052$$

$\text{cont}(\sim a_i, e) = \frac{1}{3}$

If the scientist accepts $q = 1$, he will reject H_A and H_C, and accept H_B, conjoined with (b & e) as strongest via induction.

If the scientist accepts $q = \frac{1}{2}$, he will reject H_C and accept $H_A \vee H_B$.

Index

259

mathematical necessity achieved in science (Matson), 109
See also Acceptance, Confirmation, Corroboration, Demonstrative induction
Chance, doctrine of (Kneale and Day), 7–8
Chance setups, 'probability' applied to, 46–50
Changing beliefs, Richard Jeffrey's Theorem of, 71–72
Chernoff, Herman, 151
Chisholm, Roderick, 179
Choosing between competing hypotheses
  criteria suggested, 154
  degree of corroboration as basis for (Popper), 158–59
  degree of factual support as basis for (Kemeny, Oppenheim), 159
  epistemic utility as basis for (Levi), 159
  explanatory power (Popper), 158–59
  See Acceptance, Confirmation, Statistical inference
Classes, rational, 81
Classical interpretation of probability, 29–39
  equipossible alternatives, 27–29
    as equiprobable alternatives, 30–31
  principle of indifference, 31–38
    "*a priori* rationalism" (Nagel), 32
    paradoxes of, 33–37
  ratio of favorable alternatives to unfavorable ones, 29–38
Closure, deductive
  Levi, 186–87
  not satisfied in Kyburg theory, 192
Cogency, deductive
  achieved in Kyburg system, 191–92
  defined by Levi, 186–87
Cohen, Morris R., 153, 163
Collectives (von Mises), probability

interpreted as relative frequency of members of subsequence, 41–45
Combinations and permutations, 24–26
Common usage, violated by empirical interpretations of probability, 47–49
Commutativity, used in developing probability calculus, 15
Complementation, property of sets used to develop probability calculus, 15
Conditions (necessary, sufficient, necessary-and-sufficient), role in demonstrative induction (von Wright), 111–19
Confirmation, paradoxes of, *see* Paradoxes of confirmation
Confirmation theories, 165–79
  Hintikka-Hilpinen theory, 180–85
  Kyburg theory, 190–96
  Levi theory, 185–90
Consistency, probability calculus as complex criterion of (Savage), 70
Constitutents (Hintikka-Hilpinen theory), 181–82
Content of hypotheses (Levi), 187
Context of local justification characterized by set of relevant answers (Levi), 186
Contexts of probability statements, various, with account of different approaches to probability, 84–91
Convergence and linguistic invariance, criteria for short-run and uniqueness, 132
Cooley, John C., 107
Copeland, A. H., 53
Corpora, rational, in Kyburg system, 191–94
Corpus, rational, 78–79
Corroboration, degree of as basis for

difficulties raised by enthymemes, 98

various approaches to inductive logic
acceptance theories, 180–98
confirmation theories, 165–79
demonstrative induction, 109–125
ordinary language and inductive argument, 97–108
probabilities and presuppositions, 126–36
simplicity and the hypothetico-deductive method, 153–64
statistical inference, 137–52

Inductive procedures, canon of, 103–105

Inference, statistical, 137–52
decision theory, 140–50
domination of one strategy as basis for choice among hypotheses, 146
limitation illustrated by Hacking's example, 148–49
limitations of decision theory in scientific contexts, 148–49
minimax policy, 146–48
minimizing average loss, 148
minimizing maximum loss, 146–47
minimizing maximum regret, 147
testing of statistical hypotheses, 138–42
defined, 138
null hypothesis, 138
significance level, size, and power of tests, 140–42
type I and type II errors, 139–42

Inference tickets, 99–102
Harré, R., 101
justification, not analysis, as problem of induction (Achinstein, Stopes-Roe), 102
pragmatic and descriptive approach (Hanson), 102
Ryle, Gilbert, 102
Toulmin, Stephen, 99–100, 102–3,

107
usefulness of concept, denial of (Alexander), 102

Information about real world given by probability statements (von Mises), 50

Interpretations of probability, *see* Probability, interpretations of

Intersection of sets, property used in developing probability calculus, 15

Jeffrey, Richard, 71–72, 76, 99, 174, 175, 178, 179

Jeffrey's Theorem, 71–72

Jeffreys, Harold, 66, 155, 156, 164

Justification of induction
attempts to give inductive justification of induction (Black, Braithwaite), 129–30
Hume solved his own problem (Strawson), 101
induction admits of justification, 99–102
induction does not admit of justification, 99–101
no criterion for goodness or badness of inductive hypotheses (Toulmin), 101
to say how inferences should be made is to say how they are made (Strawson), 101
information about the real world is given by probability statement (von Mises), 50
local justification (Levi), 185–86
may be made at great expense (Goodman), 129
pragmatic vindication, 99–102, 129–34
Salmon's attack on opponents of, 131–34
seeing that induction works (Ryle), 101–102
straight rule, guarantees probabi-